IN AND OUT
OF THE
IVORY TOWER

———

The Autobiography

of

Richard B. Goldschmidt

———

SEATTLE

UNIVERSITY OF WASHINGTON PRESS

1960

Zum Sehen geboren,
Zum Schauen bestellt,
Dem Turme geschworen,
Gefällt mir die Welt.
Ich blick in die Ferne,
Ich seh in der Näh
Den Mond und die Sterne,
Den Wald und das Reh.
So seh ich in allen
Die ewige Zier,
Und wie mirs gefallen,
Gefall ich auch mir.
Ihr glücklichen Augen
Was je ihr gesehn,
Es sei, wie es wolle,
Es war doch so schön!

GOETHE, *Faust II*

PUBLISHER'S NOTE

This autobiography, written in the course of so many years, was actually completed less than a week before Dr. Goldschmidt's death on April 24, 1958. At that time the author's final modifications of the edited manuscript were received by the publisher. Only minor alterations and corrections have been made since then. The publisher wishes to thank Dr. Curt Stern and Dr. Leonie K. Piternick, friends and former students of Dr. Goldschmidt, who have helped to see the book through publication. Dr. Piternick's assistance in checking the Bibliography and the Index is especially appreciated.

PREFACE

The major part of this narrative, a rather unsophisticated report on my life and time, was written almost thirty years ago while I was traveling the seven seas. Ten years later, after I had emigrated to the United States, I rewrote it in English when convalescence reminded me that it was time to record my doings for my family. Again ten years passed before I added the story of the intervening years, and another decade until I made up my mind to try for publication. Thus I should at least not be reproached with rushing into print. But with the friendly prodding of some friends I have come to the conclusion that my life story, an unusual one for a scientist, might also be of interest to outsiders as an example of a scholar who does not fit the layman's ideas of the learned man.

In addition, mine has been an interesting and rich life with its ups and some downs, its unending pleasurable experiences and some sorrows; with the intimate backdrop of private life in a rather unusual social sphere; with the reflections of the great events of our time seen from some remarkable vantage points—all this pictured upon the alert screen of a sensitive and informed mind. Actually, born with the eyes of an observer and trained *"rerum cognoscere causas,"* I have been enabled by chance to live a life much more exciting than usually falls to the lot of a man who spends most of his lifetime bent over the microscope, breeding cage, or culture bottle. Perhaps this was not only chance but the deep urge to look into all facts of life, learning and teaching, enjoying and fighting, and nevertheless—something I consider important—never taking myself more seriously than any person should. Thus I have had the rare luck of one day sitting happily inside the ivory tower and another day just as happily participating in the turmoil of the world and in all experiences of the intellect, sentiment, and mind, not to forget the body. Reliving these fourscore years, should I not be grateful for what came my way and let my family, friends, and students all over the world hear so in my own words?

R. B. G.

Berkeley, California
March, 1958

CONTENTS

ILLUSTRATIONS

IN AND OUT
OF THE
IVORY TOWER

———

The Autobiography

of

Richard B. Goldschmidt

1: THE EARLY YEARS

I come from an old German-Jewish family. This fact may convey little meaning to most people, for it is perhaps not generally known that the German Jews are a group of people who can trace their origin, at least in a general way, farther back into gray antiquity than the oldest known family, the K'ung (Confucius) in China. The reason this can be done is that many German-Jewish families, like my own, belong to the caste of the Levites, the literary and teaching caste since Moses' time some three thousand years ago. The Levites kept to themselves through the centuries except for intermarriage with the priestly caste, the Cohens, and thus the members of the Levite caste are the product of an age-long selection of intellectual performance.

It was mainly this group that migrated to Rome toward the end of the Jewish state two thousand years ago and that played a considerable role in the intellectual life of the Roman Empire. When the Romans had conquered Germany and erected the Limes Germanicus, the fortified frontier against the barbarians, Roman Jews of Levite families were settled along the Limes to teach the savage Teutons the amenities of Mediterranean agriculture. These were the first Jews to be settled in Germany along the Rhine and Main valleys. It is reported that they did not bring their wives to this military zone but took unto themselves native daughters, who embraced the Jewish faith. This condition seems to have continued long after the Limes as well as the Roman Empire had disappeared and the Jews had become steady inhabitants of this region, for, in the eighth century, a papal bull forbade German women to embrace the Jewish faith after marriage. From that time up to the eighteenth century legal intermarriages were stopped. But about five centuries of continuous intermarriage had left their imprint, and this explains why so many German Jews derived from this part of the Jewish population are tall, fair, blue-eyed, dolichocephalic, and otherwise hardly different from the western German population. From this early time there still exists—or did Hitler burn it?—a Jewish temple in Worms which is one of the oldest edifices, if not the oldest, in Germany. It is amusing to think that many of the Jews who were persecuted in Nazi Germany on account of race had more old Teuton blood flowing in their veins than did the Nazi leaders, most of whom were typically Slav and Alpine mixtures without any Teuton blood at all.

At the time of the crusades the pogroms against "the infidels who had crucified the Lord" began. A large number left Germany and fled to Poland where they have kept to this day the medieval German garb, the caftan, and the medieval German language, mixed with Hebrew and Slav, known as Yiddish. Those who remained in Germany were forced to leave the land they had tilled and to huddle together in the narrow ghettos of the medieval towns. The largest communities were still found in the Rhine-Main region and the largest and most prosperous in Frankfurt am Main, a free town, which—while there were occasional outbreaks —did not erect a real ghetto, though the Jews lived in a definite section where they inhabited houses not different from those of the rest of the town.

The older Jewish families of Frankfurt have an uninterrupted record down to the twelfth century, but my own paternal family came there only later; in 1526, a goldsmith who had learned his trade in Nuremberg settled in Frankfurt and was called Goldschmidt by the gentiles. He lived in a house—"the pitcher"—which, together with some others, remained the abode of some of his descendants until it was torn down in the nineteenth century. In the sixteenth century one of his grandsons became one of the great bankers of the day, and bankers have been plentiful in the family ever since. The family remained prominent, engaging in banking, business, and different trades until the opening of the ghettos in the eighteenth century gave them a chance to make better use of their age-old gifts.

When the Nazis came to power in Germany they published a poster with an excerpt from one of the published pedigrees of our family. The idea was to show that we had systematically set out to conquer the world. "What Aryan family," asked the poster, "has at its disposal such an abundance of positions of power as this single Jewish family? It is only thanks to the principles of the National Socialist movement that the Jews do not rule in Germany today, and that the Star of Judas does not triumph over the German people."

What actually had happened in our family was that latent gifts

4

had been used and numerous descendants of old Benedict Gold-schmidt, confectioner in the eighteenth century, had reached important positions as scientists, artists, bankers, industrialists. By intermarriage, Goldschmidts had become related to innumerable aristocratic families (up to the Dukes of Wellington) and especially to all the great banking families. Goldschmidt-von Rothschild, Warburg, Cassel, Bischoffsheim, Bonn, and many more were members of this family tree, though probably most of them did not know that they were related to the others. I think that the Nazi poster could well be used as a chart demonstrating the effect of long selection of favorable hereditary traits upon the improvement of human families.

I was born April 12, 1878, in an old house of the Börnestrasse near the former Jewish quarter, the son of Solomon Goldschmidt and Emma Flürscheim Goldschmidt. My father had inherited and ran, much against his wishes, a business that occupied our own and three adjacent houses—a coffeehouse combined with a wine trade and a confectionery, all of them famous for the quality of their products and all highly successful. Our family lived in a modest apartment upstairs so that my energetic mother could devote part of her time to overseeing the many employees. But when I was about two years old my mother succeeded in persuading my father to move to a more pleasant neighborhood, a friendly residential district near a park, surrounded by gardens that occupied the site of the former city walls and moat. In German towns at that time, as even today, the majority of the moderately well-to-do families lived in apartments; a seven-room apartment, with gas light, huge tiled stoves, and the immense luxury of a bathroom—and with the back rooms overlooking gardens—was considered a sign of affluence. Only really wealthy people owned their own homes, which were called, in awe, "houses for single occupancy."

When I was about four years old we moved farther west—the west being the fashionable residential district—and took a large apartment in a house overlooking the biggest square of the town. The children's playroom, situated at the end of a long corridor, overlooked the square, and we spent most of our time at home in that room at the windows, joined, when my mother was out, by Kathrin the cook and Rosa the nurse, both of whom had a great time flirting from a distance with passing beaux. We soon knew the favorites and announced their approach in the kitchen.

Actually I led the abominable (as I now look at it) life of a city child, constantly supervised by nurses, without playgrounds or anything that a young boy cherishes. Bicycles, coasters, footballs did not yet exist. Even when I was four years old I still wore—as did all little city boys—girl dresses, and I can still feel the shame and remember the daily fight against wearing my dress of the not very attractive salt and pepper variety. How I hated that dress, and how humiliated I felt going around in it! However, when I was a little older, I did acquire my longed-for trousers and was able to boast an especially nice white suit, which was reserved for the most important occasions such as the visits of old Emperor Wilhelm I to our town. It was against this background of a rather precious city childhood that I reached the age of six, the age at which school began.

Unfortunately, at that time, in bourgeois families, children before school age grew up as a kind of pet, and nobody was interested in their minds. There were no nursery schools or kindergartens; the child of the well-to-do played at home or was walked around the parks by a nurse or, with his mother, went shopping, calling, seeing the grandmothers—and thus had very little fun. The result was obstinacy and eagerness to play pranks whenever there was a chance. Boys with eager minds tried to occupy themselves, and I am inclined to believe the following story told by my mother. One day when my father was reading the paper I stepped up and offered to read it to him. As I had not learned how to read, everybody laughed; but I insisted, took the paper, and read it—as the story goes. Without anybody's knowledge I had picked up reading from the maids—again as the story goes. Regardless of whether the story is true, I certainly was ready to start using my brains by the time I entered school in the typical German fashion— on my back a knapsack, covered with stiff sealskin, containing the first reader and the slate, stylus, and sponge that were the writing utensils.

I vividly remember the first school session. The teacher was a fine old gentleman, known to every family in that district of the town. To put the frightened youngsters at ease—frightened because school meant discipline, and little boys had heard daily from mothers and nurses the threat, "Wait until you go to school"—the teacher had drawn on the blackboard, with chalk in different colors, the likeness of a poodle and began his lesson by explaining the features of the animal. In later life I have stood innumerable times before the greatest works of art of the Occident and Orient and have experienced the rapture, the lift beyond the world of mortal men, which really great art evokes in the susceptible mind. But the most impressive, awe- and admiration-inspiring work I have ever seen was that chalky poodle. A teacher who could produce such a miracle with his own hands was worthy of adoration, and my heart flew to him.

Indeed, education in those first years of grammar school was a pleasure. The shadowy side, however, was represented by the homework that had to be performed daily. Writing on a slate is not at all easy, even though bad strokes can be wiped out with the sponge. And my mother, like all German mothers, took the homework very seriously. A little adjustable school desk was installed in the nursery, and the homework had to be done under personal supervision of mother, who insisted upon my writing "like engraved." Of course, in those pretypewriter times an impersonal, exact, and even handwriting was one of the important assets of a business career—a fact that explains the frequent corporal punishment for uneven strokes that I received after the manner of the times.

The first school year brought to me the first real sorrow of my life, a sorrow that was to remain with me all the rest of my days. On the way to school, a one-mile walk made in the company of my elder brother, the street urchins called after us, "*Judebub*," the German equivalent of "kike," and sometimes they threw rocks. This cry, the "hep, hep" of the medieval pogroms, has sounded in my ears ever since, whether literally intoned by urchins or echoed in effect by the fraternity students in the universities or by professors on the faculties or by army officers or even by some royalty with whom I happened to come in contact. Strangely enough, however, of all these and many others, the street urchins on my way to grammar school were the most decent ones; they spoke up to my face and were ready to fight for their beliefs. All the others worked in the dark and were shamefaced enough to shake hands and pat my shoulders in public or even to ask and accept favors.

I think, actually, that nobody has a better chance to see the ugly side of human nature than an intellectual Jew who has succeeded in life. Thinking of the innumerable instances when I was stabbed in the back by those who breathed deference in my face, fellows intellectually and morally below me, I am surprised that

7

I am not a pessimist. No doubt, this thorn in my flesh has had an immense influence in shaping my character. It has made me cautious and remote, unwilling to show the warmth of my nature unless I know the other man thoroughly. It has taught me to look through people and to analyze them. It has forced me to learn to control my temper, to appear quiet on the surface when I am burning, to appear distant when I long for friendship, to develop self-observation and self-control to a perfection—all of which is frequently misinterpreted as coolness or haughtiness. It has also produced an unnecessarily deep contempt for the second-rater, the go-getter, the social peacock, and the clubman. And it certainly killed a number of qualities that I otherwise would have developed, qualities I consciously forced into the background because I knew that their development would expose me to slights and hatred that my soul was not sufficiently robust to drop off lightly. What is the use of aspiring to leadership of men if every half-wit, scoundrel, or Philistine can knock you out with the single word *Jew*?

During my first school year our family was enlarged by a baby sister. A few weeks before this event took place in our home I had watched a stork flying by, carrying a frog in his long beak. Rosa, the nurse, did not fail to tell me that the bird was carrying a baby to some family, and for many years I was convinced that I had seen with my own eyes the great mystery. When we children were admitted for the first time to my mother's bedroom to see the newborn sister, I hardly glanced at the old brown cradle that contained the quaking bundle but insisted upon seeing my mother's leg. I supposed she was lying in bed because the stork had bitten her! I guess this was the beginning of my career as a biologist.

The immediate consequences of this increase of our family to four children—one baby girl had died from scarlet fever before I was born—were, however, rather unpleasant for me. They became visible in the person of a huge, high-bosomed woman, Frau Hinzelmann, a professional masseuse who was entrusted to massage my mother back to her good figure. At that time the cold-water fad had reached Germany from England, and thus Frau Hinzelmann was asked to give the boys a daily rubdown in a bed sheet soaked in ice-cold water. How we dreaded this performance executed with great bravado and strong fists! Fortunately, Frau Hinzelmann was not employed longer than she was needed for my mother, and, still more fortunately, my father, who loved his daily swim in the river Main, decided that it was time for us little boys to learn to swim. We were, therefore, handed over to the old swimming teacher, whom three generations knew by the name of Jean.

Swimming, only breast stroke of course, was taught the following way. First you were lowered into the water from a kind of gallows, supported by a canvas belt around the waist, to learn your strokes: one, knee up, two, three. If the teacher was not content you were dunked. When you knew your strokes, three inflated pig guts, looking like huge sausages, were tied around your waist and you had to swim the length of the pool—fenced off from the river—with Jean dangling a pole in front of you. Slowly you were graduated to two sausages and later to one, always only downstream. Then came the great moment of a swim without sausage, the pole in front still giving you the feeling of safety. Finally, you swam the whole stretch without aid. Then you were taken out to the stream in a boat and had to swim for five or ten minutes upstream and downstream behind the boat, and after that you were given the freedom of the place. From that time on I spent every possible afternoon in and around the river.

There was another rather beneficial consequence of the arrival of the baby sister. The apartment became too small, and my parents decided to move to the periphery of the town, where apartment houses had gardens and back yards. I was about nine years old, intellectually precocious but otherwise a sissy, as might be expected of a city boy who was led around by nurses and governesses. The probably very small back yard, bordering many similar ones inside the block, gave me the first chance to develop my body. Indian tents were pitched, athletic contests staged, and a large gang of young boys working across the fences separating the yards made the whole block uninhabitable for quiet citizens. My father might have employed a secretary to answer all the complaints about broken fences and windows, stripped cherry trees or currant bushes, stoned cats, boys urinating out of third-story windows, and similar feats and events. But my body grew strong among such performances and was prepared for later sportsmanship. Also, at this time, my first experience with smoking occurred. My father never smoked, and ladies who smoked just did not exist. Schoolboys up to eighteen years were not permitted to smoke, and no parent would have allowed a little boy to try a smoke. But a real redskin had to smoke a peace pipe—James Fenimore Cooper and his followers were the daily literary food of little boys in Germany—and something had to be done about it. An older boy told us what to do.

From a rattan chair a piece of rattan the size and shape of a cigarette was cut off and solemnly smoked in the wigwam. I do not remember the effect, but it must have been staggering.

One other little episode from this period also sticks in my mind because it affected me lastingly. One of the neighbors, an old lady, owned a beautiful garden with plenty of fruit, which we pilfered habitually. She also had a huge cat, which did not look at us in a very friendly way when we climbed the fence on fruit-gathering expeditions. Therefore, we slowly developed the "complex" that the cat was our greatest enemy and had to be done away with. One day an expedition of three climbed over the fence after ascertaining that the old lady was out. The cat was quietly dozing in the sun when we approached. We threw a lasso around her neck and dragged her through the garden to choke her. When she lay still, but not yet dead, the whites of her eyes turned out, we became frightened and ran away, leaving the poor animal where it was. Actually the cat recovered, but I was haunted by the memory of her breaking eyes. Ever since, the idea of killing an animal has been abhorrent to me. When it later became necessary in biological classes to kill an animal, I always had somebody else do it—whether the animal was a frog, a mouse, or a guinea pig. And I have never been able to understand how perfectly decent people can enjoy shooting at little birds or rabbits or deer and even boast of such feats and call the cowardly slaughter sport. On all my later trips into remote regions and so-called hunters' paradises I never carried any weapon whatsoever and never regretted it.

2: *THE GYMNASIUM*

When I was ten years old it was time to enter the school called the Gymnasium, the only one of the many types of middle school that then prepared for the university. Students attending this school, which roughly corresponded to a glorified combination of present-day high school and junior college, all intended to take up a profession. The universities, which in Germany are not colleges but exclusively professional schools leading to the doctorate, were, at that time, open only to the graduates of a Gymnasium. Thus it had to be decided long in advance whether a little boy would be inclined and fitted for a professional career. The question in my case was answered positively by my parents and teachers, and I was sent to the municipal Gymnasium of my home town, at that time a famous, progressive school.

Gymnasium in Germany meant a humanistic school, based strictly upon the ancient languages Latin and Greek. There was no choice of subjects. Everybody had nine years of Latin, nine of French, and six of Greek, each class meeting six to seven times a week. There were in addition much German and history, and a mathematics course that led in nine years from arithmetic and geometry up to calculus. I have since had ample chance to observe the school systems in many countries and to see their products. But I do not hesitate to say that the old Gymnasium, before it became diluted after World War I, was the best school I know for training the mind. We certainly hated Latin and Greek grammar and groaned under the weight of abstract work. But the result was young men able to think logically and to express themselves logically, imbued with the classical spirit of respect for learning; idealists and optimists; boys with an immensely broad background of knowledge in all the realms that make life worth living, anxious to learn and to think for themselves, prepared to attack from a high vantage point whatever mental work presented itself. Later I had to teach students with the same training and again later, when the universities were opened to graduates of nonhumanistic schools, students of different training. The difference between the two groups was simply amazing. The Gymnasium graduates, brought up practically without sciences, understood science much better than the graduates from modern schools based upon mathematics and science. I realized, and still believe, that secondary schools are more successful if they do not impart practical knowledge, useful in later life, but teach the impressionable young mind to work, to think clearly, to finish a task to the last detail, and to cherish erudition for its own sake as one of the greatest possessions a man can carry through life. Idealism must be taught, not utilitarianism.

My first day at the Gymnasium started badly. It was customary to begin the first session in the morning with the Lord's Prayer, spoken by the class leader, a boy not selected for his popularity but appointed by the head teacher for such qualities as submission, sissiness, and tattling. During the prayer everybody stood in devout posture, hands folded and neck bent. There had been no prayer in grammar school, and I had never been present at a public prayer. I had never heard the Lord's Prayer, and, occupying the front bench, I could not see what the others did. Thus I stood quietly in attention, looking at the teacher. When the prayer was finished and everybody sat down, the teacher stepped from the dais and brusquely ordered me to get up and give my name. When I had told it, he answered by giving me a terrible slap in my face that sent me down onto the bench.

Thus I was introduced to the Christian prayer and simultaneously to my greatest enemy for the following years, Professor Jungblut. Jungblut was an excellent philologist and a very good teacher, but I think he was a kind of sadist. The students called him "vinegar bottle" because his face was always distorted with a sour expression. He never smiled and never said a pleasant word. He hated me from the very first moment and, though he always gave me the grades I deserved, usually good ones, used my slightest error or fault as excuse to punish me most severely. His lessons, good as they were, thus became for me a torture that I had to endure for four years. When in later life, by then a university professor, I met him on the street, he still looked at me with a face distorted by hate.

But one day he went too far. Another boy and I had entered the school's music room during the recess, opened the sacred piano, and amused ourselves by playing some little tunes we knew. This crime was reported to Jungblut by the official stool pigeon. During the next Latin class we both were ordered to step up front. Jungblut got out from behind his desk a rattan cane, gripped my friend's left hand with his own, and, mercilessly beating the boy's thighs, drove him screaming around in a circle until the cane broke. This finished, Jungblut sent a boy to the neighboring room to borrow another cane, this time a palm-leaf rib, which is far superior even to rattan. Then the same procedure started with me and continued until Jungblut's arm dropped. Though I could hardly sit or lie down for many days, I did not dare to tell my parents. But two weeks later Kathrin, my former wet nurse and afterward for forty-five years our cook, discovered the swollen bloody streaks on my thighs while tending to my ablutions, and reported her discovery to my parents. My father, a quiet and retiring gentleman, who usually left educational matters to my energetic mother, went himself to see the principal and threatened him with action by the board of education. His success was such that all canes were banned henceforth from classrooms, and Jungblut showed me his hate only by furious looks. But to these I became accustomed.

In spite of Professor Jungblut, however, it was during my first year in the Gymnasium that I received the impression which gave my life its decisive turn. The teaching in natural history, not very important in the traditional Gymnasium curriculum, was usually entrusted to some philologist and was of corresponding quality. But in Frankfurt, which had a long tradition of interest in natural history centered around the famous Senckenberg Museum, a special teacher was provided. This man, F. C. Noll, a zoologist in his own right, was the ideal teacher. Kindly, understanding, master of his subject and impressing the boys with his mastery, he was the most beloved teacher in the school, and his two weekly classes, unfortunately given only in the five lower grades, were considered a pleasure, which could not have been said of the Latin and Greek lessons. He taught in a special room containing the collections and apparatus, and the walls were decorated with lithographic charts. Three of these I can still see before my eyes: the sinter terraces in New Zealand, which had already been destroyed by an earthquake; the lava lake of the Kilauea crater; and the Grand Canyon of the Colorado River. Whenever I looked at these marvels I knew that

13

I must one day see them, and I was sure that I would become a naturalist and explore the five corners of the world. What was then the vague longing of a child very soon afterward crystallized into the real conception of a life as a naturalist.

It was an old tradition among the boys that, in the last session of a term, Noll had to tell a story. Noll was a full-fledged zoologist who had done good research work and who did quite a bit of outside lecturing. He was a much-traveled man, at least for a schoolteacher with a small salary and at a time when even the well-to-do rarely traveled outside the country. And he could make his travelogues charming and exciting to the youthful audience. Thus, when he entered class in the last session, everybody shouted, "A story, please!" He first winced a little and then started his yarn. Only one of these I remember.

He had traveled to Norway, and, standing in Christiania (now Oslo) at the window of a bookstore, he was strongly attracted to a picture representing a tall, fair man jumping on skis across an abyss. Skiing was at that time completely unknown in Germany, and, listening to the story then, I certainly did not suspect how much pleasure, excitement, and exhilaration I was later to derive from this greatest of all sports. The next day, Noll continued, he was visiting at the university with a fellow zoologist when the door opened and the very skier from the picture entered in person. He was Fridtjof Nansen, just back from his famous trip across Greenland on skis. Ten years later I had the honor of standing face to face with this wonderful man, zoologist, oceanographer, explorer, statesman, humanitarian, who had recently returned from the memorable *Fram* expedition after having been thought lost for years. I never have seen, before or after, a more ideal type of hero. He was a real Viking, with a face that seemed to be carved from a block of wood, a man who forced young and old alike to that genuine hero worship immortalized in literature by Carlyle.

But to return to Noll. By the time I reached my thirteenth year his influence, together with my inclination, had already made me an incipient naturalist. At first I thought only of traveling and exploring, but soon I was captivated by the great ideas behind the biological facts to which I was initiated, at a tender age, by voracious reading of such radical popularizers as Büchner, Vogt, and Haeckel.

Daily life in these first Gymnasium years ran a rather unexciting course. The education of the children was my mother's domain, whereas my father was the provider, looked at from a distance with deep veneration and awe, though he never punished his children. Actually, he was not a happy man. Fitted by his gifts and personality to be a scholar, he had been forced by his parents to take over the family business. For reasons unknown to me, perhaps his retiring nature, his parents had been less good to him than to a younger brother of his. He had to run the difficult and exacting business, while his brother, who was the partner, lived the pleasant life of a gentleman. When my father walked to his office early in the morning, his brother might pass him on horseback in gay society. My father had not been given a chance to develop his beautiful singing voice, whereas the brother had studied with good teachers and was able to sing solo parts in oratorios. My father could get away only rarely for a much-needed vacation, but my uncle found time to become a great mountaineer, at home with all the difficult peaks of the Alps, and to play golf in Switzerland—there was no golf in Germany at that time—with such success that he still won a championship when he was seventy years old. In my uncle's house, painters and musicians contributed to an interesting social life (the great Hans Thoma was one of his friends), but my father was too tired and too much occupied with business worries to entertain extensively.

Thus a highly gifted and noble man became embittered and hypochondriac and lived more beside the family than within it. Moreover, as I realized only much later, my parents' married life was not very happy. Certainly my mother loved her husband, and my father kept strictly the religious rules of marriage. But there was no community of souls, and, since my mother was very strong-willed, my father, hating any conflict, left to her the education of the children while he watched from afar and frequently with silent disapproval. My mother had a very good heart and never failed anybody in need, and she loved her children dearly, but she had no gift for education. Willful changes from extreme spoiling to unnecessary spanking, and forbidding a thousand little things dear to a boy's heart, made her actions unpredictable. She believed strictly in authority, in simplicity, and in parsimony. But she overdid all of them, and, since we children had inherited her strong mind, there were frequent conflicts, settled on mother's side with punishments, on ours with little ruses and tricks. These tricks, I think, were the worst effect of wrong educational methods. Overstrictness in things that hurt the pride of a young boy can easily make him sullen, if not worse, and we were certainly exposed to that danger.

Fortunately, there was a potent counterweight, and this was Kathrin, the cook. Kathrin had entered our house as a young "fallen" girl, to be my wet nurse. She came in her beautiful Hessian peasant garb, a kind of ballet skirt with about twenty petticoats underneath; thick, white, patterned wool stockings with a silken garter below the exposed knees; a strange, tight bodice; and on top of her head a miniature stiff hood fastened around the chin with broad, dangling silk ribbons. When I was weaned she donned city garb and remained as our cook for forty-five more years. She developed such a mastery in the fine art of cooking that an invitation to my parents' table was considered a treat, though on ordinary days we ate the plainest foods.

Kathrin bestowed all the maternal feelings she had upon me, and the love was reciprocal. Whatever nature may have failed to bestow on her by way of intelligence was fully made up by an unfailing maternal instinct and a never-ending power for love. No wonder that she was to me another mother. Whatever happened, whatever went through my mind, whatever small or large sorrow appeared, the first thing to do was to go to the kitchen where Kathrin heard what nobody else would have been told. Never did the simple mind of the peasant girl fail me or any of us children. She always provided advice, comfort, and a way out of trouble. From her own little money she bought the small things we longed for and that my mother thought would spoil us—a saw or hammer, a butterfly net, or what not. Of course there was always some fruit or dessert hidden in the kitchen when we were denied it at table as a punishment. She was my confessor, my helper, my friend, and sometimes my banker—my confidante in my young boyhood and much, much later. It was she who gave me the visible tenderness for which a child longs. I could not sleep before she had tucked me in and said the simple prayer with me.

Thus Kathrin was an inseparable part of my childhood. She lived with us while the children grew into men and moved away. She was considered a member of the family, who knew everything and was consulted about everything, but nevertheless she insisted that the distance between employer and employee, which she regarded as ordained by God, be strictly observed. I am grateful that chance made me visit at my parents' house during the last days of seventy-year-old Kathrin. She felt sick and for the first time in forty-five years she wanted to lie down. As the maid's room was not very nice we put a bed for her into one of the drawing rooms and called a nurse. The physician could not find anything wrong with her. The next morning I sat with her and found her comfortable but weak. When I had gone for a short time to the adjoining room I suddenly heard the nurse cry, "Kathrin, Kathrin," and after a few seconds of silence drop on her knees and start to pray. The noble soul had been quietly extinguished like a burnt candle. If there should be a world beyond the grave of the type imagined by the believers, I am sure that the peasant girl Kathrin sits in glory next to the throne of the Lord.

At that time, around my tenth year, boys of the solid burghers in my home town did not enjoy much freedom. School was held in summer from seven to twelve and from three to five, and in winter from eight to twelve and from two to four, including Saturday morning, with only Wednesday and Saturday afternoon free. There was much homework to be done, there were music lessons and practicing. There was also the horror of horrors, French governesses, poor young girls (and sometimes very pretty ones) who put up bravely with their difficult position between maids and employers. They had to take us out to the parks in our "good" suits, which we hated, and we had to talk French and behave, both of which we detested. Or we were sent to make our obeisance to the old grandmothers, aristocratic, stiff, and correct ladies in whose presence we hardly dared to breathe. The only freedom was on the way to and from school, a time that we stretched to the limit and filled with fighting, shooting marbles, spinning tops, or snowballing.

During the summer vacation we moved to one of the small resorts in the nearby mountain range, and here Kathrin roamed with us through the woods, gathering berries or catching butterflies, and we could forget for a short time the good manners of the city child. But sometimes part of the vacation was spent in one of the famous spas, where again we had to march cleanly dressed in the park and sit near the bandstand. I remember the fitting end of one such vacation in the hated fashionable spa of Homburg. While my mother was packing I seesawed across the back of an armchair. Suddenly the thing turned over, crashing into a French mirror that extended from floor to ceiling, and the expensive piece came down in splinters. The bill had to be paid by my parents, but it was written upon the end of my back.

Perhaps the best vacations I spent, however, were with a former maid of ours. She had married a very poor man, and, in sending me to her for a paid-for vacation, my parents could help her a little without showing their intention. She lived in a village near the Rhine in a small but clean house. The husband made a scant living as a peddler, and he was actually the type of Jewish peddler pictured in newspaper cartoons—tall and thin, with a pale face framed by a black beard. In the morning he took up his heavy peddler's pack, a kind of notion store within a large box, wandered far away, and returned at night all tired out and with the few pennies he had made. Whenever he could be persuaded to take me, I went along and felt like an explorer. I remember one day we crossed the Rhine in a rowboat in the early morning mist and the river seemed unbelievably broad. Then we walked the highway to detached farmhouses. Sometimes we entered the front gate; sometimes we were chased away with insulting words. If admitted, we went into the kitchen where the peddler, surrounded by the maids and farm hands, unfolded his treasures and tried to sell ribbons, hairpins, combs, buttons, or even cheap flannel and the like. Occasionally the housewife offered a cup of so-called coffee and a hunk of bread. I found such expeditions marvelous and could not get enough of them.

Another beautiful thing about these vacations was sheaf gathering. When the peasants in the village had finished their harvest, and wheat and oats had been brought in, the fields were opened to the poor, landless people of the village who could gather what was lying around. With the poor children I spent days in the field gathering individual sheaves, which were collected in gunny sacks and taken home on wheelbarrows to be milled. For the city child these activities of the poorest in the village were the most thrilling experiences. It was during one of these vacations that I saw my first bicycle, one with a six-foot wheel, on which a proud sportsman pedaled through the village followed by the village children crying, *"Ein Schnellaüfer"* ("A fast runner").

Outside of vacations we escaped the governesses and grandmothers on Sundays. Whenever weather permitted, my father took a hike on Sundays, at least ten miles, together with a bachelor friend and his dachshund, and one or two of us boys were allowed to

Solomon Goldschmidt, 1875

Emma Flürscheim Goldschmidt, 1875

Richard (*right*) at the age of four, with his brothers
Alfred and Bernhard

Uncle Michael Flürscheim, single taxer and utopian

come along. We walked in the countryside from noon to dusk and wound up with a glass of cider and a piece of cheese in one of the popular beer gardens. We enjoyed these hikes immensely—I have been an inveterate hiker ever since—and the more so because this was the only occasion on which my father loosened up and discussed all kinds of topics with his friend.

One of the most vivid impressions of these early years was the great Electricity Fair, the first in Germany and a national event. For the first time I saw an incandescent bulb. The fair grounds were lighted with the new invention. A power station, the first in Germany, had been erected two hundred miles from our town. The high-voltage power was transmitted to the fair, transformed, and used for the illumination and to drive electric motors, dynamos, and even an electric tramcar! No one who did not live through those gaslight years can imagine the thrill that young and old experienced: you could light a room just by pushing a button. The marvel was brought home to the excited spectator in an especially effective way by a model theater with a switchboard in front. By pushing buttons, the operator could produce all the stage effects: day and night, starlit skies, moonlight, thunderstorm, sunrise, sunset, and *Alpenglühen*—the glowing of Alpine peaks after sunset. I do not know how often I stood in front of the stage experiencing the romantic illusion of the theater enriched by the mystery of technical invention.

It was a special privilege for me to view these wonders in company of one of my uncles, who was an enthusiastic proponent of technical progress. Well acquainted with the doings in America, fascinated by technology, he prophesied technical developments that nobody believed but that today are commonplace and available to everybody. This brother of my mother, Michael Flürscheim, was a remarkable personality. He certainly was a genius, but his genius unfortunately was obscured by the faults of the autodidact who has not worked systematically on the fundamentals of knowledge and therefore falls easy prey to all kinds of quackery. As an adolescent my uncle had been sent by his parents to the United States. There he made a fortune in a few years, became interested in technological progress as well as in certain social ideas of his time, and made up for the gaps in his education by reading. He took up Henry George's single-tax ideas, translated *Progress and Poverty*, and started upon a literary career in the same field. Returning to Germany, he became a manufacturer but devoted all his spare time

19

to propagating and developing the single-tax idea, founding societies, editing periodicals, and writing pamphlets and books, some of them Utopian. He was a great fighter and fanatic and therefore had constant rows with politicians, administrators, and even his collaborators. Finally he sold his factory in order to put his social ideas into practice. At first he believed that free-trade England would be the best soil for the propagation of his ideas, and he settled there. But hating monarchies he moved on to free Switzerland. Then he tried to found a Utopian colony in Mexico, an experiment that ended with the loss of much of his fortune because the members of the colony preferred his money to his ideas. Whereupon he decided that only a new country could put his social ideas into practice, and he emigrated to New Zealand. It seems, however, that the New Zealanders were not anxious to try his schemes, and he subsequently settled in California. Then, an old man who had been robbed of most of his fortune by impostors who knew his weaknesses, he returned to Germany to die.

Uncle Michael, constantly living in high tension, was most interesting for the rest of the family, and we boys enjoyed his sporadic appearances immensely as he always brought excitement and new schemes. But he was also dangerous, for he had the ability of the reformer to talk everybody into his projects. He had ideas about everything and tried to force them upon everyone, and, since he was by nature a Utopian, his ideas were frequently dangerous because not of this world. If he talked my father into some investment, say in television, the money was invariably lost because Uncle Michael's ideas were fifty years ahead of the technical facts.

I do not know how it happened that this extremely intelligent man became a spiritualist and remained one for the rest of his life, but so he did, and whenever he appeared there were table rapping, spirit writing, and the like in the family and even my quiet father became upset and began to wonder if there could be something behind such phenomena. Two of the many stories told about these activities are worth recording. Uncle Michael's son, who later became a leading chemist and one of the pioneers of the modern valency theory, could not believe in spiritualism, a failure that worried his father. My uncle therefore sent his son to a famous medium in the United States who, he felt sure, would convert him. A seance was arranged, and after the usual hocus-pocus the medium asked my cousin with whom he wanted to establish contact. He chose his grandmother. Soon the spirit announced her presence in the usual insipid way, by rapping, and my cousin was ordered to ask questions of his grandmother's spirit. This he did, but of course in German. The medium was disconcerted and asked him to speak plain English. He answered that this would be of no use since his grandmother had not known a word of English. Thereupon the medium claimed that the spirit was actually only a control spirit who did not understand German. Unfortunately, my cousin was not convinced.

The other anecdote concerns an incident that happened after my uncle's death. He had succeeded in converting his wife to spiritualism, and so, after he died, she expected communications. For a long time nothing happened, but one day one of my uncle's spiritualistic friends telegraphed my widowed aunt that contact had finally been established with the deceased: Uncle Michael said he felt perfectly well in the other world and that his back didn't ache any more! My aunt, otherwise a clear-minded, energetic woman of the world, was happy to have the message.

It was this same remarkable uncle who almost succeeded in interfering seriously with my life. Once he made one of his sporadic appearances in our home town to visit his mother, my venerable and really remarkable grandmother. As usual, he told his relatives how they ought to educate their children. Since I was considered a gifted boy, he was especially interested in putting me on the right path. He managed to persuade my father that the humanistic Gymnasium was fossilized, that the future belonged exclusively to technology—the word technocracy had not yet been invented—and that a gifted boy had no right to play with silly ideas for his future but had to be prepared to be some kind of engineer or technical inventor. (The rise of Edison's star at this time enhanced my uncle's belief in invention by intuition.) Since Latin and Greek were of no use for such a career, he suggested transferring me to one of the so-called "realistic" middle schools, which concentrated on modern languages, mathematics, and physics. He actually succeeded in persuading my father to ask for my dismissal from the Gymnasium and register me in a "realistic" school.

Fortunately, it soon turned out that my preparation for this school was insufficient. I had had no English—it was not taught in the Gymnasium—and not enough mathematics. Therefore I would have had to lose two grades. My persuasive uncle had left meanwhile, and I was returned again, after a few weeks of this intermezzo, to my old Gymnasium class. I remember every detail of

21

my reappearance. I had already entered into the wild years of adolescence and was considered a pest by my teachers. In the first session of the morning the Latin teacher, a huge fellow with an immense stomach and a drooping, sea-lion mustache, entered his classroom. When the boys were seated—they had to stand at attention while the professor looked around the room—his face suddenly became distorted with horror. Gasping, he exclaimed: "Goldschmidt, you are back again!" and sank into his chair.

This was the most confused period of my life. When I was twelve or thirteen, puberty set in with storms and earthquakes that shook me thoroughly. Still today I cannot understand why there was no one in my surroundings, neither parents nor teachers, who understood what was going on in me. No one tried to help me out of the confusion caused by the beginning action of my glands. How many boys yearly get into trouble for the same reasons and are misunderstood and misjudged—though nowadays parents and teachers do know much more about the biological background of youthful behavior. There were many old, experienced, and well-meaning teachers who ought to have known what it means when a gifted boy of fourteen, always a good scholar, suddenly concentrates on utterly bad behavior. But the only thing my teachers knew was punishment and more punishment for smaller and larger pranks.

Indeed, I spent most of my time at school inventing and carrying out more or less harmless pranks—fixing charts and blackboards to crash down at the desired moment or putting a pane of window glass on a chair of a teacher who was inclined to dump himself heavily into his chair. I certainly was not the only one who perpetrated these crimes, but such was my reputation that I was punished whether I was guilty or not. Unmerited punishment prodded me to worse deeds, and I became a recognized pest.

For a long time I nevertheless remained a good student, since my quick memory made schoolwork easy. But this did not change my general standing, as attested each year at commencement exercises. For these exercises all the boys assembled in the biggest hall of the city and the galleries were occupied by the parents. Before the principal addressed the graduating class with one of his famous speeches, the roll of each of the nine grades was called in the order of scholarship so that everybody in town knew who was first, twelfth, or last in his grade. The three best in each grade were given prizes, usually books. I was always among the first three but never received a prize because of my bad behavior, and the whole school and all the parents witnessed this humiliation. Something very typical of German mentality occurred at these occasions. In my class there was the son of a general, the military commander of the district and hence its highest official. This boy habitually occupied the fourth to the six place in the order of scholarship, and, although in other grades there were never more than three prizes presented, in our grade there were always as many distributed as were necessary to include the general's son. The pedagogic effect of all this upon me should be obvious: I decided to avenge myself by becoming still more unmanageable.

In time, toward my fifteenth year, my scholarship began to slip. From my place among the top three in my class I slid slowly down until I was one of the last three in the class of thirty. I did not do any more homework and relied completely upon my memory. But since, instead of listening in class, I read a book held on my knees under the desk, my memory was of no use. This sometimes led to grotesque situations, one of which I still vividly remember.

Our homework had been to prepare a couple of pages of Vergil— the passage in which he describes in resounding Latin verses the sea serpent swimming toward Troy. The serpent is described in considerable detail, which means for the student a great many unusual nouns and adjectives to look up in the dictionary. This of course I had not done when fate, in the shape of the Latin teacher, called upon me to translate the passage. Glancing quickly over the pages I thought I recognized some words describing a convivial feast. Thus I started to improvise a glowing description of a feast, imagining I was covering more or less the contents of the passage. The whole class roared: I could not understand why. The teacher got up from his chair and slowly but furiously advanced toward me. When I had finished my performance, rather well I thought, he struck. Of course he was sure that I was purposely making a fool of him.

My vanishing scholarship during that year began with failure in history. In our democratic and anti-Prussian home town the government board of education insisted upon special training in Prussianism through a detailed study of Prussian history. This history, at least before Frederick the Great, is ridiculously uninteresting, the history of semibarbaric local princes and their unimportant doings at a time when the cultural history of Germany was being made in the free towns. I simply could not swallow this insipid stuff, and since my interest in the sciences had already come to the foreground I read science books secretly during history classes. When the time came to graduate from this grade, for some reason a special examination was instituted to be given to students who had failed in something. Ordinarily there were no examinations until the final one after nine years. I was ordered to take this examination in history. One single question was asked—the date of one of the minor Prussian wars called "the potato war." I did not know the answer and was flunked, to repeat the whole year. Of course this was meant as a punishment for my other sins and was well deserved, but it was not permissible on the basis of a fake examination. My father brought the matter to the school board, and a compromise was reached. There were two parallel series of courses, one starting and ending in the spring, the other in the autumn. I was taken over into the second group, and thus I lost only half a year. It turned out that the change to new teachers and new classmates was one of the great strokes of luck of my life.

One result of my restlessness during this period was a mania for devouring books—a mania aided in a peculiar way. My father was a member of the burghers' club, which owned a large library and lent the books to club members. Each week I was sent there to exchange my parents' books. The old book was presented and registered; then I went to the stacks, picked out the books my parents had indicated, and presented them again to the librarian for registration.

On the shelves of the stacks I found the most wonderful books—those of Jules Verne, innumerable books on travel, the books of the apostles of atheism, books on prehistory, and what not. As my reading at home was supervised and restricted to what my mother believed to be suitable for my age, I invented my own method of taking out the books I wanted to read. I went to the library in a wide waterproof overcoat, picked from the shelves the books I wanted, hid them under the folds of my coat when presenting my parents' books to the librarian, and then returned the books in the same way the following week. This meant, of course, secret reading at home. When I had to sit down to my desk to do my homework I held my book on my knees, and whenever my mother entered the room to see if I was doing my school work the book was pressed against the desk and became invisible. The same technique was used in school. At night I escaped with a candle to a certain unlighted cabinet and read and read in the poorly lit and unventilated water closet until my absence was noted and I had to reappear.

It is surprising that, under such circumstances, I did not read poor literature or even obscene books. Actually I read mostly good books that increased my knowledge, trained my literary taste, and prepared me for much of what I later did professionally. The great turning point came when I hit upon Büchner's *Kraft und Stoff*, the bible of monists and atheists, a book that impressed me immensely and had lasting influence. I know now how superficial this book is, but when I was fourteen years old I was ready for just that type of fare.

I had, in fact, already lost my child's faith. At twelve I still said my prayer at night and added on my own account the wish that the Lord might not send me certain much-dreaded dreams. These dreams were one of the features of puberty, and they appeared over and over so that finally I was in terror of going to bed. One of them I still remember. I visited the Natural History Museum, an old building with narrow staircases and galleries surrounding a central court. This building was actually one of my favorite haunts. There I climbed to the top of the gallery where the shells were exhibited. From this point a narrow stairway, which existed only in my dream, led higher up. I climbed it and entered a dark room. When I looked up I saw, seated against the wall, three white, phosphorescent ghosts, a terrible-looking one in the center and smaller ones at each side. Screaming I raced down the stairs and awoke in terror.

When I was thirteen I had to be confirmed. Twice a week I walked with a schoolmate the two miles to the house of a venerable rabbi who taught us the articles of faith and the ethical precepts in very much the same way that my Christian friends were prepared for confirmation. But the effect was an unexpected one—and my Christian friends had the same experience—namely, to raise doubts. On our way to and from the lesson, my schoolmate and I spent our time violently debating the existence of God, and at the time of confirmation I had already lost all the beliefs of my childhood. The reading of Büchner gave me, at the same time, a new spiritual background. Büchner's arguments, as well as those of Karl Vogt and Ernst Haeckel, were based on biology. Thus I began to realize that biology, which had attracted me mostly from the standpoint of travel and adventure, was a philosophical science, leading up to all the ultimate problems that harrowed me. This realization started me reading popular science and, later, actually studying the field that, I began to realize, was to be my eternal love. Of course many difficulties were found along the way. When I first brought home Haeckel's *Natural History of Creation* my mother discovered in the book pictures of human embryos and objected to my reading "obscene" literature at my tender age. Such was the prudery of that day. But I read the book many times and lived in its world of revolt against established creeds.

To the manifold activities of the adolescent boy was also added music. Coming from a family in which music was cherished by many members, and which has produced good amateur as well as professional musicians, I was started on the piano when I was about six years old. My teacher was a fine old lady, widow of a musician, who made a living by teaching the elements of piano playing without either training or gift. I am sure she was chosen as my teacher only to help the poor thing. Thus she taught me to play some ditties and operatic selections without any basic practice in scales and etudes. The prize piece was an insipid concoction called "Dance of the Fairies" which her deceased husband had composed and which I am still able to whistle.

When I had attained this perfection, my mother, unfortunately the only nonmusical member of the family, decided that her wonderful boy was ready to take up the higher art of piano playing. One day I was presented to Bernhard Scholz, well-known director of the famous Hoch Conservatory, for an entrance examination. He ordered me to play a C minor scale. I had never heard of such a thing. Already getting angry, he asked for any scale I could play. I did not succeed in playing any. Then with a threatening voice he asked on what basis I expected to be accepted, and I performed the "Dance of the Fairies." I do not know how my mother and her boy left the room, but one thing is sure: not physically, but morally, it was via a kick in the pants.

I certainly was happy that my piano-playing ended thus. But when I was about thirteen years old, since I was obviously endowed with a musical ear, it was decided that I should take up the study of the violin. It was unbearable for the pride of the family that some cousins of the same age were already good musicians, and one of them, later the first-rank pianist Paul Goldschmidt, was even a very good one. Unfortunately, the teacher was again selected not for his pedagogic gifts but because he needed help. Mr. Einzig, a member of the municipal opera orchestra, was a very interesting fellow, but he was lazy. He had read immensely and was a great admirer of Dante. When he found out that I was an intelligent boy, eager to learn and to discuss, he spent half or more of the violin lesson discussing literature and art. Since as a rule I had not practiced properly for my lesson, I was only too glad to postpone the moment when this would become apparent. When the lesson took place in our house, Mr. Einzig usually declared after a while that he felt nauseated. He had good reason for this, for he knew that my father kept some very good French cognac for emergencies, and this he was given as appropriate medicine. Thus I learned very little at just the time when the decisive foundation for a clean technique should have been laid. How many times in later life did I regret this, when I again took up the violin and played it in duets, trios, quartets, and orchestras without ever being able to make up for the basic faults of my technique.

In my fifteenth year, I began to engage in some less commendable pastimes. My curiosity and my ambition to take part in everything led me to associate with a bad group of boys. As a result, like Dr. Jekyll and Mr. Hyde, I would walk well-dressed and sissylike in the park with my mother or governess and then an hour later when I had escaped, using one lie or another, I would join the gang. I was introduced to this bad company by a classmate, an Austrian boy a few years older than I, who, tutored by his elder brother, had already learned to drink beer and to use obscene language. He took me to his brother's gang, low-class fellows who met in the upper floor of a beerhouse in one of the worst quarters of the town. The school, of course, strictly prohibited visits to beerhouses or cafes except in the company of parents. Such sprees, therefore, were considered heroic deeds.

I would slip out on certain afternoons from five to seven and head for the beerhouse. I was not brought up a teetotaler, but my father drank hardly anything except a glass of Bordeaux with dinner, while the children received red wine thoroughly diluted with water. Now, on these afternoons, I drank three glasses of beer, the taste of which I disliked, because it was considered manly and even heroic to be a great drinker. I learned the secrets of formal beer drinking as exercised in German student fraternities with all their ridiculous rules (called *Komment*), including duels to see who could swallow one, two, or three glasses of beer in single gulps. I do not remember the conversation at these occasions, but it was certainly bawdy. When I came home for supper, which was eaten at seven-thirty, I was not hungry and looked pale and had to invent explanations.

And there was a worse side to it. To do all these things under the eyes of my very strict and inquisitive mother, I had to build up the most complicated ruses held together by a framework of lies. In addition I had to find the money, as my extremely limited pocket money did not suffice. Thus I began to sell my books, even my daily-needed schoolbooks, and to pilfer my parents' library. There was in a narrow side street near my school an old antiquarian, a mean-looking, lean fellow with a reddish goatee, who sat in his *boutique* behind a wire partition and opened a small window when a customer came in. His customers were mostly schoolboys who sold their old schoolbooks or who bought one for a few cents whenever they had forgotten to take the proper book to school. To sell a book you shoved it over his desk, and, without speaking a word, he shoved back his price, which was final. His name was Hops, and we called the whole procedure "to hopse a book." Thus "hopsing" financed my side-stepping. Nobody noticed it, and therefore nobody helped me to get over the wild afflictions of puberty. Fortunately I did not go further than I have reported, and decisive help came finally when I flunked a grade and had to lose a semester in school.

This public dishonor, known not only to my comrades but also to all the families to whom my proud mother had boasted of the gifts of her second child, impressed me deeply. I began to realize that I had made bad use of my gifts and had behaved abominably to my parents, who believed in me. I actually threw off everything improper overnight. In my new class I did not start again with pranks; I followed the lessons with attention and immediately became again one of the top students. The association with the gang stopped, and I found new friends of a very different type. I entered a period of intensive occupation with things in which I became interested, and outside of school I read profusely on many topics, though properly counterbalancing my work with sports. As a result of my earlier readings on evolution I became absorbed in prehistory, which at that time was known to few outside the profession. This again got me interested in the evolution of language, and a book on comparative linguistics fascinated me so much that I learned whatever scripts I could lay hands on—runes, hieroglyphics, Arabic—and amused myself with writing exercises in these scripts. This hobby has remained with me to some extent. In later life, I tried to learn Chinese ideograms, and still today I enjoy following words back to their original forms. It was also during this time, my sixteenth and seventeenth years, that I first tried to read the great philosophers, but without success. I could not understand what Kant and Schopenhauer were driving at. Since that time I have tried many times again to round out my philosophical training and have forced myself to read through the tedious works of the great philosophers. I have never succeeded in getting anything out of them, and I still think that the condition of the sciences would remain exactly as it is if the books of all the philosophers were used for heating the slums.

But my real love still belonged to biology—which was not taught at all in the upper grades of the Gymnasium—and I read in earnest whatever biological works were accessible. Darwin, Haeckel, Huxley, Spencer became my heroes, and whenever my class made one of the regular school hikes I would assemble a group of boys around me and try to put over the belief in evolution and, as I was led to believe, its correlate, monism. On one of these occasions I remember overhearing our class leader, i.e., best scholar and greatest sissy, a very godly boy already destined to be a preacher, remark bitingly to another group, "Goldschmidt is again out converting people." In later life I have regretted many times not having any more of the insatiable curiosity, the intensity of conviction, and the urge to make others see the light which shook me in those years of *Sturm und Drang*. I acted like a volcano in constant eruption and made a like impression upon my surroundings.

I had the great luck that my private interest in the sciences, an interest not shared by my friends and not encouraged in school, was directed at that time—my sixteenth year—into an orderly channel. My home town was one of the most progressive cities in Germany and, keeping up the democratic traditions of the former free city-republic, took pride in its educational institutions, which were independent of the Prussian system and run by private citizens. There was a century-old natural history society, the still-flourishing Senckenberg Society, to which all citizens of standing belonged and which centered around an excellent museum. This was run entirely by voluntary workers (except for the preparators, janitors, and so forth). Men who in the daytime were physicians, teachers, and bank clerks went at night to the museum as custodians of the different departments and were fine specialists in their respective fields. The same society offered lecture courses in zoology and botany in the late afternoon, and, though these lectures were attended mostly by physicians and teachers, boys in the upper grades of the Gymnasium were admitted if the school agreed. I became a regular attendant and acquired knowledge that, in another city, I might not have gained before entering a university.

The zoology lectures were given by a great original, Heinrich Reichenbach. Son of poor parents, he had aspired to be a zoologist but had to be content with a middle-school teacher's career, for at that time a university career required private funds. For some time he continued with research in his spare moments, and his monograph on the development of the crayfish became a classic. But when he was appointed lecturer in the Senckenberg Society—without pay, since he earned his living as a municipal teacher in a middle school—he devoted all his spare time to his lectures, which were the most stimulating courses I have ever heard. He combined zoology and physiology in a way that only much later was accepted in the university. He followed carefully all new developments and discussed them with a passionate partisanship. He made demonstrations and always had on exhibit the pertinent original papers and the classic monographs. Thus I could handle, after the lecture, such treasures as the original volumes of Aldrovandi, Malpighi, Vesalius, Swammerdam, Rösel von Rosenhof, Harvey—all with their wonderful copperplates—and learned in time to respect what has been done before us. Reichenbach, who was proud of using the easygoing, singing, but vigorous dialect of our town, had a special gift for colorful, picturesque language not always fit for ladies' ears (there were no ladies at the lectures), which increased the interest in the subject and helped understanding. I learned easily the basic facts of our science and simultaneously was made to see from the beginning the great general problems hidden behind the simplest facts. So it is I remember this excellent man, one of that host of potentially great men who never become known outside their own small circle, as one of the great benefactors of my youth. When, later, already an academic teacher, I returned to my home town on occasional visits, I never failed to call on old Reichenbach and discuss with him whatever was new and exciting in science. I wish all boys could have such blessed teachers.

During these later visits I also used to meet Reichenbach in a different way. He was a bachelor and extremely fond of good wine, which belongs to a spirited conversation. It is an old German custom for a group of men to club together and meet on certain evenings in some beerhouse where a special table, the *Stammtisch,* is reserved for them. There are the *Stammtische* of the Philistines, who indulge in small talk and smutty stories; there are the *Stammtische* of the political-minded, where the politics of the day join with the beer to heat the participants' heads. But there are also tables at which really good conversation is made, quickened by the effects of moderate consumption of good wine. Such a one was Reichenbach's *Stammtisch,* composed exclusively of originals like himself, mostly bachelors.

My last years in the Gymnasium were full of intellectual pursuits, in addition to my interest in biology. Looking back I wonder how it was possible to do all these things outside school and still have time for intensive sport and the ordinary pleasures of youth. It seems that a boy between sixteen and eighteen is like a sponge expanding and absorbing to the limit. Of course, I was in an uncommonly favorable position, growing up in a town that did everything possible for education far ahead of the rest of Germany. What the Senckenberg Society did for science, the Freie Deutsche Hochstift, an organization built up in the spirit of Frankfurt's greatest son, Goethe, did for the humanities. Here I had a chance to hear evening lectures by great university teachers invited to speak on all kinds of topics, especially art.

It was here that I first learned what art might mean in a man's life, and it was here that the foundation for a knowledge and appreciation of the arts, which were to mean so much to me in later life, was laid. At the same time my interest in belles-lettres was aroused and led into the proper channels by the man who was probably the finest teacher in our school, Felix Bölte. He was very different from all the other teachers, who were very outspokenly middle-class, badly dressed, frequently queer and crankish, though very scholarly and often good pedagogues. Bölte was considered haughty and sophisticated. He was a bachelor with relatives in England, and frequent visits there had emancipated him from the provincialism of our town. He had learned to dress well and to take care of his appearance. He brought from England the sporting spirit, organized football and gymnastics, coached rowing teams, and taught us the Anglo-Saxon concept of sport, still relatively unknown in Germany. Though he was a Greek scholar, later an authority on Homeric geography, he also taught German literature, and through him I was introduced to the great literature of all countries and learned to pick out the best. I read profusely in German, French, English (which I had been taught outside of school by a private teacher), Latin, and Greek, and had the opportunity of relating my reactions to this splendid teacher of youth. It was the same man who led me systematically to Goethe, the greatest of the great, whose works have accompanied me through a greater part of my life and remain the fountain of beauty and wisdom to which I have returned again and again.

It was also during these years that the foundations of my musical education were laid. I do not mean my own poor handling of the violin as a child or my occasional participation in the performances of the school orchestra, but the beginning acquaintance with the works of the great masters. My first acquaintance was, oddly enough, with grand opera. Both my grandmothers subscribed to the weekly performances of the excellent municipal opera, a stock company with many national and even international stars. Frequently the same works were performed more than once, and the grandchildren were given the seats if the grandmothers did not feel like hearing the same opera a number of times in succession. Thus I heard all the grand operas from Mozart to Mascagni in my young years. I wonder whether this has anything to do with the fact that I now do not care any more for opera and actually consider it a low form of art. I cannot get over the ludicrous features of the performance, prostituting the esoteric beauty of music with stage settings, light effects, gesticulating prima donnas, fat tenors, and the ridiculously acting chorus. I cannot help considering opera an entertainment that makes use or abuse of the most transcendental of arts. I think that comic opera which does not claim to make serious music is far superior to grand opera, both in musical and in entertainment values. To me Johann Strauss's *Die Fledermaus* is infinitely superior to any grand opera because it does not work with false pretenses but simply entertains with charming light music. I am willing to make an exception for Mozart, whose operas are so superbly musical that one can forget the silliness of the stage, and I also except Bizet's *Carmen,* the only opera, in my layman's judgment, in which the composer has succeeded in welding drama and music into a perfect, charming, and thrilling unity.

In my young years—of which I am now writing—I was seized, like all young men at the time, with enthusiasm for Richard Wagner's operas, which were considered not only great music but deeply philosophical. But even in those early years I turned anti-Wagnerian as I became acquainted with the great masters of pure music, and today Wagner's music produces bodily pain in me. I have tried again and again to learn to cherish a master who has such a profound influence upon numerous people. But I always found his music unnatural, if not actually dishonest. The claim in some quarters that this is typically German art—Wagner has been seized upon by the Pan-Germans and their present-day successors—is, in my opinion, ridiculous. At least if one considers as typically German Luther or Goethe or Helmholtz, the typical German music is that of Bach, Beethoven, and Brahms. Of course there are also other Germans, and it is certainly no coincidence that Hitler raved about Wagner. Much later in life I once went to Bayreuth to hear *Parsifal,* thinking that this work, considered so esoteric that only Bayreuth could give it the proper setting, might convert me to Wagner. My friend, the great conductor Karl Muck, was conducting, and I could be sure of an ideal performance. In spite of the best of wills, however, I was bored to death and found this *Weihe-festspiel* even worse than *Der Ring des Nibelungen.* In the intermission Muck, who knew my feelings, came to me expecting a confession of conversion. I could not help saying to him, "I wish I could hear this marvelous orchestra, led by you, perform some really good music."

Muck retorted, "You barbarian."

Maybe he was right. But maybe I am right, too, when I say that three hundred years hence Bach, Beethoven, and Brahms will still touch people to the depths of their hearts, whereas Wagner will be relegated to music history classes.

With all these manifold activities and interests—music, art, science—I might have been a serious, overworked, shortsighted sissy. Nothing of the kind. Sport kept my body trim, and at seventeen I was the best gymnast in school and could perform without strain the most difficult tricks. All the reading and studying appeared to me just fun. I was anything but a serious boy and was inclined to be the clown for the whole class, always ready to use my facility for quick rhyming for the production of more or less witty or funny songs or skits to be performed at picnics or reunions. What a pity that such elasticity of mind and body cannot be kept up beyond the years of youth. One starts as a bird in the skies and ends as a hard-working beaver.

One little episode that happened during those years is worth

33

recording. One day in 1895 the news came from the University of Würzburg, not far away, that Professor Wilhelm Konrad Roentgen had discovered rays that made it possible to see the skeleton within the living body. This caused as much excitement among laymen as in the profession, and people simply refused to believe it. Our teacher of physics in the Gymnasium, a somewhat peculiar but very intelligent man, immediately set out to assemble the necessary apparatus. A large inductor was available, and a Crookes tube and Tesla transformer were borrowed somewhere. But the photographic outfit was still missing. At that time amateur photography hardly existed in Germany, and I was the only boy in our school who had a primitive camera with which I had already toyed for years. Thus I was made the teacher's assistant.

One fall afternoon we met in the physics classroom. We built up the apparatus and tried it out. I had brought an ordinary *cassette* loaded with a plate and had fixed a closet as a darkroom. The *cassette* was put upon the table, the teacher laid his hand adorned with a golden ring on top, and I switched on the current and let the bulb sparkle for some time. (What terrible X-ray burns we might have contracted!) Then I took the frame to the darkroom and started to develop the plate. The teacher remained outside in the greatest excitement, his ear to the door. I shall never forget the moment when the skeleton hand appeared on the plate. I yelled like a red Indian. By some chance the photograph was better than those that had come from Würzburg, and it was demonstrated at a meeting of the physical society. A note on this event was inserted into my graduation papers the following year.

In addition to my intellectual and physical development, those last years at the Gymnasium influenced me in another way. In the class I had entered after my earlier failure, about one third of the boys were sons of the hundred richest and most plutocratic people in our town. Though the political spirit of Frankfurt was democratic, the families of the old patricians and the old and new millionaires considered themselves a special type of creation, and they were called by the lesser fry the *haute volée*. On Sundays or the days of the great horse races they paraded through the boulevard in beautiful coaches drawn by exquisite trotting horses, with coachmen and footmen in traditional uniforms. The less affluent burghers lined the street, told each other the names of the riders in the open coaches, criticized or lauded the horses—all in a good-natured spirit of pride in the wealth of the community. Those were the families whose scions were my classmates.

This group of boys kept themselves apart from the rest of us as much as possible. They wore the latest fashions in suits, shirts, and neckties and deeply despised (or made believe they despised) the plebeians who could not afford such finery. Outside of school they clubbed together and enjoyed the pleasures accessible to wealth. But they were actually very nice and well-bred boys and almost all later became useful members of the community.

Nevertheless, the cleft between patricians and plebeians was there. Since I belonged to the plebeians, was badly and cheaply dressed, and had little pocket money to spend, I associated most naturally with the plebeians, sons of good burgher families, some poor, some well-to-do or even wealthy, but none of them millionaires. We behaved like fifteen-year-old boys, while the patricians already affected the sophisticated manners of rich society, had their little escapades not in beerhouses but in night clubs, talked glibly about race horses and even about actresses. I certainly did not think I wanted to belong to this group. But after awhile they drew me into their circle, and, though I always kept up my relations with the plebeians, I began to take part in the life of the patricians, at least the part which did not require pocket money. It turned out that some of these spoiled boys actually were extremely fine, and some of them became my dearest friends. The most important thing was that these friends introduced me to their homes and opened to me a new world that greatly influenced my life. This new world was not, as one might expect, a superficial world of wealth, but a refined, highly cultured world of old patrician families with great traditions, beautiful houses, and a conservative but rich home life.

In my own home I had all the care and love a child could expect, but something was missing. My father had retired into himself and lived in the house more as a deeply respected guest than as the head of the family. Only on very important occasions did he assume the paternal role, and then he retired again as soon as feasible. He was not happy. My mother, with the best of intentions, had probably too much on her shoulders. Four children, and pretty lively ones, had to be brought up. But as she was a model of filial piety a major part of her time was devoted to her old mother. We never took an apartment that was not within

35

walking distance of my grandmother's home. Day by day during my grandmother's long life as a widow my mother took her out, did her errands, and spent a great deal of time with her. (I am glad to say that my sister, years later, acted toward our mother in exactly the same way and actually sacrificed her youth on the altar of filial piety.) This absorbed my mother so much that certain aspects of our home life were neglected. Though ours was the life of the comfortable burgher, it was too bourgeois—conservative, strict, parsimonious, but without a cultured style, the enjoyment of literature and arts, or those small but highly important refinements of daily life that make up the difference between comfortable living and cultured living.

In the beautiful homes of my new friends, into which I was now taken and where I was accepted by the mothers who carefully scrutinized their sons' friends, a completely new world was opened to me. In my home town, while the bourgeois was oriented culturally toward France and employed French governesses for his children, the patrician imitated the English style of living and kept English governesses, and in this new world the pleasant English custom of five o'clock tea was observed. The children were required to be present and were allowed to bring their friends. The mother presided and watched over the manners, which had to be perfect. Sometimes the fathers were also present, and both made it a point to direct the conversation into interesting channels and to influence youth, without showing it, in the direction of cultural and ethical refinement. All these families were strictly Lutheran, and there was something of the ascetic unworldliness of the old Protestant in the background. All this was new to me, and I had to keep my eyes open to make myself fit in.

There were two families in particular whom I frequently visited at tea time. One of these, the Häberlein family, centered around the father, a lawyer, who was often at home for tea. He did not spend much time on his profession but devoted many hours to his hobby, old Roman coins. He owned a great private collection and wrote learned monographs on the subject. In addition, a room adjoining the dining room contained a beautiful collection of Greek and Roman antiquities, which the collector was glad to show to us. And there was yet another attraction in this house. My friend's mother was a granddaughter of Theodor von Sömmering, the anatomist and friend of Goethe, and one room of the house contained his large, vellum-bound library, his globes, and his instruments, including a huge microscope that looked much like a telescope with a horizontal tube. With this interesting instrument we took our first steps in microscopic work.

I was even more at home with the Breul family in the house of the dearest friend of my life. The style of living in this house, in which all arts were cultivated, was set by my friend's mother. This unusual woman, born in South America from a family of Hanseatic oversea traders, was the most perfect type of woman and mother imaginable. Nobody could approach her without worshiping her. Sitting in an armchair in her beautiful room—her perfect, nobly cut features a little overshadowed by suffering; her fair, transparent face set off against a ruffled black taffeta gown —she presented a picture that I adored as a young boy and would still adore today. Her soul was as beautiful and perfect, and also as sensitive, as her body. Her motherly understanding for youth was unfailing and limitless. The way she helped her own hypersensitive boy to get over difficulties, without making him feel that she was helping, was sublime. With sure instinct she seemed to know at once what was good in me and what was undeveloped and in need of guidance, and she began to lead me without my noticing it, to bring to the surface in me what she thought worthy and to polish off whatever specks she found. When there were difficulties with my friend, she took me into her confidence and showed me how I could help him where it was difficult for a mother. During such conversations, necessitated by my friend's labile balance, I could look into the depth of her feeling, her wonderful understanding of the psychology of adolescence, her unfailing tact, and the marvelous power hidden behind the frail frame of a noble woman. I have always considered it one of the great strokes of luck in my life that, at the most important time of youth when the personality is formed, I came into the reach of the radiance emanating from this unique woman. As long as she lived I never failed to visit her whenever I came back to my home town, and I never left her room without feeling a better man. Indeed, one of the great moments of my life was when, ten years after the period I am describing, I stood in the twilight of her room with my young fiancée on the day before our wedding. The great lady joined our hands and gave us her blessing. We have always regarded that hour as our real wedding ceremony.

My dear friend, who inherited much from his mother and was the noblest of men, inherited from his father's side two sad gifts:

37

a predisposition for tuberculosis and a tendency toward mental depression. He alternated between times of great happiness and enjoyment of life and periods of desperate self-searching and dark gloom. Later, when we were students in Heidelberg, during his times of depression I would walk with him all night long over the hills and through the forests, struggling to save him from suicide and leaving him only when I knew that the darkness had lifted from his mind. He was the type of man who wrestles with life, who takes no idea as granted before he has assimilated it after a hard fight, who seeks God all his life long, torn between doubt and belief, who is shaken to the depth of his being by a philosophical book or a great performance of a musical masterwork or a great landscape. Thus, though living an uneventful life, he felt more of the heights and depths of the human mind and soul than most others, and he had a life rich and full in its own way. Though he had a physician's degree, his health did not allow any professional work, and he spent whatever strength he had trying to master the mysteries of life, art, and religion. At forty he was an old man, and he died, unknown to the world, without having done anything for mankind. Nevertheless, he was a noble man of a greatness known only to himself and to those of us who were devoted to him.

Thus the last years of my boyhood, as a student in the Gymnasium, passed on in kaleidoscopic variety until my graduation in 1896. But, just as my entrance into the Gymnasium had been marked by the anti-Semitic hooliganism of the "vinegar bottle," my last day stood under the same star. Each year the graduating class invited the teachers as well as former graduates to a *Kommers*, a formal drinking bout with much hilarity, speeches, specially composed songs, and a play, in the form of a Greek tragedy, in which the events of school life and the weaknesses of our teachers were parodied. I had always presided at the *Kommerse* of our class, and I had again written the songs and the play for the final *Kommers* and staged and rehearsed everything. The day before the event I was told that I could not preside as it would be "insupportable" for the guests, many of them members of fraternities, to drink their beer with a Jew in the chair. So it was that the greatest sissy of the class, a perfumed dandy but a prospective "corps" member, officiated. I have always hated myself for lacking so much in pride (for the last time) as to attend and direct the prepared show.

Now—since I was ready to enter the university—came the decisive moment of choosing my future profession. German universities were not colleges, but exclusively professional schools, and the student matriculated to become a physician, a lawyer, a preacher, a high school teacher, or a scientist. My choice had long been made: zoology and a career as university teacher. But I encountered difficulties. In German universities only the full professors were paid, and the young scholars had almost no source of income until they arrived at a professorship, a success that was in no way certain. The situation was still more hopeless for a Jew, for only in very exceptional cases could he hope for an appointment; in addition, the way out in case of failure was high school teaching, and this, too, was closed to him. Thus I cannot reproach my parents for dampening my idealism and pointing out the hopelessness of such a career. They wanted me to become a physician or a lawyer so that after a reasonable time I would be able to settle in my home town near my parents and live comfortably. In my deep disappointment I asked the advice of my old biology teacher Reichenbach, who himself had foregone an academic career. His answer was, "What, a zoologist? Zoology is no science but a sport for rich people!" So I agreed with heavy heart to study medicine, secretly hoping that one day I might be able to cross over to my beloved biology. Heidelberg, only about fifty miles from my home town, was chosen as my university.

3: UNIVERSITY LIFE

"Ich war in Heidelberg, in Heidelberg Student." This jubilant stanza of a student song can hardly be appreciated any more by the present generation. In these days of freedom for youth and schools without emphasis on discipline and hard training of the mind it can hardly be understood what the entrance into a university meant for a German boy in 1896. In German universities there was the basic principle of academic freedom for both professors and students. This means that the student was the complete master of his time. He was supposed to take definite courses, but whether he would attend them or not was his own business. There were no quizzes, examinations, or tests except the final one at the end of four to five years' study and an intermediate one for medical students. At examination time a student had to show his knowledge; it did not matter by what steps he had acquired it. A minimum number of years was required, but there was no maximum, and the student could stay longer if he wished to loaf or to extend his knowledge in different directions. Certainly this was a dangerous system for the weak characters, who frequently failed beyond hope, but a splendid one for the student with a goal in mind.

Entering the university, then, meant the step from strict control, both in school and in the home, to complete liberty; from exactly set daily tasks to the mastery of one's own time; from work along lines partly detested to work for which one longed. But there was something else in that liberty. We were still close to the romanticism of a century before. We had not yet become matter-of-fact or utilitarian. The need for making a living as soon as possible was not pressing. We still felt akin to young Goethe in the period of *Sturm und Drang,* and we looked forward to the first university years as a time of romantic exuberance. Heidelberg was chosen not only for its famous professors, but just as much for the beauty of its location in the Neckar Valley, surrounded by beautiful hills and overlooked by the grand ruin of the Renaissance castle. Here there still existed the remainders of old German student life; the student was the ruler of the town, and his doings were looked upon with benevolent indulgence. There was even a special jail, the *Karzer*, right in the university building, where students were locked up under a special jurisdiction for pranks that went too far. Thus we could combine hard work in the lecture halls and laboratories with roaming all night long through the woods crowning the hills, spending our time with friends with whom we discussed the deepest problems of life with unabating zest. Even today I should not like to have missed any moment of this first year in Heidelberg: the romantic intoxication; work and play; drinking bouts; sentimental wanderings over the beautiful hills; bad pranks played upon the quietly suffering citizens, the Philistines, and the aftermath—captivity in the *Karzer;* hikes in the nearby Black Forest during holidays; swimming and boating in the river; and much singing, discussing, and again discussing.

When I came to Heidelberg as a boy of eighteen, my mother had already been there to hire a proper room for me. Americans or Englishmen can hardly understand that in the centuries during which the German universities flourished not a thing was done to take care of the students' needs. There were no dormitories, no medical examinations, no approved boarding houses. The student rented a miserably furnished room with the standard red plush furniture. There was no plumbing, no bathroom, and frequently the toilet was on a different floor or in the courtyard. The landlords or landladies were usually rather low-class creatures who lived from subletting to students. They tried to charge as much as they could for everything—hot water, the use of crockery, or what not —and if there was, exceptionally, a bathroom, its use was more expensive than a seat in the theater. The students, coming in most cases from cultured homes, had to lower their standard of living considerably and to be on guard all the time against the predatory instincts of the landlords, who renewed what furniture, crockery, and tapestries they had by charging the helpless student for imaginary harm done to the beautiful pieces.

Most students bought a simple alcohol lamp to prepare their tea or coffee for breakfast, and the landlord furnished the couple of rolls that make up the Continental breakfast. The main meal was taken at one o'clock in a restaurant and was accompanied by a glass of beer. At night the student bought bread, butter, cheese or ham or sausage and ate it in his room, alone or with friends— if the landlord did not object to friends. There were, of course,

41

no girl students yet, and no female person would have been admitted by the landlord. These rooms had gaslight only rarely, and never electric light. The student brought with him a kerosene lamp by the light of which he did his studying. Laundry was sent home weekly by parcel post, and the return package always contained a sausage, or canned sardines, or similar additions to the supper table. The only culinary luxury in which the average student indulged was a daily visit to a coffeehouse for coffee and cake in the afternoon.

When I came to Heidelberg my first action was to register for the classes of Otto Bütschli, one of the greatest naturalists of the nineteenth century, discoverer of mitotic cell division, author of the classic study of protozoa, pioneer of the physicochemical study of the cell. The *Herr Hofrat* (court councilor), as he was addressed by the students, received me in a friendly way since he came from the same town and knew my family. From the first moment I saw him I admired this noble man with his dark, fiery eyes, the finely cut nose and forehead, the pale, nervous face with the huge black beard. Though I was only one of many premedical students, Bütschli noticed my deep interest in zoology as well as my previous training and permitted me to spend free hours in the research laboratory, where I tried to make myself useful by doing little chores such as mounting insects and writing labels for specimens. I felt immensely happy to breathe the air of this famous laboratory in the shadow of a really great man. When I later returned there as a young zoologist I had already laid the foundations for what became a lifelong friendship with the venerated scholar.

There was another grand old man with whom I had to establish contact immediately, the great anatomist Karl Gegenbaur, founder of evolutionist comparative anatomy. He was already very old. Whereas Bütschli was a unique lecturer, fascinating from first to last, full of genius that carried the students away, Gegenbaur, in 1896, was terribly dull, almost unbearable. Nevertheless I attended his classes regularly for the great man was awe-inspiring and fascinating even if one could hardly hear the sound of his words. About six feet two inches tall, with a beautiful head in which a pair of piercing dark eyes looked out of a parchmentlike face surrounded by white hair, he was a commanding figure. In the dissection room he was utterly strict and exacting and scolded the students severely for mistakes or ignorance. In spite of the academic freedom, students who did not work hard were simply deprived of their working space.

There were many more great teachers for the young student to admire: the brilliant physiologist, Kühne, whose lectures were of literary perfection; the sensitive, nervous chemist, Victor Meyer; and many others. Premedical students at that time still had leisure to do something for their general education and made it a point to attend a few classes of the great scholars who abounded at that time in Heidelberg: the historian, Schäfer, who taught an aggressive Prussianism; the classical archeologist, von Duhn; the exponent of Roman law, Bekker; the brilliant Hellenist, Rohde; the radical, fiery economist, Max Weber; the hypersensitive, mystic, oratorical art historian, Thode; and the famous Kuno Fischer, whose lectures on history of philosophy and on Goethe's *Faust* no one ever missed.

The first two years in Heidelberg were the happiest of my life, filled with work and play, romantic ecstasies, exuberant enjoyment of nature, beauty, friendship, and a combination of intensive study with the wild doings of spirited youth. How many times did I spend hours at night, after a long day of classes, working out in longhand the lectures I had taken down in shorthand and illustrating them with colored drawings. But after ten o'clock I met my friends at our *Stammtisch,* drank with them much more beer than was good for me, wound up with a moonlight hike over the hills, and returned toward morning—to be found again at eight o'clock in Bütschli's class. It seems that between eighteen and twenty strength is inexhaustible, and even the effects of beer guzzling are easily offset by regular exercise. How I put all these things and many more into one day I cannot understand now. But actually there was even time left over for music. I entered an oratorio society, the Bach Verein, directed by the rough but immensely musical Philipp Wolfrum, and studied in the choir all the great oratorios, which one can actually master only after having gone through the innumerable rehearsals and the exciting public performance.

Since those days in Heidelberg fate has frequently been good to me, and I have seen much happiness and lived my days fully. But never again have I been so sublimely happy, splashing in the pleasant ocean of life, as I was in those two years. Maybe the reason is that never again was I so young; maybe that a changing world destroyed the romanticism which at that time permeated the life of a student in Heidelberg. The novel, play, and film *Alt Heidelberg* (*The Student Prince*), which many remember—sentimental, tearful, and certainly not great literature—nevertheless represents well the spirit of those days and still today draws streams of tears from audiences who knew the romanticism of long ago.

German students could change universities as often as they wanted, since all universities were state-operated. Thus, after having passed my premedical examinations, I decided in 1898 to go to Munich, famous for its faculty, its art, the free Bohemian life, and the neighboring Alps. My intention was to go at clinical medicine in a leisurely way and to devote part of my time to zoology so that I might be able to take a philosophical degree immediately after the medical one. I hoped to enter biology this way —by the back door. I arrived a few weeks before the term began and went immediately to see Richard Hertwig, one of the fathers of modern zoology.

The student who specialized in zoology, like the student of other sciences, did not do his laboratory work in regular classes as it is done in present-day America. He took the so-called big laboratory course, which meant having a table in the laboratory and working there at whatever hours were available. He was given his material by the professor, with instructions and bibliography, and then he worked out his problem as quickly or as slowly as he cared. His progress was checked daily by the professor and by instructors, who made the rounds, answered questions, helped with the technique, pointed out literature, and gave him the next topic only when they were satisfied with his slides and drawings. In this way he worked through the whole field in about two years, rather thoroughly, and with considerable independence in detail.

This training, I still think, is the only really thorough one for a prospective scholar. Today's scholar does not get enough out of standard classes, which are all right for general education or for a subject minor but not for the main field of a future scientist. This system, then, made it possible for me to start at once in Hertwig's laboratory before the beginning of the term. I felt thoroughly happy to be admitted for the first time as a student to a real research laboratory.

The Munich Zoological Institute at that time occupied the vaulted and columned halls of a medieval monastery, and from the windows one beheld a beautiful cloister with the nave of St. Michael's Church and the huge towers of Our Lady's Church as a background. This monastic setting made the laboratory a quiet and dignified oasis right in the center of the town. The fixtures and apparatus were very poor, far below what any small college has today, but there was a wonderful research spirit kept aflame by the kindly and affectionate professor who treated the few full-time students as his children and imbued them with the love of search into the secrets of nature. He was a great teacher who attracted scholars from all over the world and devoted much of his time to personal instruction.

Thus I began to learn, as the disciple of a great scholar, all the technicalities of dissection and microscopic work together with the insight into the manifold problems hidden behind each fact. Only too quickly the weeks passed until the term began and I had to start with clinical medicine. But the difference between the scholarly work in the monastic laboratory and the sights offered in the introductory clinical courses was too much for one who had taken up medicine against his will. I was shocked at the exhibition of the sick, the terrible sight of hopeless cancers, and I simply could not make up my mind to begin with physical examinations of patients. I hated it, and day after day I turned around at the door of the clinic and returned to my beloved microscopic animals.

Finally one day—after half a year of vain efforts—I went to see Professor Hertwig, who had begun to show friendly interest in me, and I opened my heart to him. I wanted to know especially whether he thought me fitted for the life of a research scholar. I still distrusted my abilities and was not sure whether I had the gift for research, the patience for incessant hard work, the strength to accept disappointments, and the will power to carry on in the face of the already mentioned difficulties of an academic career. Hertwig kindly dissipated my uncertainties, told me he had watched me and had come to the conclusion that I ought to become a biologist, and offered his assistance. This was the beginning of a lifelong friendship with the great scholar and noble man which was to last for forty years.

But the greatest difficulty was with my parents. In the Germany of that day it was impossible to work one's way through college or to make any extra money in the first hard years of the academic career. An academic career, therefore, meant that my father would have to support me for years to come, nobody knew how long.

My father, who himself suffered from a frustrated life, was willing to accept this responsibility and financial burden, but my mother found it difficult to give up her cherished dream of seeing me practicing somewhere around the corner and raising a family in affluence under her proud eyes as a grandmother. She made it very hard for me to stick to my guns. I had been brought up under the strict rule of the commandment to honor father and mother, and I suffered acutely from the sorrow and disappointment I had to inflict upon my parents, who wanted the best for me. But my decision had been made, and I meant to carry it out.

Another new world was opened to me during this first year in Munich. Through a friend I was introduced into a literary club where all the playwrights and writers of the young naturalistic school read their works, afterward adjourning to one of the famous artists' coffeehouses where violent discussions of art and literature lasted until late at night and where all the idols were dethroned and the "great men of the day" celebrated. Alas, the dethroned idols are still the great masters, and their coffeehouse successors are mostly forgotten. But it was an exceedingly interesting time in German literature. The great plays of Hauptmann and the naturalistic works of revolt by Halbe, Bierbaum, Hartleben, and Schnitzler were appearing; new poetry was being tried out in the publication *Insel;* and the graphic arts were seeking new forms of expression. Stolberg had founded a small modern theater that played in a dingy fourth-floor hall those plays of the modern school that could not be performed in the aristocratic court theater. I suppose he got his cues from the famous Moscow theater, but he certainly succeeded in impressing his audiences—mostly youths —with perfect acting and modern stage settings long before Reinhardt revolutionized the stage. Once I even had the pleasure of appearing on the stage. Every year the club produced a play acted by amateurs but coached by a professional; the novelty of that year was a rather socialistic peasant play in which I was given the role of one of the peasants—who did more spitting than talking. I enjoyed immensely this entire literary atmosphere, which, probably, was after all only Bohemian, though everybody was in deadly earnest.

That year in Germany's "town of the muses" also brought me my first real contact with art. As a schoolboy I had visited the exhibits that came to my home town, and some of the artists of the day were already known to me by their works. But only in Munich did I first find art as a companion of daily life. Everybody knew and discussed the works of the painters and sculptors of the day, and the artists who lived and worked in Munich were the leaders of social life. There were in addition the great galleries of world fame where the German, Flemish, and Italian primitives, who were just beginning to be understood in their sublime greatness, could be studied. The student could even adorn his otherwise dingy quarters with a few good reproductions, and thus I acquired my first pieces—the beginning of a lifelong hobby. In Germany the revolt against the Victorian horrors in all the arts centered in Munich. As a reaction against bad taste in home furnishings, a new style developed, the still more horrible *Jugend* (youth) style. But from this sprang a complete renaissance of the arts and crafts—a renaissance that in Germany, Holland, Finland, and the Scandinavian countries soon led to the production of beautiful and artistic household furnishings. It was a renaissance that only much later spread to England and America, whereas France has remained backward to the present day. All these developments were followed with the keenest interest in Munich, and my eyes were opened to the importance of the esthetic value of a man's surroundings. Ever since I have been deeply interested in all the arts and crafts and have derived pleasure without end from, at times, an even intensive occupation with art, which furnished to my mind the emotional counterpart to the painstakingly detailed work of a scientist. I cannot imagine the life of a man of intellect without love for the arts.

During my first winter as a zoology student, Hertwig suggested that I spend the two months of spring vacation at a zoological station on the shores of the Mediterranean. At that time there was no place in Europe where courses in marine biology were given. The few marine biological laboratories, headed by the famous laboratory in Naples, were pure research laboratories in which independent investigators found facilities for work. To visit such a place as a young student was therefore a great event.

Through Hertwig's recommendation I received a table in the Russian biological station in Villefranche near Nice, and my father made me happy by promising the traveling funds. Soon afterward, however, I caught cold walking home in an icy wind while overheated from dancing at a fancy dress ball. After a few days I felt thoroughly miserable and went to see a physician, who diagnosed pleuritis and—unbelievable but true—sent me home without prescribing any further care. This was a bad thing. The time of my departure was near, and I simply could not give up the trip to the blue Mediterranean. If, however, my parents learned of my pleuritis they would insist that I cancel the trip and return home for convalescence. As I could not afford a stay in a hospital or even an additional doctor's bill, I decided to get along by myself. Like most German students, I had a dingy room in a cheap tenement house, sublet from working people who were absent all day. After leaving the physician, I bought a little grill that used pressed charcoal, and then I went home to bed. The landlady gave me breakfast in the morning and sausage with bread and butter at night. When she left in the morning she put a basin with cold water next to my bed, and I made cold compresses for my chest, in a barely heated room. She also bought a large slice of steak, which I prepared on the grill from my bed and ate as dinner day by day, without anything else to go with it. Under these conditions I cured my pleuritis within two or three weeks. My constitution must have been a good one to survive this type of sickbed, and, fortunately, I never had any bad aftereffects. As soon as I could stand on my legs again I left for Villefranche and only from there wrote my parents what had happened.

My trip to France brought me my first glimpse of Italy, though only of that most un-Italian town, Milan, where I stayed with an old school friend and was initiated into the secrets of eating macaroni in the classic style and of sipping *caffè espresso*. Here I also saw a motorcycle for the first time in my life. It went rushing by at the terrific speed of twenty miles an hour. I had already seen, in Heidelberg, a motorcar making about fifteen miles while everybody ran to safety at its approach, and all the coachmen descended and held their trembling horses.

Without much delay I proceeded to Villefranche, the French naval harbor near Nice where the Russian government had leased an old prison to erect the marine biological station. The building was located within military grounds, and one had to pass the barracks of the Chasseurs Alpins to reach the station. This famous troop seemed to regard the bugle as its most formidable weapon; from morning to night, hundreds of soldiers practiced bugle calls, and one could not get away from the more or less correct signals. The laboratory still had prison windows with iron bars, and huge iron rings set into the stone floor testified to none too pleasant methods for treating prisoners. The place was run by a charming Russian zoologist, Davidoff, who did not care for hard work but loved to have a good time and to share it with others. (Unfortunately his wife, a former German waitress, watched carefully over his inclination toward side-stepping *in baccho et venere,* and many a day after a happy party he returned to the laboratory with his face scratched all over.) At noon he presided over the lunch party of the group, which took place in one laboratory. Everybody brought bread and cheese, and Davidoff furnished tea from a huge samovar tended by one of the fishermen. Frequently this simple repast was enriched by a huge pot of splendid caviar. The shrewd Davidoff had his friends in Russia ship caviar to the laboratory in little barrels marked (absolutely correctly) "fish eggs" and thus free from customs' duty. I learned to eat caviar in the approved Russian style, not as a thin spread with a lot of bread but by the spoonful. It was thirty years before I had another chance to practice this pleasant art.

There was at Villefranche an excellent company of young biologists, some of whom, like Hartmann and Koltzoff, later became leaders in their field, and we all had a fine time together. We lived in the "best hotel" in town, where half of the rooms were usually occupied by sailors and their passing sweethearts. Room and board cost seventy-five cents a day, and that included as much wine as we cared to drink. After work hours and on week ends we hiked over the beautiful hills, occasionally climbed a real mountain, or walked across the hills to Nice where we observed the fashionable life, which we utterly despised. At night we frequented the sailors' cafes crowded with crews from whatever warships were in port. We enjoyed the low-class shows presented and frequently watched serious fights between sailors of different nationalities. Once we saw a real battle between English and Russian sailors which ended with the Russians swimming to their ship under a hail of rocks.

But the greatest excitement for the young biologist was the daily study of the beautiful marine animals of the region. Villefranche is especially rich in plankton, the completely transparent, glasslike flotsam of the high seas. When we entered the laboratory early in the morning the fishermen had already brought in their catch, and the entrance hall was filled with glass jars containing the strangest creatures. It is difficult to describe the beauty of snails ten to fifteen inches long and so transparent that you see, at first,

49

only the black eyes; or an animal called Belt of Venus, up to twenty inches long, ribbonlike, and completely crystalline; or the mixture of transparent and vividly colored parts in the tribe of jellyfish and their beautiful relatives, the Siphonophora, not to speak of the microscopic plankton of inexhaustible beauty. It took hours merely to observe and to draw the host of never-before-seen animals before dissecting and microscopic work could be started. It is impossible to describe the thrill I experienced facing for the first time these wonders and finding out for myself what I beheld, since there was no instruction. The present-day student who gets everything ready and well prepared in crowded classes can hardly know what this first experience with the wonders of marine life meant to me.

So passed two wonderful, happy months. Then I had to return home to be back in time for the summer at Munich. I also had to leave because my meager funds were gone. When I reached Switzerland I had only six pfennige (one and one-half cents), which bought two pretzels to sustain me until I reached my home town. When I drove up to my parents' house in a taxi they knew I was penniless and sent Kathrin down to pay the driver. If I had owned a nickel I would have come by streetcar.

During the summer term of 1899 at Munich, I became involved in my first piece of research. While working at my usual laboratory course I found a few things in a slide of the dangerous parasite echinococcus which did not agree with the description in literature. Hertwig encouraged me to follow up the subject, and I started and carried through my first piece of research. When the term ended, however, it was not yet finished. My parents did not want me to return to Munich after the pleuritis story came out, and I realized myself that it would be better for me to return to Heidelberg. Hertwig, who liked me and my work, wanted me to take my degree at once with that piece of research work as a thesis. I felt, however, that my training was not yet as broad as I wanted it to be and that it would be wiser to enter Bütschli's laboratory and take another couple of years at least for training as well as for a better piece of research. Hertwig regretted my leaving him but, kindly as he always was, permitted me to take my microscope and equipment with me in order that I might finish my work during the summer vacation. At home I rigged up a frightfully hot attic as a laboratory and worked there all day studying my

Gymnasium graduate, 1896   Army recruit, 1902

Elsa Kühnlein, the author's fiancée, 1905

Hans, Ruth, and Elsa Goldschmidt, 1913

slides, making drawings, and writing my paper. The heat under the roof finally made me so nervous that I could not sleep any more and kept seeing before my eyes the thousands of little dots of my drawings. So I was happy when this, my first paper, was finally ready for press.

I went back for a couple of weeks to Munich to return the borrowed instruments and to attend the great meeting of naturalists, which, that year, promised to be of extraordinary interest. There was the exciting event of Grassi's lecture on the life cycle of the malaria germ, just discovered. This great Italian biologist has received hardly any recognition for his splendid work. Most of the credit has gone to the English surgeon Ross, though Grassi deserves a considerable share. I was attached to Grassi to help him find his way around, and my work consisted mostly of hunting for his spectacles, which he left in the most impossible places. The other great attraction was Carl Chun, the zoologist who had just returned from the deep-sea expedition of the *Valdivia* and who gave a brilliant account of his discoveries and arranged an exhibit of the most amazing forms of deep-sea life. But the lion of lions was Fridtjof Nansen, back from the drift of the *Fram* across the North Pole. Munich, the artists' town, made it a point to give the foreign guests an idea of its beauty, and at the close of the meeting an unforgettable party in the park and the halls of the old Schleissheim castle was arranged by the leading artists.

For the fall term I returned to Heidelberg to finish my studies in Bütschli's laboratory. Here the atmosphere was very different from that in Munich. Hertwig, though politically conservative, even reactionary, was in his laboratory a friend among friends, and work was done in a very free atmosphere. Bütschli, however, a confirmed republican who accepted many slights from his government in the form of being snubbed at the regular distribution of titles and decorations, ran his laboratory in a dictatorial way. Students and assistants alike held him in such awe and veneration that they treated him as a superior being. The professor reciprocated with a deep affection for his students which did not, however, prevent him from asking the maximum of work. Assistants and technicians trembled at his approach as no error or failure was overlooked but produced an outbreak of his nervous wrath. A student who showed him a poor slide or an untidy dissection at his daily rounds of the laboratory, or who could not explain the subject properly, was publicly called down. Good work was correspondingly lauded and put him in such good humor that he assembled all of us around him and joked. But there was always a distance, the cause of which I realized only later when we became friends and he opened his heart to me. The great biologist was an unhappy man. After many difficulties in his youth—he had been a complete autodidact who had done some of his classic work privately, without the backing of a university—he had lost his beloved wife in childbirth, and an unsuccessful second marriage had turned him into a dark pessimist. Thus he lived an unsocial, secluded life, did not take part in the easygoing pleasures of his colleagues, read mountains of literature and philosophy, made music, painted, and wrote poetry—he once confessed to me that he had translated Shakespeare's *Tempest*—and was always unhappy.

I worked very hard these years without giving up the pleasures of student life in Heidelberg, and I finally started on my thesis. While I was taking a summer vacation with my father in the beautiful spa of Baden-Baden to recover from overwork, I received a letter from Bütschli offering me the newly established second assistantship at the royal salary of seventy-five marks (eighteen dollars) a month. At that time there were in the department only the full professor, Bütschli, and an unpaid associate professor, Schuberg, who was simultaneously a paid assistant. The third newly created job was the one offered me. I certainly felt greatly honored, as it was unusual for an assistant's job to be given to a man before he got his doctor's degree. I had visiting cards printed at once with "second assistant" after my name and was thoroughly offended when the first recipient of the card, a spoiled and wealthy young girl, laughed heartily at the great title.

One of the conditions of my appointment was that I had to learn the art of round hand, a kind of artistic script written with a special pen, in order to write labels for the museum specimens. The typewriter was unknown then and for a long time afterward in a German laboratory. My new duties were rather menial, aside from assisting in the laboratory work. I had to make up museum specimens, especially dissections and injections; make slides for demonstration purposes; act as librarian; collect living laboratory material like frogs, newts, worms, insects, and microscopic animals to be ready when needed; and paint the charts used in the lectures. Lantern slides had not yet come into use. The chart making was my most precarious job, for Bütschli was himself a real artist who

52

painted fine watercolors and was not easily satisfied with my amateurish work.

In my spare time I continued to work on my thesis. Since I was more self-reliant than was warranted at that age, I had not followed the usual course of asking my professor for a problem but had proposed my own. This was in a field, cytology, which was just beginning to develop but in which Bütschli was no longer interested though he had been one of its pioneers. Thus I had to find my own way and had much trouble with the technique as well as with the interpretation. I finally finished a piece of work that was acceptable but rather behind the times in technique, actually nothing to be very proud of.

The two years as Bütschli's assistant meant much work, since I was preparing for my degree at the same time. Usually I worked at night, but nevertheless I somehow found time to meet with interesting or amusing groups of young men of the most diversified types. There were still some of my fine old friends around for serious conversation and real friendship. There were the young zoologists, among them many foreigners, especially some very fine Russians, who initiated me into their interminable discussions over the samovar late in the night. There was another group of snobbish Berliners, from whom I learned some of the superficial ways of metropolitan playboys. There was a group of young Viennese men, deeply interested in music, in whose rooms quartets were played and vehemently discussed. There was a spirited, intelligent, and very amusing group of young lecturers, some of them later well-known scientists, who loved to hike six or eight miles over the hills at night to take supper in one of the lovely country inns, followed by considerable wine drinking and the long walk home. There was the tennis club, rather swanky as tennis clubs were at that time, where I played daily before supper and took part in many a tournament. There was a cousin who was a passionate saber fighter and had a special fencing room in his apartment, and who trained with me in heavy German saber fencing daily after lunch; as he was much better than I he cut all my shirts to pieces and adorned my chest with red streaks by heavy blows that bruised the skin through the thick padding.

What I liked less was that I had to make calls and dine and dance in official academic society, which at that time, in a small university town, was certainly the most boring of all pastimes. But there were also a few nice houses to which I was invited.

There was the famous historian of mathematics, Moritz Cantor, who lived with his spinster daughter and an elderly housekeeper. His main extramural interest was the theater, and the conversation turned mostly around the stage. But once, during dinner, he suddenly started addressing me in Latin. At first I did not know what it was all about, but finally I understood. He had started keeping hens in his large and beautiful backyard, and he wanted to know whether he would have to supply a rooster in order to have his hens lay eggs. This question was thought to be improper in the presence of his thirty-five-year-old daughter, and so he put it in Latin.

Another interesting house was that of a distant relative, the crystallographer Victor Goldschmidt. He was a great art collector, and in his house I could handle the most beautiful things. He was fond of good conversation, good food, and good music and attracted interesting guests. One whom I frequently met there was the later famous "traveling philosopher," Count Hermann Alexander Keyserling. At that time the worst pessimist could not have predicted what was to befall this noble family. In his old age Victor Goldschmidt gave all his art treasures to the university as the Von Portheim Foundation, called after his wife's maiden name. Fortunately he died soon afterward. When the Nazis came to power they began to harass his widow, an unusually fine lady. They forced her to add the contents of her house to the foundation and fined her for keeping back pieces "belonging to" the foundation. One day they found out that an old painting Goldschmidt had bought as an original was a copy. In typical Nazi fashion they accused Mrs. Goldschmidt of having cheated the foundation and made her pay the value of an original. In this way things went on until the day came when all Heidelberg Jews were arrested and deported. Eighty-year-old Mrs. Goldschmidt was warned and committed suicide before the Gestapo arrived. The foundation still exists and is now well taken care of by the university.

I associated occasionally with Rudolf Binding, later to become a famous poet. One day Heidelberg was startled by the appearance of a student ten years older than usual, extremely fashionable, with a Kaiser Wilhelm mustache and the manners of a cavalry officer. With him appeared a beautiful lady, dressed more fashionably and expensively than had ever been seen before in the old university town, and a dogcart with two beautiful horses driven in tandem. This was Binding, former officer, former law student, *bon vivant,* gambler, horse racer, son of a famous scholar, who now, with his mistress, made his debut in Heidelberg. To everybody's surprise he appeared with perfect regularity in medical courses. After some time his mistress disappeared with another similar type, the dogcart followed, and Binding turned into a serious student who now associated also with ordinary mortals. At night, however, he had his dinner, always accompanied by half a bottle of champagne, alone in the most fashionable restaurant. In his conversation he was just an ordinary, well-mannered, uninteresting man of the better type of German army officer of that time. Nobody would have thought it possible that this man could develop into the author of *Der Opfergang,* one of the most sensitive, pastel-like pieces of German literature ever written.

The year 1901 brought a great event in my young life. The International Zoological Congress was to be held in Berlin. International congresses were at that time rarer and therefore more important events than now, and sometimes were actually landmarks of scientific progress. Bütschli had been invited to deliver one of the chief addresses on a philosophical topic, and for many months he kept the whole laboratory excited with discussions of the questions that occupied his mind. I was assigned the special task of preparing a short version of his manuscript for a magazine that had called for it. Subsequently the same magazine invited me to report on a paper by a Viennese physician Schenck, a fake, who had claimed to be able to control the sex of children. Thus at the age of twenty-three I wrote for the first time on the problem of sex determination, not foreseeing that one day I was to discover decisive facts and write books and dozens of papers on the subject, the last one as late as 1951.

This first international meeting meant much to me. To see and to hear all the great men whose names were mentioned in the lectures and whose books I had studied, and, occasionally, even to be introduced to one of them, was marvelous. I remember one meeting my attendance at which will fill any young biologist of today with envy, a meeting of the experimental embryologists. Spemann, later to win a Nobel prize, then a young lecturer, read a splendid paper. Oscar Hertwig, discoverer of the fertilization of the egg, was in the chair. Among those who took part in the discussion were W. Roux, the founder of experimental embryology, and Driesch and Herbst, two of the pioneers in that field. There were about twenty-five men present, twenty of them world celebrities. The great foreign specialists were a special attraction, since travel overseas was still a rather rare thing among German scholars. I was especially impressed by the Japanese Ijima, one of the pioneers of modern science in Japan, who spoke German fluently. He had brought a marvelous collection of the beautiful glass sponges found in the depths of the Sagami Bay, that delightful bay to which Mount Fuji forms the grandiose background. I certainly would not have believed it if some good fairy had whispered in my ear that thirteen years later, as guest of honor of the same Professor Ijima, I would sit on the lovely porch of a Japanese house overlooking Sagami Bay, the glorious Mount Fuji glistening beneath its snowcap across the waters.

No less than the scientific program, I enjoyed the festivities with which rich Imperial Germany treated its guests. The style of these receptions has probably disappeared from the world: invitation dinners with eight courses and a selection of the best wines, gala opera to be attended in full dress, and, on top of all, a reception by the senate in the magnificent town hall of the free city of Hamburg, at which an army of lackeys served the most expensive delicacies of the world, washed down with French champagne. Not everything was ideal in Imperial Germany, but certainly science and its makers were ranked near the top of society.

My father had made it possible for me to proceed from Hamburg after the congress with one of my cousins, a chemist, to Scandinavia for a hiking trip across beautiful Norway. We proceeded by way of Copenhagen to the Swedish town of Göteborg, where I made my first acquaintance with Swedish bathing customs. We went to a public bath—hotel rooms with bath, if at all available, were only for millionaires—and each took a cell with a tub. When I got out of my tub, a huge middle-aged woman suddenly entered without much ado, took hold of me, and gave me a terrific cold rubdown. At dinner time we went to a restaurant and asked what we could get. The waiter, who spoke only Swedish, repeated over and over the word *kräftor.* So we ordered *kräftor,* which turned out to be crayfish, of which we ate an unbelievable amount without any ill effect. About five years later I developed such a strong allergy for this delicacy that a spoonful of crayfish soup now produces a dangerous complete collapse. From Christiania, now Oslo, we hiked across Telemark to Hardanger Fiord and Bergen on the west coast, a most beautiful trip at a time before the motorcar had encroached upon the hiker's paradise.

In Bergen I visited the professors of the marine biological laboratory. Hospitably they invited us young students to a dredging party in the bay, certainly the strangest dredging for marine animals I have ever participated in, and I have seen much dredging in all the oceans of the world. When the boat was loaded at the wharf with the nets, battery jars, alcohol, and whatever else belongs to deep-sea dredging, I noticed that the baskets contained more bottles of beer and aqua vitae than specimen jars. The boat was manned by two sturdy oarsmen, and we started.

When we were a mile or two from land a big four-master bound for the north crossed our path, dragging its lifeboat behind it. We crossed just when the rope to which the lifeboat was attached was in front of us. Then our great oarsmen conceived the idea —I am afraid they had already sampled the contents of our baskets—of slipping under that rope between schooner and lifeboat. The result was that with a terrible crash the lifeboat was pulled right across our boat, and there it remained. By a miracle nobody was hit and we did not capsize. In this strange condition we were pulled behind the fast sailing vessel crosswise with a whole boat on top of ours. The skipper of the four-master finally noticed our plight but refused to change his course, and only after long palavering did he turn into the wind and give us a chance to free ourselves. Somewhat upset, we reached our goal, a flat rock way out in the bay. We had hardly landed when we heard a terrific noise nearby and turning around saw a huge whale, his whole back out of the water, blowing by only a few yards away. Professor Apellöf, our host, had now had enough excitement and sent the boatsmen out to do the dredging, i.e., to sink the dredge in deep water and haul it in from the shore. We, however, started picnicking and taking care of all the bottles in the basket. From time to time the fishermen interrupted the spree by bringing in their haul and Apellöf explained the animals that were new to us. I am still surprised that we finally got home safely, the battery jars filled with deep-sea animals, the other bottles empty. I am afraid that Apellöf, a charming man, with whom I kept up correspondence, made many such scientific excursions, for he died rather miserably from the effects of alcoholism.

The trip home to Germany was my first long sea voyage. The small, bad-smelling coastal steamer *Mira* contained, besides minuscule cabins, one dining and social room of about ten feet square. As long as we could stay on deck we could stand the rolling in the always ugly North Sea. But when we had to go below the terrible smell was too much. I must admit that, when I read forty years later that the steamship *Mira* had been sunk by a German bomb, I could not help feeling a certain satisfaction.

A half year after my return from the beautiful Scandinavian trip, I received my doctor's degree, and the time had come to make plans for my future. I had decided to try an academic career, in spite of the difficulties, mostly due to academic anti-Semitism, which have already been mentioned. But Heidelberg did not seem the proper place to start. There was ahead of me the first assistant, Professor Schuberg, a man more interested in his position as a reserve officer in the army than in his scientific work, difficult to get along with, and with little chance of being called away to a professorship and thus of giving me an opportunity to rise beyond my eighteen-dollar-a-month job. Such was the organization of German universities at that time. Moreover, I realized that I could not throw in my lot with Bütschli, though I had the deepest reverence and affection for him. First, he was too overpowering a personality to give a young assistant a chance for independent development. Second, his interests had shifted to a border field—the structure of colloidal matter—which did not then interest me, and at the same time he had lost interest in the recent important developments in biology. He was even opposed to them, partly as a result of the overbearing attitude of some of the representatives of recent experimental biology who showed their contempt of everybody who worked in different lines. From this difficult position an unexpected way out opened.

In the spring of 1902 I went to the marine biological laboratory at Rovigno, Istria—then a part of the Austrian empire—on the shores of the blue Adriatic. I intended to study certain problems that had grown out of my thesis. On my way south I called on Richard Hertwig in Munich. To my surprise he told me that he was about to dismiss his first assistant, an intelligent fellow but a drunkard who neglected his duties. Hertwig also told me that he intended to offer me the job with the permission for "habilitation." The meaning of this is difficult for Americans to understand. In the German universities there was only one full professor in a field like zoology, and he was the only paid member of the teaching staff. He had one or two paid assistants to share in the laboratory teaching and the general management of the laboratory, and these might or might not be simultaneously lecturers or assistant or associate professors in the university—titular positions without income. But in order to be eligible for a real professorship one had to be admitted first to "habilitation" as a *Privatdocent*, or lecturer. This was completely independent of the assistantship, but since the lecturer was not paid only a man of independent means could afford to become *Privatdocent* without holding an assistant's job at the same time. Hertwig's offer therefore opened a wonderful and unexpected way of entering the academic career with a paid job (about 140 marks a month) in one of the greatest universities and under a great scholar. I had to tell Hertwig that I had not yet served my obligatory year in the army, but this suited him well for it gave him time to make things less hard for his unsuccessful assistant. In happy spirits I continued my trip to the Adriatic.

The two months in Rovigno are among my most splendid reminiscences. Life at the small marine laboratory, where only half a dozen scientists were working, was always most interesting. The dredging expeditions in the small laboratory steamer; collecting trips in the rowboat; land excursions in the beautiful surroundings, with or without zoological ends; life in a small southern fisherman's town; work and pleasant association with aspiring, idealistic young men—all made such a stay an ideal holiday. In this spring in Rovigno I had many additional reasons for happiness. I had a first success in my work, which, though scientifically of no importance, pleased me very much.

There is a group of small, transparent marine animals, somewhat akin to fish, the *Appendicularia,* the development of which had never been seen. I had come with the intention of finding and observing this development, and after a few days I discovered the tiny eggs and embryos in the plankton. But more important than this little achievement was the meeting with a great biologist and wonderful personality, a meeting that developed into a friendship. This was Fritz Schaudinn, already a leading protozoologist though not yet thirty years old, soon to be one of the great benefactors of humanity as the discoverer of the syphilis germ. Schaudinn had done extremely important work as assistant to F. E. Schulze, a professor of zoology in Berlin. But that conceited, jealous, and spiteful man had done everything to make things difficult for Schaudinn. At that time Robert Koch, the great bacteriologist, who had become interested in the malaria problem, noticed

Schaudinn's gifts and had him appointed to the staff of the imperial health department, an appointment that sent him to Rovigno to make an experiment in the sanitation of a bad malaria region nearby.

Schaudinn was one of those happy creatures to whom youth feels attracted immediately. A blond giant with sparkling blue eyes, he had the manners of an overgrown child. He loved fun and also strong language and accepted the young beginner with the unaffected simplicity so frequently associated with greatness. He had an uncanny power of observation and was an indefatigable worker who could spend twenty-four hours at the miscroscope when a continuous observation was needed, and in spite of his huge body he had the nimblest fingers to perform difficult microdissections. I was often permitted to accompany him on his regular visits to the village, towering above the fiordlike Cul di Leme and accessible only by boat, where he succeeded in eradicating the malaria he had found in each house when he first arrived. I spent many a pleasant hour with this fine man, who impressed me greatly, and later on I met him repeatedly at different occasions and kept up some correspondence. Only from a distance could I later follow his tragic fate.

Soon after I left Rovigno, Schaudinn was recalled to Berlin. The Kaiser had been deeply impressed with statistics on the spread of syphilis in the army and had ordered the health department to attack the problem seriously. Schaudinn received the order to search for the unknown syphilis germ, and an army surgeon, Hofmann, was assigned to him as an assistant to keep him supplied with material from fresh infections. Once work had actually started, it took Schaudinn only a single day to discover the hardly visible germ, the *Spirochaeta pallida.* He was absolutely sure of his discovery, but when he announced it at a meeting of the medical society the chairman, von Leyden, rose after the paper was finished and said in effect: "Gentlemen, you have listened in this hall already to one hundred announcements of the discovery of the syphilis germ. This was the hundred and first." Accompanied by the laughter of the hostile meeting Schaudinn left. For many weeks attacks and insults were heaped upon him, and in the front line stood his former chief, F. E. Schulze. This so maddened the young biologists, who stood firmly behind their idol Schaudinn, that the dignified, white-haired Schulze was booed when he appeared at the next meeting of the zoological society, and he never again showed up there. Meanwhile Neisser, Levaditi, and Metchnikoff had come out for Schaudinn, his discovery was accepted all over the world, and the way was opened for Paul Ehrlich's discovery of Salvarsan.

When an English university called Schaudinn to a newly founded chair, the Institute for Tropical Diseases in Hamburg realized what the loss of such a man would mean for Germany and offered him a suitable place. No German university, how-ever, had honored itself by inviting him. Schaudinn, who had recently married and had never before had a decent income, was happy and embarked upon a cruise given him by the Kaiser him-self. He returned a dying man. In the heat of his work and his fights with stupidity and ill will, he had neglected to have a small operation for hemorrhoids; an abscess developed, and when the operation was performed it was too late. Not yet thirty-two years old, the great discoverer perished miserably. And even this did not end his tragedy. Years later, during the misery of German inflation, I learned by chance that Mrs. Schaudinn and her children were living in abject misery. A collection was started by a few of Schaudinn's friends, and it was very successful. Many contribu-tions came from all over the world, and especially the Japanese scientists, led by my friends Shiga and Hata, responded wonder-fully. But the abysmal inflation that followed destroyed these funds, which had been established as trust funds and could not be touched. Once more the friends had to save the unfortunate family, and they succeeded in inducing the Hamburg senate to vote a pension for the widow of the great discoverer. But a worse fate was in store for the harassed family. When the Nazis came into power it was discovered that Mrs. Schaudinn had a Jewish mother; the fine, tall, and fair children were "non-Aryans," and all were thrown out of their careers, back into darkness.

But let us return to Rovigno in 1902, when the world still ap-peared rosy and "the sky full of fiddles." The end of a successful season of work and play was celebrated with a hike across Istria to Fiume in the company of a highly cultured and interesting young Russian biologist, Petrunkewitsch, later professor at Yale and a lifelong friend. Traveling home I took a steamer from Trieste to Venice and landed for the first time in that unique city. When I arrived I found that my traveling funds were completely exhausted, but I could not forgo the pleasure of being rowed around the canals in a gondola and visiting the famous churches and art galleries. On the steamer I had made the acquaintance of a nice old Austrian gentleman, who suggested that I send a telegram home and meanwhile accept the necessary money from him. This I did and had a beautiful time sight-seeing with my new banker until the ransom arrived one day in the mails. Though I visited Italy a great many times afterward, it happened that I returned to Venice only once. It was almost thirty years later that my wife and I landed there on our way back from India. Passing the Piazza di San Marco we stood at the railing, and at the pier our grown-up children welcomed us home. In memory of my first visit, we put up in the same cheap artists' inn I had been in before. But Venice did not seem as beautiful as the first time. Maybe it was the absence of sunshine; maybe it was because I was older.

My last term in Heidelberg was unpleasant. It was an exceedingly hot summer, and the close valley was unbearable. Moreover, I had outgrown my surroundings and was longing for a new field of activity. Thus the approach of my year of service as *Einjährig-Freiwilliger* (one-year "volunteer") was a welcome change. In the fall of 1902 I reported for service as a private in a mounted artillery regiment.

By law every citizen of Imperial Germany had to serve two years in the army, and even three if conscripted for cavalry. But all those who had graduated from certain types of middle school had the privilege of serving only one year and could choose their own time and also their regiment. They did not live in the barracks but had their private quarters in town, bought their own food and uniforms, were supposed to spend a good deal of money, and were entitled to be promoted to the rank of a reserve officer after two additional training periods of eight weeks each. Service in a mounted regiment was quite expensive, and I was grateful to my father for permitting this extravagance, which cost him more than I ought to have accepted. But at that time it was not considered improper for a man of twenty-four to accept his father's money. Those were, of course, times of prosperity, and nobody worried about the future, which seemed safe and rosy in the rich and successful German Empire.

Being strong of body and fond of exercise, I liked being a soldier though the harsh discipline was rather tedious to a man who already had a start in science. The first weeks were especially tough. The *Einjährigen* started six weeks before the regular recruits were called to the colors, and we had to live in the barracks during that time. As the *Einjährigen* of the foregoing year had painted the town red, orders had been given to show us from the beginning what military discipline meant. The sergeants to whom we were entrusted certainly enjoyed this order and did their best to give us a rough time. From four in the morning, when we started cleaning the horses and stables, to seven at night, we were chased around with only a few minutes for swallowing some miserable food and no time for washing. There was constant shouting and swearing at us in the most obscene language. Riding school was held not with the regular saddle horses but with the huge old mares of the howitzer teams, and since we rode without stirrups we were thrown high up into the air with every step. After six weeks we were certainly broken in but were full of resentment against the brutality of our treatment. It was one of the most pleasant moments of my life when finally the recruits came to occupy the barracks, the *Einjährigen* were dismissed to their private quarters, and I was able to soak for hours in a hot tub after six weeks without a bath or even a decent washing.

The winter brought the usual barracks life. There was excellent training in horseback riding. I learned to jump a hurdle without stirrups or rein, doing arm exercises at the same time, and to perform various tricks on a galloping horse—jumping off and on its back, changing position in the saddle to face to the side or the rear. Later I was taught the dangerous art of breaking in young broncos, a feat that takes every ounce of a man's strength. There was much gymnastics, and the artillery training itself was interesting. The only tedious work was practicing the goose step, which even the mounted troops had to learn. This outrageous invention, though useful for loosening up the heavy joints of the peasant boys and for training a man to act like a part of a machine, cannot be appreciated by anybody who has not practiced it, as I did, for three hours, at zero temperature, with a sharp little rock lodged inside my boot. But there were also compensations, for the *Einjährigen* were allowed to leave the barracks at five in the afternoon, don their fashionable and colorful town uniforms, and have a good time in town, where the boys and their open purses were rather popular.

The least pleasant part of the barracks life was the young officers. Most of the higher officers belonged to the aristocracy and came from old military families. They were soldiers by instinct and tradition and knew how to handle recruits and to keep discipline without shouting and name calling. But the training was usually entrusted to young lieutenants, most of whom happened to be commoners. It was a strange fact that the haughty *Junker* had the sympathy of the private soldiers, who recognized their competence and their natural habit of commanding. But officers who came from families of civil servants and the like seemed to believe that they had to show their superiority by constant shouting, threatening, and punishing. Moreover, they were militarily inefficient, and the soldiers hated them. The worst one in our battery was a preacher's son, probably handicapped by poverty, very unintelligent, ugly, and spiteful. He believed that discipline meant making life miserable for the private soldier, and he acted accordingly. He especially hated the *Einjährigen,* many of whom had academic degrees, and he despised the young businessmen, "businessman" being about the worst name an officer in Imperial Germany could call anybody. These poor fellows were treated like the scum of humanity and exercised to the point of breakdown. Since the lieutenant could not boast of intellectual superiority over the hated *Einjährigen,* he tried to impress them with feats of the body. But he had bad luck. One day he appeared while we were having gymnastics and ordered a long jump over the horse, adding that he would show us how to do it. He took off his sword and made the jump as poorly as it could be made, with bent knees and crawling along the horse with his hands. I was the next and, since I was at that time a top-notch gymnast, performed the jump in the proper style. The lieutenant was furious and commanded next a little insignificant-looking Jewish boy. It was his bad luck that the small boy also happened to be a first-class gymnast and performed a perfect jump. With distorted face the lieutenant left and never again performed gymnastics in our presence. I wonder if later in World War I he was not one of the officers killed by shots in the back from their own lines.

The first of July finally approached—the date at which customarily the *Einjährigen* were promoted to noncommissioned officers. This promotion was the first step toward the reserve officer's patent, which each *Einjähriger* aspired to receive, not only as the natural goal of his service but also because in Imperial Germany a man without such a patent was considered inferior and had difficulties in a governmental career, including, of course, a university career. The day arrived and I was not promoted though I knew that my captain had told his cousin, one of my best friends, that I was his best soldier in every respect. Of course I knew the reason, confirmed via my friend: anti-Semitism. My pride was deeply hurt, for I enjoyed being a good soldier and had made it a point to excel in what are called soldierly virtues. Shortly afterward I took advantage of an illness to secure a leave of absence which I succeeded in prolonging again and again until a few days before dismissal from service, and I did not don my uniform any more except for those last days. My captain, a fine man, but powerless against orders from higher up, told my friend later that it was a great relief for him that my long absence gave him a proper pretext for not asking for my subsequent promotion, which he knew would not be granted.

The last day in service was characteristic. The commander of the regiment, a rather unintelligent *Junker*, assembled the *Einjäh-rigen* and shouted a short speech at them, the gist of which was that whoever had not been promoted had to ascribe the fact to his own incapacity. Planting himself in front of a Jewish lawyer who had had a conflict with an officer and had been foolish enough to inform him that he would demand a duel after the year of service, the *Junker* asked, "Do you know why you have not been promoted?"

"Yes, Colonel," was the answer.

No businessman, no son of a shopkeeper or artisan, and no Jew had been promoted, but two members of the feudal students' fraternities who could hardly mount a horse without provoking laughter were at the top of the list of promotions.

Yet these things had already become unimportant to me for my life had entered a new phase. While on leave in Munich I had met a young girl, Elsa Kühnlein, the daughter of a professor of classical philology, and had fallen head over heels in love for the first time in my life, a condition that at once became chronic. There was a new goal to my life. But not being a poet, who alone is entitled to lift the veil from his innermost feelings, I finish this story of my youth simply with thanks to the good fate that brought me this crowning blessing, not yet ended after more than fifty years.

4: MY PROFESSIONAL LIFE BEGINS

In the autumn of 1903 I started my work in the department of zoology at the University of Munich. And in the following year 1904, the great event of my habilitation as *Privatdocent* took place. I had published half a dozen or more papers, as required, and my thesis, a large piece of work, had been accepted by the faculty and was in press. I had passed the so-called colloquium, a kind of friendly examination by those members of the faculty who wanted to ask questions, and I was ready for the formal "test lecture" to be given in the big auditorium to whoever might care to attend. The head of the department presented to the faculty sealed envelopes containing three topics, of which one was chosen by lot. Three days before the event the envelope was opened and I was told on what topic I was to lecture. The next day I had to call on all the full professors of the faculty, in full regalia including top hat, to present a copy of my thesis and an invitation to the lecture. I hired a taxi and went to the homes of the professors all over town. All were absent save one mathematician who accepted my visit. After we were seated in the parlor he took the thesis and turned over the pages, hoping to find an idea for starting a conversation. But he did not succeed, and after five minutes of silence he rose and I backed out.

The great day came and, trembling, I took my seat on the semicircular, elevated row of benches reserved for the professors. Again I was in full evening dress at ten in the morning. When the time came to start only Hertwig, the dean, and the professor of mathematics who had accepted my visit were present in the rotunda. The large hall with its marble pillars and walls covered with paintings made a strange impression. The janitor, knowing that not many attended such lectures, had refused to put chairs into the hall. He could be induced only to put up a single chair for my father, who had come to Munich to be present at the great event. Thus my father sat alone and forlorn in the center of the empty floor. Along the walls the students from our laboratory leaned uncomfortably; in the background stood two lean, black Jesuits who had happened to drop in; and in a corner near the door stood a rather ill-matched pair—my best friend, a fellow six-foot-six in his boots, and my fiancée, Elsa, reaching hardly to his armpits. To this great audience I delivered the lecture on which I had worked hard the three preceding nights. Afterward I had to defend some more or less extreme statements, which were handed in print to the audience. Only Hertwig and one fellow assistant attacked my statements; I responded, and the critics declared themselves convinced. Thus I became a full-fledged lecturer.

In the first year I did not have many students because my lectures were not among the obligatory ones. But in the course of the years I built up lectures for advanced students in different fields like cytology and genetics, and these, though not in the curriculum, were well attended. This meant for me not only the satisfaction coming from successful work but also bread and butter, for students meant students' fees, which I, as lecturer, received. How often at the beginning of the term did I enter my lecture hall with trembling heart! A full hall meant a vacation trip, a doctor's bill paid, a new suit, or a piece of furniture; an empty hall meant tightening the belt. I developed the art of counting my students and computing the expected income without interrupting my lecture for a moment.

These lectures were always given from six to seven at night and ended a long day of work. It took me a long time to stop having the jitters before each lecture. I always prepared my lectures very thoroughly and spoke without notes though I had the notes available on my desk. In time I succeeded in earning the reputation of a good teacher, a reputation reflected in bigger classes, and I reached an income larger than that of many a full professor. Old Reichenbach, who had told me that zoology was a sport for rich people, was definitely beaten. But the funny thing was that I never enjoyed being a good lecturer. In spite of an inborn gift, I disliked my lectures for they took too much out of me. If my eyes fell upon a student who yawned or talked to his neighbor, the whole lecture was spoiled for me, and afterward I felt depressed and low. Maybe this is why I got more pleasure out of the popular science talks I had to give on many occasions. The audiences at such events swallow avidly every word of the lecturer, and immediately there is established a pleasant and stimulating contact that is frequently prevented in university classes by the bad manners of some students.

Another kind of teaching I greatly enjoyed, though it took much time and strength, was the work with advanced research students. It was my duty to look after Hertwig's research students; with each I consulted daily and watched and controlled each step of the work. In these years Hertwig's laboratory in the old monastery became a great attraction to the scientists of the whole world, and in addition to our own students we always had numerous guests from everywhere in the world doing research work. I had to take care of all of them, a task that was very stimulating, gave me practice in a number of languages, and helped me to make friends. It meant also a huge amount of work. Because of the increase in the number of research workers I soon had to take on students working on their doctor's theses, and I built up in time a considerable school of excellent men, many of whom later became fine scientists and leaders in their chosen fields.

There was only one drawback—the lack of independence. The organization of the German universities was such that I remained, as far as the university was concerned, Hertwig's assistant, though I had gradually become a scholar in my own right. For personal reasons—the death of a son and a subsequent breakdown—Hertwig could not do his full work for some years, and I actually ran the laboratory and had all the research students to take care of. But officially they were Hertwig's students and I was the assistant. Hertwig himself, the noblest of characters, probably did not notice this traditional condition, and he could not have changed it. He certainly did everything in his power for me, recommended me for lectureships and traveling and research grants, and was a father and a friend to me; and he never interfered with my research, which tended away from his own interests. But I longed to be my own master and to do my own work in my own way. Externally I got all the promotion available, even a position with tenure and pension, newly created at that time, as a kind of laboratory chief comparable to the French *chef de laboratoire*.

Among the many different things I did in these years—during long working days and frequently into the evenings—was university extension work. Hertwig, politically extremely conservative but with a socially minded heart, was greatly interested in this work and gave much time to popular science lecturing in night classes. He got me interested, and I gave many a course of such lectures, sometimes for large audiences. I found that popular lecturing, to be successful, requires much clearer thinking, clearer expression, and more logical organization than university teaching. When I boast now that I can make the most difficult topic clear and give a well-organized lecture even without preparation, I think I owe my ability to the popular lecture work of those years. In later life this practice stood me in good stead, for many times and in many countries I was forced to improvise suddenly a popular science talk to the most incongruous audiences; actually I have given such completely unprepared talks to Japanese, Chinese, Korean, Ryukyuan, Formosan, Philippine, and Hindu, as well as European and American, audiences. This work also led me to popular science writing. During those years in Munich, I began to write an occasional popular science book or article and ever since have enjoyed doing so from time to time as a kind of relaxation from highly technical work.

It is a strange fact that scholars frequently are strongly prejudiced against popular writing, thinking that it lowers the standard of a research scholar and makes him a superficial writer. The great examples of Huxley, Tyndall, Helmholtz, Haeckel, and Fabre are usually forgotten. Actually, in my opinion, it is the duty of the research man to write popular science, provided he has the gift for it. Next to the successful artist the scientist is the freest of all human beings. His hobby is simultaneously his work; he is able to create without outside interference or control; he is responsible only to his scientific conscience; he lives in the ideal atmosphere of a laboratory, associates with the most interesting people, lives for an ideal, has leisure time, and frequently has extensive opportunities for travel. All this is made available to him by the community that pays him for doing his research and for teaching the results to students. Is it not, then, his duty to help the hosts of active, interested minds of the nation, to whom the technical works are inaccessible on account of the difficult terminology and special requirements of scholarship, to learn the results of science? Of course there are professional popularizers who do this; but how do they do it? Not having first-hand information, they usually cannot discern what is important or unimportant, essential or nonessential, certain or controversial. In addition they tend to exaggerate, to be sensational, to promise future developments, to cater to the taste of the lower class of readers. It is therefore the duty of the man with the first-hand information to disseminate it, though I realize this is not an easy job. To write popular science requires mastery of the language, clear thinking, scientific tact, ability for logical organization, power to feel where results are not yet fit for a general discussion, and good taste and artistic sense in selecting

69

examples and inventing comparisons and similes for the sake of clarifying difficult points—more than is required for the writing of treatises or textbooks. A scholar who tries and succeeds in fulfilling that duty ought to be not slighted but praised.

This was the shape of my professional life between 1903 and 1909, rounded out most pleasantly by my private life in what was at the time a most charming place to live. William Lyon Phelps, who stayed for some time in Munich during these years, asserts in his autobiography that there was no place in the world where a man could be happier. Munich, the artistic center of Germany, at that time combined the charming levity of Vienna, the Bohemian extravagance of Paris, the happy-go-lucky life of Florence and Naples, all with its beautiful location in the grand Isar Valley near the Alps.

The most important thing that happened to me in those years was, of course, my marriage to Elsa Kühnlein, the young girl I had met in Munich. After an engagement of two and a half years, we were married on March 15, 1906, at Frankfurt. Fifty-two years of my life as husband, father, and grandfather have passed since that time. They constitute our most precious private possession, which we are not willing to share even with the most friendly reader. The innumerable friends of both of us will understand this and respect our privacy.

The young family—two children, Ruth and Hans, had been born in 1906 and 1907, respectively—now lived in Munich the simple but rich life of a young scholar among many friends, mostly scientists and artists with broad interests. There were the best concerts, the violently discussed new movements in painting and music, the hikes and occasional climbs in the Alps. Music was not neglected in our home, and my violin again came into its own. Under the influence of the artistic milieu I began to acquire here and there a modern or an old etching or engraving and became acquainted with the points, quality, and stages of the prints, all of which a collector has to know. Whenever funds permitted, and sometimes also when they did not, a piece of china or brass, a painting or sculpture, or a piece of antique furniture was hunted down and our simple household embellished.

Friends in all walks of life were plentiful, and many a pleasant night was spent at one of the gay and colorful artists' balls. Social intercourse was easy and simple. Frequently we bought cold cuts, bread, and butter and went with friends at night to one of the famous beer gardens where we ate our simple supper accompanied by a huge stein of the best beer in the world. Or we surprised a friend, a painter and accomplished pianist, bringing the supper (and a little more to leave behind), and had him play Bach and Beethoven for us for hours on end. I cannot think of these long-past evenings without feeling the shock of subsequent events, so characteristic of our times. Our charming friend, Henrik Moor, a brother of the composer and pianist Emanuel Moor, was of Jewish-Hungarian descent. Probably he was the only one who knew this, since he had been born in the United States of America while his parents were traveling there. When the Nazis came to power, Henrik had the artist's levity not to declare himself a "non-Aryan." In fact he went on as before and even painted the portraits of some Nazi bigwigs. But somehow the Gestapo got suspicious and started investigating him, meanwhile confining him to his house. One day he came down with acute appendicitis. But the Gestapo refused permission for him to see a doctor, and he died miserably from a ruptured appendix.

But who would have expected such future happenings in the happy-go-lucky town of Munich in the first decade of this century? In our life outside the laboratory there were also elaborate parties and gay dances during the carnival season in the homes of wealthy friends, parties that invariably ended with breakfast the next morning. Eight to ten hours of continuous dancing did not mean much in those days. But best of all were the days of skiing, and occasionally also tobogganing, in the Alps during the winter. For weeks we waited for the snowfall and the beginning of the skiing season. When I first came to Munich only a few people had discovered the Scandinavian sport, and it was possible to ski for a whole week end in the mountains without meeting a soul. But when skiing became popular, around 1910, the station from which the trains to the mountains left early in the morning looked like the forest moving on Dunsinane castle.

I had started skiing as one of the pioneers, completely autodidactic with a self-invented technique, and when I think of the bindings with which we dared to mountaineer on skis I shudder. Later on, no week end or winter vacation was missed if possible, and many a beautiful day was spent on the peaks of upper Bavaria and Tyrol. There was a whole group of student skiers in the laboratory, and during the week at tea time the plans for the next week end were laid. It is sad to think that all my companions of this greatest of all sports, all younger than I, have passed away—Kupelwieser, the charming, indefatigable, daring Viennese, the best of mountaineering companions; von Kemnitz, the passionate Alpinist of huge strength, who later was killed by an avalanche; the brothers Mulsow, promising young zoologists and excellent sportsmen, both killed in action in the first months of World War I. Kupelwieser, who happened to be one of the richest men in Austria, owned a beautiful castle in the Alps surrounded by a whole range of mountains. Once we spent a Christmas vacation there. We stayed at a hunting lodge high up and could make another peak each day without ever leaving his property. Returning from a day's sport, we frequently played trios all evening in his cozy parlor.

Life in Munich was frequently and pleasantly interrupted by more or less extended trips abroad, not to mention trips and hikes into Tyrol and other nearby beauty spots. German universities had almost five months of vacation, distributed over Easter, Christmas, and summer. In summer we went to a lake near the mountains where we rented a small and utterly primitive old farmhouse without any comfort or sanitation whatsoever. But we all—Elsa and I and the children—had a happy time swimming, hiking, and resting. In spring, after the long, cold, and dark winter of Munich, we longed for sunshine and, whenever funds were available, tried to get to the Mediterranean. Marine biological laboratories made it possible to combine travel with work.

Our most impressive spring was probably that of 1910 at the famous zoological station in Naples, to which I was to return many times. All winter long we had prepared ourselves for the sights of Italy by studying history and art history, and when we finally reached Florence we already knew every stone. We soaked ourselves in the architecture, sculpture, and painting of the Renaissance and raved about the beauty of Tuscany. In Naples we combined work with strolling around the picturesque town, which had not yet been cleaned out and still gloried in the unbelievable but utterly attractive filth of the Santa Lucia quarter. Every cab ride meant a fight with the coachman; every purchase was a contest of wits; every waiter returned us fake money as change. But I must confess that Naples was a much more desirable place then, with all those little taints, than later when Mussolini had made it more respectable but duller. We reveled of course in the beauty of the Greek sculpture in the famous museum; leisurely visits to

Pompeii were great events; and hikes over the uniquely beautiful Sorrentine Peninsula were not to be forgotten. But the greatest impression came toward the end of our stay.

News came from Sicily that Mount Etna was in eruption. Since this volcano has the peculiarity that its eruptions last for weeks, even increasing in intensity, here was a chance to witness an extraordinary sight. With a few friends we sailed at once to Sicily, where we were greeted by the ghastly sight of the city of Messina, destroyed by an earthquake the year before and still in a condition of complete destruction. From Messina we proceeded to Catania where we were told that the lava stream had reached the hamlet of Nicolosi, some thousand feet up the slopes of Etna. Surrounded by a crowd of gesticulating, excited townspeople who took part in the difficult proceedings, we bargained with a driver for a carriage to Nicolosi and finally drove out of town.

Toward dusk we reached the endangered hamlet. Here we learned that the new crater had formed at the flank of the mountain at about nine thousand feet altitude and that the lava stream had reached the outskirts of Nicolosi, having run down for about ten miles. It was surprising that there was complete calm in the village though everybody could expect that within the next few days the whole town might be buried by the slowly proceeding lava. But all day long processions with the statue of the Holy Virgin went around and toward the lava stream. Once before the Virgin had stopped the lava near the village, and a chapel erected on the spot attested to the miracle. Actually, the miracle repeated itself this time, though a skeptic might have pointed to the configuration of the bottom of the valley near the village.

The lava stream, ten miles away from its origin, looked not like a stream but like a huge pile of coal, twenty feet high and with a frontage of about seven hundred feet. Black in the daytime, at night it glowed red, and we saw its forward movement in the form of small cascades of red sparks. It moved on extremely slowly, about two yards a day, destroying everything in its path. We watched a farmhouse being slowly wrecked by the giant serpent in the course of three days. In the garden stood a flowering peach tree, already surrounded by some lava. Suddenly a blue, sulphurlike flame—and nothing was left. I have never forgotten the sight of the dying tree, which would be a lovely topic for a Chinese poet.

We found a native who had climbed to the crater and told us that it was located not too far from an Alpine refuge, the *can-*

tonièra. This news presented a chance of staying overnight near the crater. If the lava stream did not change its course there would be no danger in approaching the crater. We started the next morning with our guide and climbed the steep slopes of the mountain over old lava streams until we reached the *cantonièra.* A short walk brought us to the edge of the lava stream and within a few hundred yards of the new crater, which looked like a giant anthill on the flanks of the mountain. With a thundering noise the white, glowing lava fell in a huge cascade out of an opening and poured downhill, as liquid as water. At the point where we stood at the edge of the stream upon blocks scarcely cool, it was about seventy feet broad and moved eight yards a second with a terrible noise like the breaking of thousands of bottles. The noise was produced by the friction of the liquid mass against the cooling clinkers at the edges. Bluish sulphur fumes took away our breath and hurt our eyes. Within the crater there were terrible explosions, and fiery rocks flew to heaven like skyrockets in a constant fusillade, fortunately falling down upon the walls of the crater. A terrible heat emanating from the stream scorched us in front while the cold mountain wind made our backs shudder. Finally we returned to the *cantonièra,* exhausted by the fierce and unearthly spectacle. The night was not very pleasant in the small room, which was filled with sulphur fumes and had only three undersized bunks for six people, three of them oversized. Before dawn I could not stand it any longer and went outside, soon followed by one of my companions. It was a starlit night, and we walked again to the lava stream, guided by the infernal clattering. When we stood at the edge of the fiery glow, listening to the bombardment from the crater and watching the distant cascade of fire breaking out of the mountain, both of us were suddenly seized with a feeling of abject terror, which lasted until the sun rose gloriously over the Mediterranean at our feet.

The end of this, my first encounter with the subterranean powers, was less pleasant. We proceeded to Palermo to see the glorious monuments of Norman-Arab art, the Capella Palatina and the Cathedral of Monreale. We climbed Monte Pellegrino to see the view of one of the great beauty spots on earth, and we made an excursion to the magnificent ruin of the Greek temple at Segesta. Returning to Palermo I felt rather miserable and soon realized that something was wrong with my appendix. At night we embarked for the trip to Naples. Soon a terrific gale began to blow, and the small steamer rolled terribly. All night long the entire contents of our stateroom, baggage and all, rolled from one corner to the other. Toward midnight there was excited shouting, and we learned the next day that hundreds of Sicilian enlisted men who were being transported to Naples had gone mad with fear and tried to storm the bridge to force the captain to turn back. I was very seasick, and I can affirm that the combination of seasickness with appendicitis is not a pleasant one. I did not return to Sicily until more than twenty years later, when Elsa and I, with our children, took a silver-wedding trip and revisited all the old sights.

It was about this time that I began to feel unhappy with the type of work I was doing. I had spent years upon a tedious piece of microscopic work, trying to unravel completely the structure of a simple nervous system. Though I carried out my task and published a monograph, I felt that the really interesting points could not be attacked by microscopic work but needed physiological experimentation. I began to be tired of my purely morphological line of research, which no longer satisfied my analytical mind. I felt unhappy and came to the conclusion that I must find a way to live for two or three years without a job and take up again a thorough study of physics and chemistry so that I might carry on an experimental study of cell phenomena. I had in mind a line of research that has now been successfully developed by present-day biochemists, and I racked my brain to find a method of financing such an undertaking. Meanwhile, during a vacation at our country place, sprawled under a plum tree, I read Johannsen's *Elements of Exact Genetics*. Though I had followed the development of this new science in a way, the clear, exact exposition and the critical evaluation of the facts in this really great book opened a new scientific world to me. I was so fascinated that I decided at once that this was the work that would give me satisfaction, and, dropping my other plans, I immediately began to study the literature and to plan experiments.

In order to organize my knowledge I announced a lecture course in genetics, actually the first offered in a German university, and was pleased that not only numerous students, but a large number of young lecturers, assistants, and visiting scientists, registered for the course. From the course I developed a textbook that became very popular and went through five editions until its sale was prohibited by the Nazis twenty-two years later.

75

In starting my experiments I had nobody to lean on or to consult and had to work out my own methods. I chose as my material butterflies and moths, knowing this group of animals to be suitable for the attack upon the problems I had in mind—sex determination and evolution. Chance and luck, but perhaps also knowledge of the material and hints in the literature concerning odd phenomena occasionally observed, made me select especially one animal, the gypsy moth, *Lymantria dispar*, which turned out to be most interesting and kept me busy for more than twenty-five years. Hertwig, always helpful, secured grants to pay for equipment and help, and the next summer saw me already raising thousands of caterpillars, later to become hundreds of thousands. Again I was thoroughly happy in my work, which extended continuously and led into many interesting directions and to fascinating and stimulating discoveries, and which still keeps me happy almost fifty years later.

The following year, in 1911, an international meeting of geneticists was held in Paris, and for the first time I had the opportunity of meeting the foreigners who led in this field—Johannsen, Bateson and his school, Nilsson-Ehle, Cuénot, and many others. There were only two German botanists in the field at that time, Carl Correns and Erwin Baur, as well as the Austrian Tschermak. The meeting was rather a strange affair. Official French science, which until rather recently was hostile to genetics, boycotted the meeting. It was run, and paid for, as a kind of private affair by the Vilmorin family, the great nurserymen. Apart from science the atmosphere was a bad one, overshadowed by the Morocco affair. The hostility toward Germany was all too evident. The shop windows displayed caricatures of the Kaiser with bellicose texts, and the statue of Strasbourg in the Place de la Concorde was covered with wreaths with black ribbons and the inscription *"Revanche!"* Parades of nationalistic students cried for war. The few German delegates to the meeting were badly treated, and when the Swede Nilsson-Ehle made a dinner speech in German some Frenchmen were rude. When the proceedings of the congress were printed, the French translated all the German papers into French without asking permission of the authors and added English summaries—an act contrary to the established rules of international scientific intercourse. One must have seen these things to realize that the world war had been in the air for a long time before it finally broke out, and that the French were not poor harmless sheep attacked by a wolf, as they succeeded in making the world believe. But this time the storm blew over, and the following year I was able to return to Paris with my wife for a delightful holiday.

At about this time the tragic death in a sailing accident of my chief's son indirectly resulted in an immense overburden of work for me. Hertwig did his duties and spent all day in the laboratory, but his nights were sleepless, and this impaired his work in the day-time. It fell to me to do a considerable share of his work and to make things easy for him. This meant that with one other assistant I practically ran the large laboratory with about thirty research workers. It was too much work, and I began to loathe teaching, especially the beginners' courses. I envied men who had independent means and could pursue research without being tied down. There was even a rumor that in America research professorships existed. If only such a thing could come to Germany and, of course, to me! And there was another reason to envy the gentleman scholar. I had reached the age and the reputation to be eligible for a call as full professor. A number of times my name had been in the run-ning, but in every case academic anti-Semitism had decided against me. Thus I longed to get away from the university into a pure research position. But there was none in Germany, and I had to resign myself. Actually, unknown to me, fortune was already around the corner.

In 1910 the University of Berlin had celebrated its centenary and, on that occasion, the Kaiser, advised by Harnack and Schmidt-Ott, had collected twenty million marks from rich industrialists (paid for with decorations, titles, and invitations to tea) to found a society for the advancement of research. The membership fee was immense, but, since the Kaiser himself was honorary president, all wealthy people rushed to join. The idea was to found research institutes in fields not sufficiently taken care of by the universities, and especially in fields in which work required more space, funds, and time than were available in universities. The state added from public funds the salaries of the directors, fixed at a level near that of secretaries of state. A beautiful site in a fashionable suburb of Berlin, belonging to the crown, was purchased, and the Kaiser's favorite architect, Ihne, was entrusted with the building (which was done, according to expectation, in the worst artistic taste). The institutes even received their own flag, designed by the Kaiser, and at court functions the trustees could wear a uniform, also designed by the Kaiser, which I never saw but which must have been staggering. The first institutes founded were for electro-chemistry (Haber), chemistry (Beckmann, Willstätter, Hahn, Meitner), and serology (Wassermann). Soon the advisers of the society suggested also an institute for experimental biology, and a large sum was set aside for this purpose. Theodor Boveri, at the zenith of his brilliant, classical work in biology, was invited to organize the institute. He planned to have five departments: his own; one for experimental embryology for which he selected Hans Spemann (later Nobel prize winner); one for experimental biology of lower forms, to be headed by Max Hartmann (today Germany's foremost biologist); one for cell physiology with young Otto Warburg (later Nobel prize winner) at the head; and one for genetics. For this I had been selected, and one day in the winter of 1912–13 Boveri announced his arrival in Munich to talk over the invitation.

I certainly was excited when suddenly my most cherished day-dream seemed to come true: work in a research laboratory; freedom from teaching, administration, and university politics; freedom to choose my collaborators; and all backed by a large budget. I gladly accepted, if my requirements in regard to space, assistants, and budget could be sufficiently met to make successful work in such a conspicuous place possible. Of course my personal needs had to be taken care of, and full independence and freedom in the work as well as in the application of the funds to this work were asked. After some quibbling about details, the society finally agreed upon the terms of my appointment. But soon other difficulties appeared. Boveri, who had always lived in the quiet atmosphere of a small university, was an idealist and no match for the Berlin officials, who tried to drive as hard a bargain with him as possible, according to the old traditions of the ministry of education. This offended him and added to the weight of doubts that he nursed regarding his ability to fulfill the expectations. He feared that he would be driven in his work, forced to produce quick results. A highly artistic personality, he asked himself whether he would not be happier among his old friends in his accustomed atmosphere, and, since he was in addition a typical Bavarian, he mistrusted a priori everything coming from Prussia. When he fell sick about this time with severe influenza, he suddenly decided to decline after all and informed Berlin (and also me) of his decision. Maybe he already knew that a treacherous illness was preparing its onslaught, an illness to which he succumbed three years later in his early fifties.

Boveri's refusal was a hard blow for me. None of the other four candidates was old enough or famous enough at that time to be put into the foremost position in German science. No other biologist with all the needed qualifications was available. Nothing was heard any more from Berlin, and I went about my work, believing that the great plan had been abolished. Then I heard from Hertwig, and from August Brauer in Berlin, that the plan would be carried out if a proper director could be found. I suggested confidentially that, since no zoologist in the proper age class was available, one might include a botanist in the group, and I pointed to Carl Correns, the rediscoverer of Mendel's law of heredity and the leading German plant geneticist. I had met him in Münster, when both of us gave formal addresses at the meeting of the Society of Naturalists. Hertwig and Brauer, who were greatly interested in saving the project for biological science, convinced the Kaiser Wilhelm Society that Correns would be a proper substitute for Boveri, and new plans were laid in Berlin, though I did not know it.

A year passed, and again I spent my summer vacation in our little farmhouse, not thinking any more about Berlin. Then one day a letter with a huge seal arrived from Adolf Harnack, theologian, philosopher, historian, and organizer, the president of the Kaiser Wilhelm Society, informing me that Correns had consented to take Boveri's place and that otherwise the institute would be organized as planned. A meeting was to be held in Berlin within a few weeks to work out the organization. Also, an invitation was enclosed to attend the Kaiser's solemn inauguration of the serological institute. This letter fell like a bomb into the summer peace of our Tusculum.

At about this time, my work had come to a critical point. I had hit upon a strange and new phenomenon for which I later coined the term "intersexuality." When Japanese races of the gypsy moth were crossed with European races, all would-be female offspring were transformed into something between the sexes, and this according to definite rules. Certain observations led me to conclude that different races of this moth must be found in Japan, different in regard to their sex-determining action in crosses. In addition, observations I had made concerning other characteristics in these racial crosses suggested that the Japanese forms must be extremely interesting from the standpoint of evolution. Thus I felt it necessary for further progress in my work to go to Japan to try to find the races whose existence I suspected and to analyze them. I had tried to get the necessary funds from academies, but the few grants of sufficient size had already been awarded to others. Now I conceived the idea that the time that would elapse before the Kaiser Wilhelm Institute was ready for occupation would be the proper time for my work in Japan, and that the material I would bring home would give me a fine start in the new institute. I immediately worked out the plan, calculated the minimum cost, and asked Harnack to interest the Kaiser Wilhelm Society in its execution. No answer was received.

Finally the date of the meeting in Berlin came. Harnack presided, Schmidt-Ott (later minister of education) represented Prussia, Trendelenburg (later secretary of state) was the secretary, and we five chosen scholars sat around the table in great expectation. Harnack, one of the great men of Germany, whom I now met for the first time, led the discussion in a way I never witnessed before or afterward. Though not a scientist, actually a theologian, he seemed to know all about science, kept the discussion in a straight line, made short work of unimportant points, and brought about quick decisions on important ones. The funds available were very large for German conditions. Each of us announced the share he wanted for his work, his helpers, and his equipment, and also the floor space and special rooms he needed. In a surprisingly short time Harnack succeeded in welding into a workable whole the claims of five scholars without practical experience, and everything was settled.

When this was done, Harnack said, "Let us see if there is anything left for discussion. Oh yes, here I have Mr. Goldschmidt's request for a trip to Japan." My heart started bumping. "There is no objection to that." I felt dizzy. "Let's see. How much had you asked?" I had asked for six thousand marks. Then, addressing Schmidt-Ott, Harnack said, "Are you not also a member of the board of trustees of the Kahn fellowships? How about presenting Goldschmidt's name to His Majesty the Kaiser for award of the fellowship for next year?" Then, turning to me, "I am afraid the fellowship carries over thirteen thousand marks and there is the condition that the trip must go around the world. Would you object to that?"

I felt stunned, and I must have stuttered the most ridiculous answer. Spemann later told me that I offered a very funny sight, suddenly splashing helplessly in a stream of gold.

Only later I learned about the marvelous Kahn fellowships. A wealthy banker in Paris offered seventeen thousand francs every year to four governments (the United States was one of them) to be given to scientists as fellowships *autour du monde*. No special work was required; the incumbent was to travel around the world, keep his eyes open, and simply profit from the opportunity to see the great world. Mr. Kahn expected the fellows to call on him on their way home and report upon their experiences. In his beautiful park at Clichy, near Paris, he had established *le club autour du monde*, which was open to all fellows. World War I prevented me from paying Mr. Kahn my respects while I held the fellowship, but seventeen years later, while visiting Paris as a guest lecturer at the Sorbonne, I had dinner at *le club* with the charming and refined old gentleman. I understand that after his death his fortune was lost, and a beautiful institution for fostering international understanding no longer exists.

At the dinner party following the meeting with Harnack, I had an interesting conversation with Schmidt-Ott, all-powerful boss of Prussian universities. He told me that the Prussian Academy had proposed to call to the post of research academician, vacant since the death of the great chemist Van't Hoff, a young physicist by the name of Albert Einstein, about whose rising genius all kinds of anecdotes were told. The ministry, which had to approve the invitation, had tried to find out about the man, his personality and *antecedentia*, but was completely unsuccessful. Schmidt-Ott spoke of him as of a mystery man and added that he would have to take the risk of appointing him according to the wish of the profession, though he felt rather unhappy about appointing a man about whose origin and former life he was left in the dark. Einstein was appointed, and the rest of the story is known to the world.

Mentioning Einstein I might add that though I met him many times, as a fellow director of a Kaiser Wilhelm Institute as well as socially, it happened that I never had any real contact with him. But I owe him an interesting experience. When the University of Jerusalem established a new institute of biochemistry in the early thirties, he asked me to attend a meeting of a small advisory committee held in his apartment in Berlin. The interesting part was that Professor Chaim Weizmann, the actual father of the state of Israel and a very impressive personality, was also present and took part in the discussion.

Returning to Munich, I had to rush my preparations for the impending world trip. At that time only a few German scholars had had such an experience, and a trip to the tropics and around the world was an immense affair requiring thorough preparations. Literature had to be studied, a smattering of Malay and Japanese acquired, my work in Japan prepared by correspondence with colleagues, and tropical clothing bought (which turned out later to be completely out of style and worthless). A traveling kit was made up of the most impossible medicines, which I just threw away later; photographic plates for a stereoscopic camera were purchased (both camera and plates proved to be unfit for tropical use); and two huge, heavy, tin-lined and rubber-tightened trunks made for tropical expeditions were filled with unnecessary things. Two ordinary suitcases would have been the proper thing. So provincial were people at that time in the German empire, or at least in Munich! As a last preparation I had my rebellious appendix removed, and finally I was ready. There was a last excitement because my letter of credit was held up by ministerial red tape and had not yet arrived when it was time to leave. But fortunately a rich friend put up the money pending the arrival of the grant, and on January 4, 1914, I prepared to leave, hoping to return in the autumn. I actually was not to return until five and a half years had passed.

5: *THE TROPICAL WORLD*

I sailed from Genoa. My trip was to take me by way of the Red Sea and the Indian Ocean. The overcrowded S.S. *Derfflinger* sailed past Sicily, then Crete, along the shores of North Africa toward Suez.

While we were out on the Mediterranean, a great and almost unbelievable event occurred, and I noted in my diary: "Today I visited the wireless operator. He actually receives his telegrams from a station at the North Sea! How miraculous! I myself have listened to the Morse signs received by telephone! During the whole trip there will be wireless communication with some land station!" How I pity the present generation to whom motorcars, electric lights, trains, telegraphs, X-rays, airplanes, long-distance telephones, radios, movies, and television are matter-of-fact things —inventions that to my generation meant or would have meant unbelievable thrills!

Port Said at the entrance of the Suez Canal gave me my first impression of another continent, but it was not a pleasant one. The traveler was surrounded by mean-looking fellows of all shades of skin color, whispering, in German, French, or English, "Buy dirty pictures," or, "Come see little girls belly dance." Most travelers made for the Simon Arzt department store to buy pith helmets and Egyptian cigarettes, but a stroll away from the port with its curio shops selling Egyptian and Indian merchandise (made in Germany and Czechoslovakia) took me to the Arab quarters, which were at least genuine and therefore impressive to the inexperienced traveler, though they were poor and filthy. Without regret I left the miserable port when the steamer began to plod slowly through the Suez Canal. There was not much to be seen except the unbelievable number of wild birds inhabiting the lakes connecting the canal stretches. The hundreds of flamingos were certainly a beautiful sight to me, a northerner, who knew the picturesque birds only from the zoo.

When the steamer emerged from the canal and traveled through the fingerlike appendix of the Red Sea, which three thousand years before was crossed by the Israelites leaving Egypt for the Sinai peninsula, the landscape began to be interesting. On one side were the sand dunes and, in the background, the hills of the Egyptian desert, completely uninhabited but for a lonely lighthouse; on the other side the ragged, bare mountains of the Sinai group, silhouetted with sharp contours against the flaming sky. At night glowing, golden sunsets made an unforgettable sight.

The Red Sea brought the usual terrific heat, though I think now that New York and Boston could easily beat the famous waters. Since I had read so much about the machinists who, crazed by the heat of the engine room, jump overboard, I went down to see for myself. It certainly was hot, but I do not think that the men, accustomed to working in the heat, were overwhelmed. It was here, however, that I first became acquainted with the toughest race on earth. At the hottest stations near the fires only Chinese did the work, the only race that can work hard in any climate, hot or cold. Whatever I have since seen of these people has increased my admiration for them. They are a race able simultaneously to be the toughest and the most refined.

Approaching the strait of Bab el Mandeb, separating Arabia from Africa, we saw at least from a distance the white houses of Jidda, the port for the holy city of Mecca, and in the background the bare hills of Arabia, at that time still mostly terra incognita. In the morning the bugler awakened us with the German *Lied* *"Freut euch des Lebens . . ."* ("Enjoy your life . . ."), which turned out to be a practical joke.

As we approached the Indian Ocean, a monsoon began to be felt. Long waves splashed over the decks, and many passengers did not enjoy life. On January 18 we landed at Aden, the famous British stronghold controlling the entrance to the Red Sea and certainly one of the most forsaken places on earth. High, rugged, black, and completely bare mountains looking like giant coal heaps, crowned with forts, surrounded the harbor. Near the landing jetty stretched a flat region through which passed the highway connecting the quarters of the British barracks near the harbor with the native town behind the hills. Hundreds of vultures sat around waiting for carrion, and hundreds of buzzards covered the sky searching for food.

Across a narrow pass the road led into the native town. There I had my first glimpse of the real Orient. I could stand for hours in the bazaar watching the crowds made up of all the African and Asiatic races: Bedouins on beautiful Arab horses, wearing wide, white burnooses that showed only their fierce, brown faces; giant Sudanese Negroes, completely naked and black as ebony, towering on the backs of loaded camels; turbaned Indians, Afghans in embroidered skull caps, and a lonely bearded Sikh policeman in khaki shirt and shorts, regulating the scrambling traffic. The most famous sight at Aden, however, was the cisterns, built in concrete in a kind of canyon to collect the rain water, which fell only once in four or more years. When I visited the cisterns it had not rained for many years and the huge reservoirs were completely dry. But in a rock near the cistern the greatest sight of Aden was to be seen—the only tree, a large *Ficus* tree, in the branches of which I saw a lonely rock dove.

Quickly the six days in the Indian Ocean passed, hot but exhilarating and followed by indescribable evenings, well known to any traveler in tropical seas. The air is soft and moist and seems to pet you tenderly; you feel a pleasant languidness enveloping your whole being; and you feel charmed and far away from the turmoil of real life. I would travel again through the Indian Ocean any time in order to experience once more those magical nights.

On the twenty-fourth of January, almost three weeks from Genoa, we arrived in Colombo, Ceylon, which for me meant the first glimpse of the tropics—a glimpse I had longed for since early childhood. Every sight was known to me from Haeckel's enthusiastic letters, which I had devoured as a young student. The two days—to be followed fifteen years later by an extended stay—passed as in a dream. This was my first sight of an old culture outside of Europe, a culture represented by the dignified, beautiful Singhalese and the dark, lower-class Tamils from south India. The life in the bazaars, in the streets of the artisans, in the villages with their open huts where all the life of the people displayed itself as if seen on a screen was an unending source of observation and wonder. My first sight of the native fruit gardens with the noble coconut palm, the fruit-laden bananas, the huge breadfruit trees was simply overwhelming. And the first ride in a ricksha, drawn by a black, sweating Tamil, was an event worthy of those grand days. Later on I was to return many times to the tropics and to fall again under their spell, but never did the tropics make an impression on me as breathtaking as that first time.

Only too soon the steamer left for the very hot trip to Penang, an island near the base of the Malay peninsula. For the first time

I experienced the downpour of tropical rain and the subsequent moist heat, which is rather trying. On the ship's table appeared the delicious tropical fruits mango and papaya, with which I made my first acquaintance. Soon we reached Penang.

The entrance into Penang harbor was of sublime beauty. To the right were the high, forest-covered slopes of the Peak (which I was to visit only many years later) and the residential parts of the town, with the setting sun illuminating the villas and gardens of the wealthy inhabitants; in the background the mountains of the Malay peninsula, over which a thunderstorm brooded; in the foreground the sea, completely becalmed, green, and filled with a myriad of large, milk-white jellyfish. The air was as moist and hot as in a greenhouse. From the wharf, herculean Chinese runners took us in rickshas through the quiet residential quarters with gardens of beautiful and strange trees, flowering shrubs, and an indescribable scent in the air. Still more than in Colombo I was actually smitten by the new type of beauty and could have stayed on indefinitely. But suddenly, as always, the tropical night with the shrill concert of thousands of insects broke in, and we had to return to the main area of town. How many times have I later experienced the mysterious fascination of the last moments of daylight and the sudden change into tropical night, always a wonderful experience.

Here, too, at Penang, I had my first sight of a real tropical Chinese quarter. The endurance, thrift, adaptability, and organizing capacity of the Chinese are overwhelming, and there was no better education in some of the problems of the tropical East than a stroll at night through the Chinese quarter of Penang, or for that matter of Singapore or Surabaya. In the open shops half-naked, strong craftsmen worked long after midnight, and I could watch their skill at any imaginable trade or craft. In better houses fat, which means wealthy, men lolled on quilted chairs and smoked long pipes. The rich merchants lived in huge European-style mansions, but through the open doors and windows I could see the Chinese settings and the large altars of the ancestors. It was surprising to see here young men playing the Western violin. The ladies were rarely visible, but the sweetest children in gay costumes played around late at night. I never got tired of these sights and later spent many an evening here as well as in similar towns just watching the fascinating life in the Chinese quarters in the days before they began to stir with political unrest.

But this time my stay was short, and soon the trip south to Singapore was continued. Singapore did not appeal to me this first visit, but when I returned there later and stayed longer I rather liked the busy and cosmopolitan city. The strangest mixture of races could be seen there, all living in their own quarters. The white men worked and sweated in the open halls of their offices under noiselessly turning fans, repairing at night to the beautiful residential quarters far out of town, now easily reached by motor-car but at that time only in a ricksha pulled by a half-naked, speedy Chinese runner. Here the houses were hidden in beautiful gardens, dinner was served on screened porches by a host of servants, and material life was as pleasant as the heat permitted. On the other hand, the Chinese lived in their quarter, which at night looked like a beehive and was immensely fascinating. More to the east were the Malay quarters where native and insular Malays had their open shops and their simple dwellings, and still farther out lived the black southern Indians with their sad faces and their frequently very good-looking women, dressed in a wide gown which left back and waist free. Though these were the larger ethnical groups, there was hardly an Oriental nation not represented in Singapore, and the street scenes were enlivened by the costumes, skin colors, hairdresses, and jewelry of Arabs, Afghans, Parsis, Hindus, Sikhs, Siamese, and every shadow of half-castes.

From Singapore the small Dutch steamer *Van Cloen* took me to Batavia. Batavia, now Jakarta, was not very interesting, damp and hot, and the only remarkable experience was my first stay in one of the marvelous tropical hotels, the famed Hotel des Indes. Its center was formed by a lawn occupied by one of the most amazing waringin trees (*Ficus*), the roots of which grew down into the soil like stems and made out of a single tree a whole shady grove. All around flat buildings with open galleries led to the central hotel building, which everybody could reach without exposing himself to the sun. The windowless, relatively cool rooms opened onto the veranda, where one could rest upon strange armchairs with footrests high up in the air. A bed sufficiently large for a whole family was covered by mosquito curtains. Under these one slipped cautiously at night and searched for the mosquito that might have succeeded in getting in. If he was not caught, the night's rest was gone. I usually took a flashlight into bed to use during my nightly hunts. In the large and airy dining room at noon we were served *rijstafel*, that native dish, improved upon by the

Dutch, which knocked us out for at least two hours. In the best style twenty Malay waiters, each carrying two trays, passed in a line, and the diner took some of all the delicious side dishes on top of a mountain of rice and hot curry sauce and finished the mixture with a sprinkling of little spices, at least forty different ones, a pinch of which burned the tongue terribly. After having finished this delicious lunch I felt like the python who swallowed a whole goat, and the two hours of obligatory siesta were really needed.

But I had no patience here, for I wanted to reach my first real destination, Buitenzorg ("without sorrow"), now Bogor, the residence in the hills where the world-famous botanical garden with its laboratories was to be my headquarters for some weeks. I did not intend any special research but just wanted to admire and to observe tropical animals and their surroundings.

Buitenzorg, where also resided the governor general (whose palace is now the White House of Indonesia), is situated on a hill above the valley of the Tjiliwong River. At that time there existed a small inn, Hotel Bellevue (I understand it is now gone), which contained one of the most marvelous surprises I ever had. From the village street I entered a rather dingy and simple hotel and asked for a room. The Malay *mandur* asked whether I wanted an ordinary room or a *bergkamer* (mountain chamber). I did not like the cheaper, ordinary room and wanted to see the *bergkamer*. We went across the house to a veranda from which one entered the windowless rooms, and I was completely speechless. Before me spread the valley through which, way down, the river flowed among native hamlets surrounded by coconut palms, bananas, and tropical fruit trees. For a long distance the meandering river was visible, and in the background stood, clear in the blue skies, the almost ten-thousand-foot-high volcanoes Salak and Gede. During the next weeks I spent as much time as I could on this veranda and never got tired of the unspeakably beautiful sight. If I had to name the most beautiful landscapes of heroic size that I have beheld in my life, I should divide the honor among the Grand Canyon in Arizona; Kinchinjunga Mountain in the Himalayas in early morning light; snow-capped Fuji-no-Yama in Japan, seen from the Ten Provinces Pass in the Hakone Mountains; and this view from Buitenzorg's Hotel Bellevue.

The days in Buitenzorg were full of the most interesting things. There was the most gorgeous botanical garden in the world where one could spend weeks on end observing the many peculiarities of tropical flora. There was a market place in town where the strangest fruits and vegetables were sold, many of them completely unknown to me. The smell here was nauseating, for Chinese venders sold piles of dried fish and squids, and Malays brought to market heaps of the huge durian or "stink fruit," a terrible-smelling fruit the smell of which remains with anyone who eats it regularly. It is said to be delicious, but I could not make up my mind to taste it. In the side alleys of the little town one could see women squatting in front of their houses and making their garments (the sarong, or skirt; the *kain kapala,* or headwear; the slendang, or scarf) in the exquisite batik technique. From little copper pots with long-drawn-out snouts of different size and shape they poured hot wax onto a densely woven cotton cloth, holding the little containers by means of a bamboo handle like brushes and using the snouts like pens. Thus the negative of the most charming and intricate patterns was laid out, and, after dyeing, the pattern appeared in the spots not protected by wax. The wax was then removed with hot water, and the next pattern for another color was designed. At that time the beautiful batiks were still made by hand, and one could see the women working at them all the time. Today this craft has been replaced by factory work using stencils dipped in wax, and the beautiful old freely designed patterns are gone as well as the beautiful colors. Already in 1914 printed imitations imported from Holland were used instead of the expensive batiks, especially by the poorer classes, and once I beheld with horror a big woman wrapped in such a sarong on which the story of Little Red Ridinghood and the Wolf was represented in gaudy colors. I was happy to acquire a number of old batik pieces, mostly from the government pawnshops, which did a brisk business with the natives, who were inveterate gamblers and always broke.

Frequently I took one of those amusing carts called "sado" (corrupted from dos-à-dos), where the driver occupies the front seat and the guest the backward-looking seat between two huge wheels. A little pony draws this light conveyance in a brisk trot, and the ride is most pleasant, if the driver has not eaten durian. Usually I went down to the river and strolled through the kampongs (villages) to observe the life of the population in their open huts surrounded by fruit gardens and separated by the well-irrigated rice fields. Everywhere numerous children were seen playing, mostly naked or dressed with a silver-gilt necklace carrying a capsule with verses from the Koran. Huge water buffaloes worked in the rice fields and gave the white man, whom they hate and attack when given a chance, an ugly look. The men were frequently seen squatting and idling on the lawn in the shade of coconut and areca palms, bananas, melon, and breadfruit trees, rambutan, mangosteen, and djukdjuk (all of them bearing delicious and strange fruit). The women worked around the house, frequently clad only in a skirt, milling rice, nursing the babies, or sewing with an imported Singer sewing machine. There was no furniture in the houses, which were built of bamboo and matting. But poverty was certainly less hard to bear there than anywhere else. There was always a little rice, and a few low-backed black pigs, a few frizzly chickens, and bananas and coconuts to keep the mouths fed. The river was near, where everybody bathed all day long and where the women washed a few sarongs, all the clothing they needed unless they went to town clad in a kabaya, a kind of dressing jacket introduced by prudish foreigners.

At night there was life in the dark streets. At one corner actors rigged up a primitive stage and performed a play in which one actor appeared in a dinner jacket and was spoken to as "Mistair." At the next corner the entrancing music of a gamelang orchestra (a set of tuned copper kettles) was heard and some very young girls in fantastic costumes danced the strange Malay dances, mostly consisting of movements of arms and hands. Maybe also a shadow play was performed with the classical wajang figurines cut out of leather. From the kampong down at the river the rhythmical play of drums in never-ending sequences was heard, flying foxes shot through the air, and a myriad of cicadas sang in the shrillest voices a choir that did not stop before dawn. The mixture of strange sounds, the mellow warm air, the shadowy appearance of the barefooted natives in the dark streets, the silhouettes of giant trees, the heady scent of the flowers, all together made me feel as if I were floating through a fairy realm. I wish I could experience all this again for the first time in a peaceful world.

Dr. Koningsberger, the director of the botanical garden (later minister of the colonies), who had been already the most charming host and guide, invited me to accompany him for a week to Tjibodas, a hill station at the foot of the volcano Gede, where

the garden had a branch laboratory in high altitude directly adjacent to the glorious virgin forest covering the slopes of Gede.
The train ride gave me a chance to observe the densely settled
country in its typical pursuits. The train climbed toward the
mountains through *sawah* (rice fields) covering the hillside in
elaborate and cleverly built terraces irrigated by a complicated
system of canals and pipes. It could be said that the whole agricultural law was built upon the right to water for the paddy
fields. In the fields I could see in one corner the fresh young shoots,
densely planted, and I could watch, nearby, peasants setting out
by hand the individual young shoots in proper distances, and not
far away a harvest going on, each ear being cut singly by hand,
while the straw remained to be used separately. In empty fields
the carabaos (water buffaloes) were resting almost completely sub-
merged, and women and children hunted with baskets for a fish
(silurid) that lived in the mud. The small banks between the paddy
fields served as pasture for sheep and brown, white-flanked goats.
Myriads of glittering dragonflies filled the air—in addition to their
beauty they are very useful animals since their water-living larvae
feed on mosquito larvae, but, as things happen in nature, the
dragonflies are fed upon by a bird that lays out its nest with the
silvery wings of its prey.

The slow trains, which at that time were run only in daytime
because no native would expose himself to the spirits of the night,
stopped frequently, and there was always something to be seen at
the stations: the station master with his official cap on top of his
native headgear; boys and girls offering a dish made of rice and
beans and wrapped in fresh leaves, or whole twigs covered with
fruit or sugar cane for chewing; crowds of natives in their colorful costumes; and coolies balancing heavy loads on the ends of a
bamboo pole carried over their bronzed shoulders.

Farther up in the mountains new cultures appeared: tea, which
grows best in the mountains; and dammar trees, looking like
cypresses, which furnish the resin dammar. When the train had
reached the pass we left it and rode by horse and buggy through
beautiful mountain scenery to the end of the road, to the summer residence, Tjipanas, at about thirty-three hundred feet. From
there we climbed a steep path about eighteen hundred feet higher,
soon leaving behind us the last villages, passing fields of potatoes
and cabbages, which thrived at this altitude. At nightfall we
reached Tjibodas, where a mountain garden contained trees and

flowers that would not grow in the heat of Buitenzorg. A small laboratory building with a few bedrooms occupied the center of the garden. We brought all our food in tins, and an old Malay did the cooking.

The first thing in the morning was of course a long walk in the virgin forest, the edge of which stood behind the house like a huge green wall. Numbered trails had been cut through in all directions to enable the scientist to work alone without danger of being lost. The first impression after entering the dark moist thicket was bewildering. Everything grew so wildly and on such a gigantic scale that it took time to realize what one was seeing. After some time one noticed that hardly two trees were alike, that every trunk and stem was covered with multitudes of creepers of all description, every inch was used by some growth, and everything tended up toward the light. In the forks of the trees were huge ferns, the bird's-nest fern; creeper palms climbed the trunks of giant trees; tree ferns grew where a little hold was left; herbs tried to catch the enlivening sunlight with huge leaves, large as umbrellas. Occasionally the trees were thinner, and patches of sunlight pierced the green roof. Contrary to expectation animal life was much more difficult to see. Of course the little pests of leeches dropped on us from everywhere to suck our blood. We heard the birds but had difficulty in seeing them, and only in more open patches could we see the marvelously colored butterflies. But frequently a shrieking herd of monkeys or apes passed high above us over the treetops. I felt perfectly happy and thought that the sight of this great forest, where the struggle for existence and the marvelous adaptations it had produced were still visible at every step, was alone worth the long trip from faraway Europe.

During the night the temperature in the house dropped to sixty-five degrees, and we felt terribly cold after Buitenzorg. Dr. Koningsberger, who had lived for years in the tropics, had water for brushing his teeth warmed; water of sixty-five degrees affected him like ice water.

The following days were spent in long walks to the different parts of the virgin forest with unending pleasure in studying the ways of untouched nature. A pleasant interlude was a formal dinner given by the native workingmen to celebrate the completion of a greenhouse they had built. When all preparations were finished, Dr. Koningsberger and I were called and seated on a couple of chairs. We were supposed to be the guests of honor, who only looked at the feast without partaking of it. The floor of the greenhouse was set as dinner "table." Palm-leaf mats were spread and covered with small baskets, one for each guest, each basket covered by another conical basket. Between the baskets were arranged plates heaped with meats and vegetables. After we were all seated the men and children squatted cross-legged on the mats behind the dishes, the women forming an outer circle squatting at a little distance. The *mandur* (foreman) sat among the women and started the festivity with a speech in Malay ending with *salamats* (cheers) for the guests of honor. This done, he put a pair of immense spectacles on his nose and read with singing voice a prayer from the Koran. While he prayed the guests covered their faces with their hands, but giggled behind this screen. The moment the prayer ended the conical baskets, which hid piles of rice, were removed. The women, who did not eat, distributed large leaves of a kind of lily to serve as plates, whereupon everybody helped himself and ate with his fingers. Within fifteen minutes the silent repast was finished. The leftovers were put in the rice baskets and everybody took his mat and basket and disappeared. This was the shortest, driest, and quickest dinner party I ever attended or, more correctly, watched.

The next days brought a great event. Years before I had read in a travel book a glowing description of climbing Mount Gede, and when I came to Java I hoped that I might be able to make this tour. Now this actually happened. A few other guests had arrived from Buitenzorg to make up the party, led by the *hortulanus* (chief gardener), and one morning the caravan started. Eleven native porters carried the camp outfit and food, and they ran up the steep mountainside as if the weight and the moist heat were nonexistent. Only once they were distressed—when we had to wade a stream of hot water. It was unpleasant for us in our shoes but especially trying for the barefooted natives. The higher we climbed the more indescribably beautiful became the rain forest. The thicket was dense, the creepers and lianas formed impenetrable entanglements, the tree ferns increased in number and size. Moisture dropped from all the trees like a steady rain. There were not many flowers, though begonias and a few orchids were found. Finally, wet and hot, we reached the saddle between the twin peaks Gede and Pangerango at an altitude of eight thousand feet, a place called by the natives *kandong badak* (rhinoceros crossing).

At this point a corrugated iron shack had been built by the botanical garden for the convenience of naturalists and also a small palm-leaf hut for the native porters. We enjoyed the warm and dry clothing we had brought, but the half-naked natives felt terribly cold. One after the other each asked for *obat* (medicine) against the cold and received a small dram of liquor. This he accepted with his left hand, the right hand under his left elbow as a sign of respect, and then he squatted down and drank the medicine, making terrible faces while swallowing it. A little later one of them tried to get a second drink by coming in limping terribly and declaring that he had fallen and hurt himself and needed medicine. But he received only a moist compress and an aspirin tablet, which cured the leg quickly.

After dark the shivering natives started a fire and squatted around while the *hortulanus* and I stood nearby. Suddenly a new guest appeared out of the dark woods, an old native hajji, that is, a holy man who had made a pilgrimage to Mecca, distinguished by a yellow turban instead of the native headdress of batik cloth. He approached the fire, asked permission to warm himself, and squatted down. The Dutch *hortulanus*, a young man who, I later found out, drank heavily, suddenly flew into a wild rage, grabbed the hajji, threw him down, and chased him away into the night. I could not understand the scene, for everything was spoken in Malay, of which I had only a smattering sufficient for small talk. But the unprovoked brutality might have had unpleasant consequences as we shall see.

The next morning we started early to climb Gede (about ten thousand feet). We first climbed through forest—the most fantastic woods I have ever seen—which looked as if it had been taken from a fairy tale, a real enchanted forest. The trees were low in this altitude and assumed strange shapes like fantastic animals. They were completely covered with moss, and garlands of hanging moss intertwined with lianas connected them. Many trees had fallen, and their trunks, over which we had frequently to climb, were covered with a wild growing vegetation. Finally we reached the bottom of the crater, with the rim on one side only rising perpendicularly seven hundred feet high. The bottom was covered with blueberry trees (*Vaccinium*) and high bushes of Javanese edelweiss covered with flowers. Two secondary craters rise from this old bottom; one was a little active and fuming, the other dead and filled with water. To get a proper view we climbed the steep rim, hewing a path with bush knives and pulling ourselves from tree to tree on the almost perpendicular edge of the rim. Traversing the cliff we descended again into another old crater bottom, completely covered with silvery edelweiss, using for our descent through the thicket the small paths made by wild boars. This bottom, through which a little rivulet trickled, was warm in the midday sun, and we cooked our lunch there. Then we climbed the rim again and reached the highest point, from which all western Java was seen at our feet with the ocean in the distance. The pattern of the rice fields made the plain look like a checkerboard over which groups of white clouds were sailing beneath our feet.

While descending on the other side toward our headquarters, we noticed on a small hill a short distance away a group of thirty to forty men. The field glass revealed them to be hajjis. Now it became clear why the lonely hajji had climbed the mountain the night before. A secret meeting of the Mohammedan society Sarikat Islam was taking place on the mountaintop, which was considered to be far away from the eyes of men. The *hortulanus* became silent, and the three natives who accompanied us showed all signs of terror.

In the camp at night we felt that something was wrong. The natives were sullen and shy and could be seen whispering in groups. The *hortulanus* was nervous and frequently went out to talk to the men. When the rest of the party had retired he told me that our men feared an attack by the irate hajjis in revenge for the maltreatment of one of them and that we had better sit up and keep watch. So we sat behind the table with the oil lamp burning, the *hortulanus* with three bottles of liquor in front of him. From time to time he looked through the door into the dark night. But nothing happened. After midnight we heard the hajjis passing by, walking around the hut and talking in whispers, but the light shining through the door cracks probably discouraged them if they were bent on revenge at all. Nevertheless it was an unpleasant night.

The next morning we climbed the other peak, the Pangerango, a little higher than Gede and covered with forest to the very top. The virgin forest was, if possible, still more beautiful. The moss-encased tree trunks were covered with large blue orchids; albizzia trees were laden with yellow blossoms; huge rhododendrons were in bloom; and occasionally we saw the three-foot-high yellow-flowering imperial primrose, which grows only in this place and on a few isolated peaks in Sumatra. Arriving at the top we found at an altitude of more than ten thousand feet flowering straw-berries and the ripe, delicious fruit itself. The view surpassed even that from Gede, and in the flat old crater bottom was the most delightful grove of thick, short blueberry trees and ten-foot-high edelweiss. We were sorry to leave this beautiful spot and retrace our steps back to Tjibodas. When we passed the hot stream again it was much hotter than two days before, and the poor natives screamed with pain. Farther down we had the pleasure of being accompanied for some time by a herd of apes (gibbons), which chased through the tops of the highest trees with loud shrieks.

The next morning I started early and walked in pouring rain with two native porters down into the valley. I must have looked strange in my long yellow oilskin, for all the natives stared at me as at an apparition. A herd of carabaos passed, and the calves ran away frightened when they saw me. But an old fellow with im-mense horns turned grunting toward me, and I was glad when the cowherd noticed it and drove him away. Down in Tjipanas I took a rickety car with three ponies down the mountain road to the railway station. I noticed that the natives I passed looked at me in a rather unfriendly way, which was then not usual. I was told later that Islam was especially strong and active there against the white rulers. My diary of February 16, 1914, adds here: "Sooner or later a revolt will happen. If the natives are capable of organizing properly, which I doubt, it will be hard for the few Dutchmen. I wonder whether Japan will then appear on the scene."

My next visit took me to the native "independent" states of central Java, ruled by their old princes, though a Dutch adviser saw to it that there was no nonsense. There, in Jogjakarta, native life could be observed at its best, and the charming place was full of attractions. The population there was racially different from that of west Java and though less good-looking more free and upright. Blue was the color generally worn there, whereas it was yellow and brown in the west. The batiks had different pat-terns, and more good handmade ones were visible. Life in the streets was full of color. The main street, which led to the palace of the ruler, was lined with huge waringin trees in the shade of which old women sold goods and children played. The men walked with great dignity, wearing gaudy jackets over their long batik sarongs, which they held with one hand on their lower backs, just as Western ladies held their skirts in my youth. Here the cart of a nobleman passed, a coachman in front wearing a black-lacquered topper over his batik headdress. On the running board stood an extravagantly dressed servant holding a sunshade. In the rear another servant stood, and the courtier sat stiffly, wearing a white European jacket, a beautiful batik sarong, and a tropical helmet on top of the native headdress. Around the next corner a nobleman in beautiful native dress galloped on a white stallion, holding the stirrups with the big toes of his bare feet. In a side street I found a gamelang orchestra playing plaintive mellow tunes interrupted occasionally by a deep strong note produced by a copper plate hung over a clay pitcher as resonator. A very graceful girl with light yellow skin danced to the music. Needless to say, I soon succeeded in finding a Chinese pawnshop where I could acquire some really good old batiks and practice my Malay in hard bargaining.

The *kraton*, the sultan's palace grounds, must have been a marvelous sight in the season of the big dancing festivals and court receptions. Outside of this season there was not much to be admired in the residence of the puppet king. A large series of walled courtyards contained open halls built of carved teakwood. When I visited them nobody was visible except servants who were taking the fighting cocks of the sultan for an airing, just as pet dogs are taken out in Western countries, one servant to each cock. The gates between the courtyards were guarded, and the grade of the guards increased with each enclosure. First I passed a gate watched by soldiers with swords and lances. Later I passed a gate guarded by sons of princes of the fifth grade, who looked terribly bored and were playing cards. At the next gate two ministers of state were in attendance, old gentlemen with spectacles who sat on the floor surrounded by numerous attendants. Finally I entered the innermost courtyard where His Majesty lived. Of course, I was armed with proper introductions and permits. A nice little girl clothed in a sarong and a golden necklace was playing there, guarded by many maids, and the little princess, the granddaughter of the sultan, stepped up briskly and shook hands. But she protested at being photographed for she feared that the camera could look through her clothes. One side of the courtyard was faced by the harem, in front of which some hags were on guard, certainly fit to frighten away anybody. In front of them on the floor stood their food, white and red-colored rice in conical cakes. Only the antechamber of the sultan could be visited. It was filled with innumerable examples of the worst in European taste. But there was one thing there I loved seeing—a few cages with beautiful wild jungle fowl, and one with a gorgeous bird of paradise.

From Jogjakarta I could easily visit the great ruins of Borobudur and Prambanan, the only works of art (except for a few similar ruins on the Dieng plateau) existing on the island. Strangely enough a thousand years ago a powerful Hindu and Buddhist empire existed there, but it disappeared, leaving hardly any trace but these temple ruins. The much described Borobudur is a Buddhist dagoba, a huge pyramid crowned with stupas, which is supposed to cover some Buddhist relic. Staircases lead to the top, with doorways on each of the many terraces. Everything is covered with stone carvings and sculptures, some better preserved than others. The terraces are built as circuits flanked on both sides by miles of bas-reliefs, many of them commonplace, but some really beautiful, depicting the life of Buddha. The scenes are very vividly presented, and houses, trees, ships, animals, and men, women, and children are worked out with great realism. From the top of the pyramid, covered with stupas each containing the image of Buddha, there is a marvelous panorama of plain and mountains.

Less well preserved are the ruins of Prambanan, a huge group of temple buildings composing the mausoleum of a ruler. Though the architecture, in the style of the south Indian gopura (temple towers), is rather wild, the details of the sculpture are very beautiful and some of the statuary is among the best that old Hindu art has produced. But it was frightfully hot among these ruins, and since I could reach them only by walking a considerable distance in the burning sun I was glad to find on my way back to the station an old woman of unbelievable ugliness who sold bananas. I handed her the smallest coin I had, about a nickel, and she gave me a whole stem with I do not know how many dozens of bananas. When I kept only two and returned the rest, she just burst out laughing at the stupidity of the *orang blanda* (white man).

Proceeding from the Jogjakarta area to the coastal town and trade center of Surabaya I passed through a tropical rain that really was everything I expected. Within a short time the whole countryside was one huge lake, in which the houses stood like lake dwellings on poles. Old and young enjoyed splashing in the floods, for bathing was one of the favorite pastimes of the Malays. The thunderstorm following the rains with lightning all around was the wildest I have ever witnessed. Surabaya was a typical port with foreign hotels, business houses, and restaurants—and a place not worth mentioning. But it was the starting point for eastern Java, where I wanted to visit at least the famous Tengger Mountains.

Traveling toward eastern Java I noticed at once that it was inhabited by people of a different race, the Madurese. The people were much better looking, clean, and nicely dressed. They also had lighter skin, and their faces were flatter. All the women wore clean white kabayas over their sarongs, and silver anklets, bracelets, and necklaces like Hindu women; their heads were covered with a kind of veil, and around their necks they wore silken batik scarfs. The children were all at least partly clothed and wore jewelry. Best of all, the horrible sight of betel-chewing women was rare.

Pasoeroean was the station for the cool mountain resort of Tosari, and a motorcar waited there for guests. But I preferred to make the ascent my own way, and, since my Malay was sufficient for making my own arrangements, I took a little horse cart and trotted comfortably from the station to the small town of Pasoeroean at the foot of the Tengger Mountains. Here I changed the cart for another one drawn by two strong stallions which took me up to a place about two thousand feet high where I dismissed my car and hired a native to climb with me to Tosari and carry my heavy knapsack.

Through a beautiful forest, full of monkeys who trumpeted at us, we climbed in a considerable heat, and when a tropical downpour started I could not have become wetter than I already was. My porter took his bush knife and cut himself a few wild banana leaves, which made an excellent umbrella. After some time we came to the villages of the Tenggerese, a tribe that still preserved the Hindu religion (as was also the case in Bali) and that considered the volcano of the Tengger Mountains a sacred mountain. Most of the natives we met were on horseback, and they were amazed to see an *orang blanda* walking. One young fellow even interviewed me about the strange phenomenon, but I am afraid that my Malay explanation was not sufficiently clear to satisfy him. Wet and tired I finally arrived at Tosari, located at a height of almost six thousand feet and completely hidden in clouds.

A few days of rest were not unpleasant after rather strenuous weeks, and the temperature of sixty-eight degrees was greatly refreshing after the heat of the plains. Mornings and evenings were always clear, and the days clouded. To sleep under a blanket was a great experience. But on the third day I could not wait any longer to visit the volcano Bromo, one of the greatest sights in Java —indeed, on the earth. The Tengger is an old extinct volcano of immense size, rivaling the craters of the moon. Its flanks, the Tengger Mountains, slope steeply toward the sea, and between huge ribs deep, extremely fertile valleys have been washed out. Here the Tenggerese grew potatoes, corn, and vegetables for the tables of the Dutch residents. The houses were located on top of the ribs, doors pointing toward the sacred mountain.

As a party was to climb the mountain on horseback, I also mounted a huge mare, and before dawn we went up on one of those ribs, later through forests, until a break in the old crater wall was reached. There I beheld suddenly the unbelievable spectacle of this volcano. The old crater rim forms a circle many miles in diameter so that the opposite side of the rim was hardly visible in the distance. The walls fall like cliffs into a huge bowl filled with sandlike ashes, called the Sand Sea. From this rise three secondary craters, one a whole mountain range, the two others exact cones looking like huge coffeecakes with regular ribs and ravines between radiating down from the top where the crater opens. Early in the morning the whole old crater was filled with silvery clouds upon which I looked down from the old rim as upon a waving sea out of which the three secondary craters rose like dark islands. The Bromo, the one active crater of the three, puffed out dark smoke. It was an unforgettable sight.

Leading the horses, we climbed down a steep path to the Sand Sea while the ocean of clouds was slowly rising. In a lively canter we crossed the soft sands of the bottom and skirting the second crater we reached the foot of Bromo, which rises about eight hundred feet above the bottom. The Tenggerese, who performed yearly religious rites here, had built stairs up the steep walls, and thus we could easily climb the cone and look down into the perfectly conical crater, with its steep walls falling down seven hundred feet into the mouth, in which lava was boiling and from which a thick puff of smoke was extruded with a hissing noise.

Later, after this first visit to Bromo, I decided that I must see the grandiose sight again without being bound to a party and horses. At one point the rim of the old crater rose to nine thousand feet and looked from the distance like an independent peak. From that point, the Penandjaan, the view was said to be still greater, and so I decided to climb the peak. By chance I found excellent company for this tour. In my hotel I met an old American gentleman who was conspicuous by his gaunt, sinewy appearance. It turned out that he was an explorer and collector, a Mr. Abbott, who had collected specimens for museums all his life and had worked in the Archipelago, in central Africa, and everywhere else, under the most amazing hardships. Now Mr. Abbott was an old man, his eyesight had deteriorated, and he could not collect any longer. But he just had to travel, and here he was with his sister to do a little more climbing.

Long before dawn Mr. Abbott and I started, hoping to reach the peak before the day's heat made it too hard. I flattered myself on being a good mountaineer in those days, but Mr. Abbott, at least thirty years my senior, set such a pace that I needed all my energy to keep up with him. The higher we climbed, the more marvelous became the view. The coast line way down to the Straits of Madura appeared, and inland the huge volcanoes of eastern Java stood in perfect silhouette against the brightening sky. When we reached the summit after some three hours of stiff climbing, the sun rose and illuminated one of the most gorgeous views human eyes can behold. Between high blueberry bushes we looked deep down upon the Sand Sea, now free of clouds. The whole immense circumference of the old rim was visible, and in the background rose the perfect cone of the highest mountain of Java, the active volcano Semeroe, over twelve thousand feet high. In the east the volcanic chain of the Dieng Mountains was partly hidden by clouds, and even the sea far south across the island was visible.

Unfortunately my time was up and I had to return to Buitenzorg, stopping on the way at the beautiful hill resort of Garut, where I climbed a few more volcanoes and enjoyed the unusual luxury of hot baths in an exceptionally well-managed hotel. At Buitenzorg I found that my charming host Dr. Koningsberger had a most pleasant surprise for me. I had mentioned how I longed to visit a real tropical coral reef, the El Dorado of a naturalist. Now he had arranged that a revenue cutter which was to make a tour of inspection to the Thousand Islands Archipelago north of Java would take two botanists and me along for a visit to coral islands and coral reefs. The days aboard the little *Brak*, run by a Dutch captain and two Madurese sailors and machinists, were delightful, though the hottest I have ever experienced. The sun, right at the equator, shot arrows of heat at us, and even a pith helmet was not sufficient protection. Only a few of the innumerable small coral islands were inhabited, and they were exactly as I had imagined South Sea Islands: white glaring sand of bleached corals, huge coconut palms silhouetted against the fiery sky, and simple native fishermen, who specialized in making elaborate fish traps of wickerwork. The inhabitants were descendants of Buginese pirates from Celebes, and their houses were built on high poles and covered with elaborate mattings.

From the coral islands we visited the coral reefs, which are among the most beautiful of their kind. The botanists, who were less interested in the animal life of the reefs, took the rowboat, but I went with the captain and a sailor in a native dugout that could easily be paddled over the reefs, though crossing the choppy open sea to get there was rather trying because of the numerous sharks.

The corals thrived there in the warm surface water in a depth of two to six feet. It is impossible to describe the beauty of such a tropical reef. In later life I visited others, including the Great Barrier Reef of Australia, and even saw them from below with a diver's helmet, but all were poor compared with these. Any number of coral species grew in dense masses and looked far different from the dead skeletons one sees in collections. There were deep red antlerlike colonies with blue tips, white corals with a strange pattern simulating the surface of a brain, the flaming red fans of the gorgonid coral, small pink organ corals, white and blue mushroom corals, and innumerable others. Between them grew the beautiful coral-like colonies of related groups of so-called Hydrozoa; sea anemones of sometimes giant size filled the holes, one of them about two feet in diameter with violet body, white disc, and red tentacles. Frequently we saw the huge shells of the giant clam *Tridacna*, opened only partly and showing the bluish fringe of the animal. Innumerable crabs, shrimps, and prawns in lively colors sat in every crack; strange sea urchins with zebra-striped poisonous spikes ten inches long and a quarter of an inch thick were abundant; also starfish and multicolored naked snails.

In between, in the crystal clear water, the beautiful coral fish clad in the most unbelievable colors shot through. Some of these coral fish can nowadays be seen in modern aquariums, but they look infinitely more colorful under the equatorial sun in the natural pools of a reef. No naturalist ought to speak of adaptation and similar subjects who has not set eyes upon this most remarkable of all associations of living beings.

We visited a few more islands. The botanists wanted to study the strange mangrove trees with their breathing shoots surrounding the main tree like a field of asparagus. But the heat in the mangrove region was so intense that we were glad to steam away again, while the most impressive of all flying things, the albatross, circled majestically around our small craft. The whole trip was a fitting end to a glorious tropical holiday—if intensive study of innumerable new things in all possible fields can be called a holiday.

My last days around Batavia I used to see a few things I was especially interested in. I visited one of the newfangled batik factories where an industrialized version of the old craft was manufactured—genuine batiks, but how different from the homemade ones. On the floor of an open hall a dozen natives squatted. In front of each was a small brick fireplace upon which wax was heated in a pan. The cloth to be printed was spread on a board covered with flannel, and with a stencil made of copper plate and dipped into the wax the workman printed the pattern, setting stencil beside stencil so that the pattern remained continuous. He could lay out the wax pattern of ten sarongs a day, whereas real handiwork took weeks for a single one. The "artist" received about three cents for each sarong he made. In the next room dyeing with German aniline dyes was done. Brown and yellow colors were rubbed into the cloth, and one cloth was pressed upon the other in stacks. Indigo, however, was dyed in barrels into which the pieces were hung from a kind of gallows. In large hot-water basins the wax was removed before the pieces were returned to the artist for application of the next wax pattern.

Many an hour of my last days I spent in front of the silversmith and goldsmith shops, all owned and run by Chinese. Malay women, who used jewelry for a savings bank as so many other Eastern peoples do, brought their own silver and gold bars, and the clever Chinese craftsman worked them into the desired piece under the eyes of the cautious customer. Once again my respect for the

103

Chinese, who can do anything to perfection, was increased. Finally a little heartache was in store for me: in the shop of a Chinese curio dealer I found the most beautiful seventeenth-century Dutch furniture, the like of which it would be difficult to pick up in Europe. But I withstood the temptation.

6: JAPAN

I left Java and returned to Singapore on the spick-and-span Dutch steamer *Melchior Treub*. In Singapore I had a few more days to observe the kaleidoscopic life of the city. Many hours I spent in the Chinese quarters, watching the picturesque street life, seeing all kinds of craftsmen at their work, smelling the odors of the open-air kitchens and the fish market, and watching the charming, well-kept Chinese children at play. The Chinese as well as the Malays, and of course the Japanese, treat their children with indescribable patience and love. I felt rather miserable when I read right there in Singapore in a German paper that in Germany during the year 1913 there had been thirty-one thousand sentences for cruel maltreatment of children.

Finally my steamer arrived, the north German Lloyd liner *Yorck*, which was to take me to Japan. On the way we made the usual stopovers in Hong Kong and Shanghai. Though these international ports were anything but Chinese in character they were extremely interesting. The port of Hong Kong is one of the great beauty spots on the earth, rivaling Rio de Janeiro, the Golden Horn, the Golden Gate, and the Bay of Naples. I have since entered Hong Kong two more times, and the fascination has always been the same. Each time I went up to the Peak, where there is a glorious view, and the sunsets were among the most gorgeous riots in color I have witnessed. Otherwise Hong Kong was a busy, orderly, well-managed, typical English colony in which the Chinese were relatively modern and well kept.

Traveling toward Shanghai and already shivering in the brisk spring air after the heat of the tropics, I had a chance to observe the dangers of the entrance into the mouth of the Yellow River in the days before radar. A dense fog made it impossible to see more than a hundred yards ahead, and the steamer plodded slowly along, blowing the foghorn incessantly. There was no chance to sleep at night with ten seconds of horn following fifty-second intervals of silence. Then I heard the steamer stop dead during the night and drop anchor. When the fog lifted next morning, we found ourselves headed directly toward one of the steep rocky islands strewn here and there over the yellow waters. The captain had heard the sound of the horn reflected from the rocks and had stopped just in time.

Shanghai in 1914 was rather different from the way I found it ten and fifteen years later; and again in the thirties, after two wars and bombardments, the great changes in the foreign concessions, the appearance of tens of thousands of Jewish refugees from Germany, it must once more have become a very different place. The little we hear about the condition of this amazing metropolis today makes the Shanghai of 1914 seem like old history. At that time there were no skyscrapers, and the small park near the Bund actually displayed the signboard: "Dogs and Chinese prohibited." The foreign colony was certainly not too adventurous in composition, but still strange types could be met, like a well-known German butcher who sold his sausages to all the Germans in east Asia, drove around in a hansom and four, used the most obscene language, and was said to have had a hand in the murder of his wife by thugs. Next to the concessions there still existed the old Chinese walled city though parts of the walls had been torn down. Here the life went on as in any typical Chinese town, just as if the port and concessions around the corner did not exist. The streets were so narrow that only one ricksha could pass through them. All the shops were open and exhibited the products of clever craftsmen. The market, the bird market, the teahouse in the pond in the center of the city, the noisy running, going and coming, in the narrow lanes—everything was just as I had imagined real China to be and not different from what I found later in the interior.

Two stormy monsoon days brought me finally to my goal, Japan, and the first impression of the country of which I had read so much was as charming as anticipated. The port of Nagasaki is located at the bottom of a narrow fiord. The landscape was typical of the Japanese setting so well known to me from the art of the woodcut: the clear silhouettes of the hills, the small rocky islands topped by a few bizarre pine trees, the wooden houses nestling along the slopes covered with blooming cherry trees— everything small and charming. As we spent only one evening in Nagasaki I did not see much and actually was to see this ill-fated town and some of its beautiful surroundings only many years later. But in order to get at least a first impression I strolled into the town, which was brightly illuminated on account of the cherry blossom season.

Like a real greenhorn, I asked for a teahouse, not knowing that teahouses may be not only the most expensive restaurants where one goes only for dinner parties, but also rather disreputable places or anything in between—but never places where one goes for a cup of tea. Thus I squatted on the floor and asked for tea, and the landlord and maids sat around grinning and certainly at a loss about what I had come for. But, not knowing that, I made a fool of myself and enjoyed it immensely. Returning to the steamer, I found a sight that since has disappeared together with the coal-burning boats. Hundreds of small women stood on bamboo ladders leaned against the sides of the boat and handed up from hand to hand, with unbelievable speed, small baskets filled with soft coal. A great many of the women carried their babies on their backs, and I am afraid that the air, black with coal dust, was not the best for the poor lungs of the helpless children.

Two days later I arrived in Tokyo where my work would soon start, as soon as the caterpillars I was to breed hatched with the oncoming spring. The first days were rather amusing and somewhat trying. I had made the mistake of not announcing my arrival and of putting up in a small hotel in the harbor quarter instead of at the Imperial Hotel, where all foreigners alighted. I had wanted to get away from the globetrotters and dip immediately into real Japanese life. But at the small place where I stayed there was nobody to interpret, there were no city maps, no rickshas accustomed to foreigners, and I was as completely lost as if I had landed on the moon. The little Japanese vocabulary I had acquired turned out to be useless, for I had learned it from a book and pronounced everything wrong. In addition it rained incessantly, the unpaved streets were mudholes, and the distances in Tokyo are such that all my attempts to get anywhere on foot failed.

I wanted to get to the laboratory, located in the suburb of Komaba, to see my colleagues, find my mail, and get settled. But nobody knew of the existence of Komaba, which actually was located outside the city limits. In my plight I remembered a letter of introduction to a German named Lehmann, supposed to be one of the oldest residents, whose office address was in the same quarter as my hotel. I actually found what I believed to be the house a few blocks away, and the signboard, with the name of a German firm, was encouraging. I entered, and soon a young man appeared. I asked for Mr. Lehmann. He answered that Mr. Lehmann, who had lived next door, had died a long time ago. But then it turned out that the young man was a cousin of one of my colleagues in Munich, and when I told him my difficulties he put an English-speaking Japanese clerk at my disposition, and I was able to start on my errands.

With great difficulty and much sweat on the part of the poor ricksha pullers we found the laboratory in Komaba, about ten miles away. But nobody was there, as it was still vacation time. The janitor, however, knew the address of Professor Toyama, who was to be my host, and there we went. Later on I found out why it took so long to find the house: Japanese houses are numbered not in the order of their location but in the order of their erection, so that No. 200 might follow No. 1, and in addition the numbers go around the whole block. Thus it was next to impossible to find a house without the assistance of the police officer of the beat or a rice or sake dealer who served the neighborhood. Finally we were lucky enough to find the house. The professor was out but was expected to return soon. With this information my Japanese helper left me, and I entered the house. Already knowing a little about the customs, I left my shoes outside and entered the lovely Japanese room and squatted down on a cushion spread on the clean matted floor. As Japanese houses were not heated I felt rather cool in my stocking feet and wet clothes.

After some time one of the sliding screen doors was pushed open and a fine-looking middle-aged lady in a quiet striped kimono of heavy silk entered. She kneeled and then bowed, the palms of her hands on the floor in the prescribed position, the forehead almost touching the floor. I immediately went down on all fours myself, watching the lady closely and doing everything she did. She murmured some extremely polite phrases of greeting (as I later found out when I acquired the necessary knowledge of polite behavior in old Japanese style), which I did not understand. Then she sat up. So did I. After a few seconds she went down again. So did I. Finally the ceremonial welcome was finished, and we faced each other sitting flat upon our inwardly bent feet. Mine hurt terribly. As no means of communication existed, Mrs. Toyama soon left with another series of ceremonial bows. When she had left I pulled my sore feet out into a more comfortable

108

position and could not help laughing aloud at my perfectly ridiculous position. After a pause the screen was pushed open again and a maid was seen crouching outside, her forehead on the floor. She entered carrying a *hibachi* (charcoal burner)—the only heating existing in the cold, damp house—to warm my hands, and a tray with green tea. Again formal salutations, which I again copied carefully. Exit the maid.

While I was warming my stiffened hands and sipping the green tea, which also was a new experience, I looked around and admired the perfect beauty of the room. I later sat hundreds of times in similar rooms, small simple ones in the houses of friends, larger and very large ones in the houses of the great of the earth, big businessmen, bankers, viscounts, marquesses, and princes. The rooms were all alike in style and arrangement and differed only in size and in the quality and finish of the woodwork. Just as on this first occasion, I was always impressed with the perfect beauty of Japanese interior decoration. There was no furniture, no paint, no bric-a-brac, no wall decoration. All lines were simple, all proportions perfect. The effect was achieved by the soft finish of beautiful, perfectly joined woodwork, with the larger panels interrupted by elaborate, lacelike latticework. There was the ceremonial niche, *tokonoma,* on one side, raised one step, containing some shelves, simple or beautifully painted, a stand with a vase holding a flower arrangement, and a painting (*kakemono*) selected to fit the season. In rich houses the contents of the *tokonoma* —the vase, the picture, a few lacquer implements—might be priceless, but the general style and arrangement were the same as in the simplest house. I have no doubt that the beauty and perfection and harmony of those rooms put to shame any known Western style. One must compare the overwhelming beauty of the reception hall of Nijo castle in Kyoto with the gilded ugliness of Versailles, or the drawing room of the well-to-do and even the not-well-to-do Japanese citizen with the ghastly bad taste of a French salon, to be impressed with the perfection of Japanese taste in interior decoration. Of course the modern movement in arts and crafts, which started the rebellion against Victorian horrors at the end of the last century, was greatly influenced by Japanese crafts.

But there I was still squatting on the floor of the impressive room, feeling cold and forlorn, when the screen slid open again and in came a boy in a student's uniform. Of course we went through all our polite exercises, though the boy did them less ceremoniously than the ladies. With a happy grin he said, "How do you do?" This was exciting—finally somebody who spoke a foreign language. But, alas, it turned out that no other English word could be extracted from him, and thus we grinned at each other again until he left. Some time passed, and then the younger son entered. Again the same wigglings on the floor. This time he said, *"Wie geht es dir?"* I made only a feeble and unsuccessful effort to extract more German from him, and then he left. Finally a young daughter appeared, very shy and embarrassed, perfect in the performance of the greeting rites, and she whispered, *"Comment allez-vous?"* I gratefully acknowledged her skill in French but did not try for more. I was already stiff from cold and dampness, my legs and feet upon which I squatted hurt badly, and I was completely resigned to my fate. Finally, after two hours, excited and happy voices of both sexes were heard talking simultaneously: father Toyama had returned. I had difficulty getting up on my feet to shake hands with the excellent scholar, who had a complete mastery of English.

Within a few days I was able to start my work, for which everything had been prepared by my colleagues. The department had even furnished a laboratory with new furniture, had purchased all the necessary equipment, and had engaged graduate students to assist me. I learned to my surprise that the great geneticist Toyama with whom I had corresponded was only an assistant professor and worked most of the time in a distant silkworm laboratory. The head of the department, who actually turned out to be my host, was Chiyomatsu Ishikawa, whom I now met for the first time. We became great friends for life, and he did more than any other, except my friend the botanist Miyake, to help me understand Japan and the Japanese.

Ishikawa, who spoke English and German perfectly and knew the mind and psychology of the Western world, was at the same time a Japanese deeply interested in the lore of his nation and willing to give reliable information. This was a most important feature of that noble man. Most Japanese have been trained to prevent the foreigner from getting correct information regarding things Japanese. This is not, as one might think, secretiveness and falsehood, but the outward sign of an inferiority complex. They are afraid the foreigner might criticize what is different in Japanese life and therefore do not tell. For this purpose they have invented all that flowery language of the travel agencies—"from the land of flowers," "eternally smiling childlike people," "the heroic Bushido." The carefully guided foreigner is led to see what he ought to see and might make an extended trip to Japan and return with completely wrong information about everything.

Ishikawa helped me to see, study, and like the real Japan. His answers to my inquiries were always honest and reliable. Some of my finest experiences were leisurely trips, in old Japanese style, which I made with him to different parts of the country. Everybody knew him, as he was a highly popular personality, and wherever we went we were royally received. He was, in addition, the most charming traveling companion; he loved good inns and good food and drink, and he knew all the interesting places and where to get the specialties of the region. He was familiar with all the lore and history, was full of amusing and characteristic anecdotes, and loved to laugh and to have a good time. I am glad to pay tribute to the memory of this extraordinary, noble man of whom any nation might have been proud.

In 1914 it was not easy for a visiting scientist to work in Tokyo. The only place with Western comforts was the immensely expensive Imperial Hotel. I should have loved to live with a Japanese family, but I was told that every house was overcrowded on account of a fair. In fact, nobody wanted to take in a foreigner, and this one can understand since Japanese houses do not afford any privacy and customs like the method of bathing make the presence of a foreigner a nuisance. The small downtown hotel where I stayed was situated in an unpleasant quarter and ten miles away from my laboratory. At that time there were only a few motorcars in the huge city. One ride in them sufficed. There were no traffic rules, and the contraptions dashed in a zigzag through the crowded streets, dodging each pedestrian or ricksha, so that one was in a constant fear of becoming a murderer.

The general conveyance for covering the great distances of the capital, which then housed over two million inhabitants in individual houses, was the ricksha. At each corner there was a ricksha stand. Most people of the middle class had their own *kuruma* and *kurumaya* (ricksha and puller), and wealthier people had two uniformed *kurumaya* running in tandem. After the first shock of being pulled by a human horse has subsided, the *kuruma* is a most pleasant vehicle to ride in. I actually became fond of the *kurumaya*, unfortunately referred to as ricksha coolies in travel books. These

poor men certainly had the hardest and most unhealthy job existing. How frequently a middle-aged, even elderly man ran with me
ten minutes or more, at a brisk pace, without stopping, arrived
completely soaked but politely smiling, and had to wait for another customer in his wet clothes, maybe in rain and wind. I
found most *kurumaya*, in spite of their low station and poverty,
really charming men. When they had women and children riders,
they chaperoned them, helped with the errands, and carried the
babies. How often when visiting a new town did I engage a
kurumaya who took me around, served as a guide, gave reasonable
information, showed his own pride in the beauty of a temple or
a park, and was a pleasant, helpful, reliable companion. (This
was later, of course, after I had acquired a smattering of Japanese.)
When I returned to Japan ten years later, the motorcar had put
the *kurumaya* out of business, and I wonder whether he still exists
at all. This poorest of the poor and still so decent group of men
in Japan deserves a monument more than many a military leader or
prince.

But my daily rides to Komaba I had to take in streetcars, and
this was the only disagreeable part of my otherwise enchanted
first weeks in Japan. I succeeded in hunting up a streetcar map
with English explanations, and I learned to read the Chinese
characters marking the different lines. But the rides in the cars
were an ordeal. The streetcars were used almost exclusively by
the working population who could not afford rickshas. The fare
was very small with as many transfers as were wanted, so that you
could ride for hours with one ticket. As a result the cars were so
overcrowded that the passengers hung to the outsides like grapes
on the vine. Inside it was very unpleasant. The Japanese people,
who were otherwise models of politeness, behaved most rudely
in the cars. Everybody coughed or sneezed into your face. If
you were seated, three men standing in front of you, hands up to
grip a handle, alternately brushed their filthy kimono sleeves
across your face. They did not mind standing in their wooden
getas (clogs) on your toes. Everybody sucked his teeth or produced some other unpleasant sound with mouth and nose. When
I finally read in the papers that three thousand cases of plague
had occurred in town, I found it time to look for quarters that
could be reached without the pleasure of streetcar rides.

It was Ishikawa who heard of a small hotel, run in Western
style, in a residential suburb, Omori, from which the laboratory

could be reached by a half-hour train ride and a pleasant walk of a mile. Today Omori is a highly populated and rather expensive residential district. At that time it had only a few villas and the hotel on the top of a hill in a pleasant park, and immediately beyond it began the villages and rice fields spreading over a charming valley. There I lived for the rest of my stay, and I returned there when I revisited Japan. It was just what I wanted. When I returned from work in the afternoon I could take long walks in the countryside and observe the life of the farmers in the villages, their ways of planting, tilling, harvesting, threshing. I found the Japanese farmer or peasant so similar to the peasant of southeastern Europe—aside from the differences in clothes, implements, and crops—that one might easily substitute one for the other, and I do not doubt that their outlook on life was identical, and probably many of their problems were also. This observation applies, of course, similarly to many walks of life. A Japanese scholar looks upon life very much as I do; a grammar school teacher may be picked out of a Japanese crowd as well as out of a German or French group. The same applies to businessmen, shopkeepers, bankers, and aristocrats, and shows that national and racial differences are in many respects overcome by similarities in occupation and in stations in life.

My favorite haunt in the surroundings of Omori was the old Ikegami temple, the central temple of the powerful Nichiren sect of Buddhism. The temple, actually a park covering a whole hillside with the many different edifices making up a Buddhist temple precinct, could be reached on the highway along the shore of Tokyo Bay. But I had found a charming walk through the valleys behind Omori which led in about half an hour to the rear of the temple hill, and many an evening I strolled there to be present when the marvelous-sounding old bronze bell was struck for vespers. The hillside was covered with huge old cryptomeria trees in the shade of which a picturesque graveyard slumbered. The plateau on top of the hill, reached from the main street by a huge stone stairway, contained all the buildings forming a Buddhist temple—the larger prayer hall, smaller halls, library, stage for religious dances, pagoda, and belfry. Usually the grounds were deserted except for a few visitors offering their prayers. Sometimes a special service was held for some party, probably mourners, and then I squatted in the background, half hidden by one of the huge wooden pillars, following the ritual which has so much resemblance to the Roman Catholic ritual. But the most beautiful thing in the compound was the abbot's residence, to which I had access once. Located at the edge of the plateau, it seemed to be an ordinary and rather new Japanese mansion. But when one entered it one came to a series of beautiful rooms all facing a garden, the existence of which could not be suspected. This garden, the first in old Japanese style that I beheld, was the most beautiful piece of landscaping imaginable. It filled a natural amphitheater topped by a grove of dark pines. Using the natural features of the ground, the landscape artist had succeeded in producing an impression of indescribable beauty. One has to have sat in one of the rooms facing the garden, sipping powdered tea in the company of the priests and looking down upon the glorious view, to realize its beauty.

Many years later I had the opportunity of seeing the grand Ikegami temple in a completely different light. Each year on a certain day the adherents of the Nichiren sect made a pilgrimage to Tokyo to take part in a midnight parade to Ikegami. This night march was one of the weirdest and most impressive things I ever saw. I can compare it only to a visit at night to the great temple of Madura in India. Toward evening a parade of half a million or more men started in Tokyo and marched for some fifteen miles to Ikegami. All participants, mostly workingmen and artisans, marched in groups according to villages or guilds or associations of employees. All wore the white pilgrim's suit, and as they marched along they worked themselves into a religious frenzy. Thousands of drummers beat incessantly a hypnotic rhythm. Each group of men carried one or more elaborate lanterns built in the shape of a temple, some very large and carried on top of high poles. The sturdy working-man who carried this heavy piece performed with it a wild dance to the rhythm of the drums, swinging the lantern in a complicated rhythmical pattern, a very difficult and terribly exciting per-formance. When his strength gave way the next workingman grabbed the pole and continued the dance. So it went for hours while the parade proceeded through the dark streets of the suburbs. The performers refreshed themselves with considerable amounts of rice wine, and the frenzy, both religious and alcoholic, increased as the procession approached the temple.

I went with the parade from Omori to the temple, fascinated be-yond description and carried away by the hypnotizing, exciting rhythm of drumming and dancing. At the foot of the high stair-way the crowds and the frenzy were such that I considered it

A ricksha ride in Kyoto, 1914

Old-fashioned bath, Japan, 1914

The *oiran* and attendants in the Yoshiwara parade, 1914

unwise to be carried up the stairs within the parade and got out of the stream. My intimate knowledge of the temple grounds stood me in good stead. I was able to climb the hill from the rear in the dark and reach the entrance to the main temple hall hidden in the shade of trees. Here I could watch the groups arriving after the long march at midnight. The strongest man, standing on the wooden platform of the temple, performed one more wild and grandiose lantern dance and then made room for the next group pushing up toward the temple. For a long time I watched the spectacle, fantastic beyond words, and then walked home to town through the quiet valleys. One must have seen this sort of night pilgrimage to understand how it is possible that a disciplined army, made up of decent peasants and laborers, could suddenly be transformed into a frenzied horde of rapists and murderers, as happened years later in the massacre of Nanking.

When my day's work in the laboratory was finished I used to walk for hours through all the quarters of the huge town and watch the people at work and play. At that time Yokohama, the treaty port, was a bad imitation of a Western city, but Tokyo still retained its Japanese character. The Imperial Theater and Mitsukoshi's department store were about the only foreign-style buildings in a quarter that is now covered with skyscrapers and huge stone buildings in an un-Japanese style. The Ginza, the main business street, was flanked by small Japanese-style business buildings with open fronts behind which the salesmen sat on mat-covered platforms and offered tea when one entered for a purchase. There were no bars, and there was only one place where good foreign food could be eaten. Not a single woman could be seen on the streets in foreign dress, and very few children. Even the majority of the men wore native garb. In hot summer the workingmen worked clad in nothing but a G-string, and women frequently sat in the open shops or in streetcars with their kimonos wide open in front.

In the less central quarters and in the densely populated districts of the poor, life in and around the street was completely Japanese. The temples were crowded with worshipers, and the foreigner was treated with politeness wherever he went. I visited, of course, as many different types of eating places as possible, for nothing is more characteristic of a nation than the way people eat. Nations of an old culture are usually fond of good food. The Chinese, for example, have invented the best dishes of the world. There is nothing in culinary experience to compare with a big Chinese dinner with its dozens of courses, one more elaborate than the other. But the Japanese are, I think, the masters of refined eating. Chinese eat good food in ugly surroundings, throw leftovers to the floor, use one bowl for many dishes, and neglect form completely. Frenchmen eat delicious food in poorly furnished and not all too clean places. But a good Japanese dinner in a well-known restaurant, teahouse, or hotel is a unique combination of delicious food and the most esthetic setting.

The room is a marvel of interior decoration in old Japanese style. The guests sit on silk cushions upon white mats. The food is put in front of them upon lacquered trays of different heights and beautiful designs. Each dish is served in a different type of bowl or platter: soup in beautiful lacquer bowls, eel in a lacquer box with drawers, other dishes on china, each piece different but the same for each guest. Behind the tray squats a waitress, or a geisha when money does not count, and pours wine. The chopsticks are brand new, and everybody behaves according to strictly observed rules. Even in smaller or less expensive places all these things are perfect, and in expensive places they are very sophisticated.

During my second visit to Japan I was frequently taken to the so-called "gourmets' club," meaning that only members were served. When I entered, the landlady and half a dozen beautifully dressed waitresses received me at the entrance with ceremonial greetings. Then I was offered an opportunity to bathe before dinner. The room reserved for the party was perfect in architecture, flower arrangement, and painting in the *tokonoma*. In summer it opened upon a small, charming garden into which the guests looked from their seats on the floor. The food was indescribably good and was served in perfect style upon valuable lacquer and china dishes and bowls. Once the restaurant owner joined us at table and entertained the party by writing poems on beautiful gilt paper in highly artistic characters produced with graceful strokes of the brush admired by everybody. When he asked me to reciprocate I felt like a clumsy barbarian; I concocted a little poem with suitable allusions to the place and wrote in my poor handwriting which looked, beside his beautiful Chinese characters, like the scribbling of a child. Afterward the proprietor, who made his china in his own kiln, showed me the china closet of the place, which certainly surpassed anything I have ever seen, and, noticing

my admiration, presented me with a set of plates of his own design, worth more than my dinner bill.

But not only such select places demonstrated the refinement of
formal dining. Parties in private houses, to which I was frequently
invited after it became known that I liked Japanese food and
customs, were just as elegant. According to the old custom the
lady of the house did not eat with the guests but sat near the door,
where she received the dishes from the maid, and she herself served
the guests. Among the dishes there were a number that nobody
touched. But every guest when he entered left his *furoshiki* (wrap-
ping cloth) with the maid, and when he left the party he found
the untouched dishes wrapped to be taken home to the children
and servants.

I could fill pages with descriptions of odd eating places—the wayside noodle restaurants in the country where for a few cents one
could get a dish of hot buckwheat noodles in gravy; the eel houses
where the most delicious of all Japanese dishes, eel fried in soy sauce,
was served; the different types of houses serving some special food
like turtle, whale meat, the poisonous fish fugu, pickled jellyfish,
fried prawns, and even one place in the suburb Ryogoku where
monkey and badger meat was obtainable; and the cheap shops where
one ate, standing, *zushi*, a kind of rice ball boiled in vinegar and
dressed with raw fish or seaweed, ginger, and many other delicacies.

An interesting sight in Tokyo was the streets on rainy days.
Most people carried the Japanese umbrella made of split bamboo
and oiled paper, which offered much better protection than a Western umbrella. As the streets, even the large thoroughfares, were
not paved, they were soon covered with a deep mud that looked
like chocolate sauce. The Japanese walked on wooden sandals with
two cross boards almost four inches high, and I always admired the
students who jumped with these stilts from running streetcars.
Once I saw a priest who had a single ten-inch-high board under
each sandal and walked cleverly through the mud on these queer
contraptions. People with foreign clothes, however, usually wore
high rubber boots up to the knees. Pressed pants were of course
not known. And sometimes there could be observed combinations
of costumes that would not be believed by anyone who had not seen
them. The owners were probably visitors from small towns who
had no proper notions of the use of foreign apparel. I remember one
man clad in a pair of cotton underdrawers over which he had rolled
high rubber boots. Around his waist he had a woolen knitted belt

to keep his stomach warm. Over all this he wore an old morning coat and vest with collar and tie, and a derby hat crowned the performance. One summer, during my next visit, some enterprising businessman had sold a large number of long white shirts that looked exactly like ladies' nightgowns; they were even adorned with some lace around the neck. This sort of shirt was worn by working people as a light summer dress, and my own laboratory boy went around wearing nothing but one of these women's nightgowns. He did not know, of course, where the pattern of his comfortable summer dress came from.

People who at that time knew the Japanese only from the serious, correct scholars and the stiff, dry, vinegary government officials who traveled abroad would have found it hard to believe that Japan was the jolliest nation on earth. The Japanese loved to have fun, and they made use of any pretext to get it. Walking around a big city like Tokyo one could find any day of the year a street or precinct where a local festival was being celebrated. The streets were decorated with lanterns, flags, and garlands and were filled with happy crowds and with booths selling little playthings and sweetmeats for the children. Each of the innumerable Buddhist temples and Shinto shrines in the city had its yearly festival, so there was always at least one in progress. At these festivals the young men of the district carried around on their shoulders a miniature shrine built upon heavy wooden beams. This duty was performed, not with the seriousness we associate with a sacred procession, but in a wild spirit of intoxicated enjoyment, with shouting and jostling for a place under the beams, so that one wondered when the heavy structure, so violently tossed about, would crash. But it never did.

One of the favorite pleasures of the people was traveling, and the trains were crowded all year round. A trip to visit one's relatives or home town was an excuse for a pleasure trip. Since everybody slept on the floor in rooms that in the daytime were living rooms, and everybody bathed in the same water, even a poor man could take into his house numbers of visitors. The whole country was covered with famous sights, and every Japanese tried to visit as many of them as he could. In the course of my three visits to Japan I saw all the best-known ones and many others just as beautiful, and everywhere I found crowds of sight-seers and merrymakers. All these places had their teahouses, eating booths, and picnic grounds, and everybody enjoyed a perfect merry holiday. The poor man did his traveling in the form of pilgrimages to holy places. He lived on alms, hiked for weeks, worshiped where there was an opportunity, and had a grand time in addition.

Whoever could afford it gave and attended dinner parties, which were always jolly and full of laughter. On my many lecturing trips all over the world I have been wined and dined to any extent but nowhere more frequently or more lavishly than in Japan. A Japanese of standing had hardly an evening without a party—a simple one in a home, an elaborate one in a restaurant, or a very elaborate one in a geisha house. Half of his day was spent in calling on others or receiving callers, who began to appear at seven in the morning, or seeing somebody off at the railway station, or welcoming an arriving friend.

Even the seasons of the year served as reasons for merrymaking. The cherry blossom season has been widely advertised abroad as a sweet, gentle festival of sentimental flower worshipers. But in fact the crowds thronged the suburban places where groups of the flower-laden trees were found, and masqueraded, picnicked, and drank tremendously. Every man of the lower classes had a two-quart bottle of sake strung around his shoulders, and many were dead drunk before noon. This was the case at the famous cherry blossom places like Mukojima. In the public parks and streets flanked with cherry trees the crowds were very orderly.

Plum blossoms, cherry blossoms, iris, wisteria, peonies, azaleas, and chrysanthemums furnished pleasant excuses for outings, picnics, and merrymaking all year round, and I certainly did not fail to join the crowds on all such occasions. Under these circumstances I also learned to enjoy rice wine (sake or *masamune*), although when I first tasted it I thought it an abominable drink with a flavor like soapsuds. The two greatest flower seasons of the year, *sakura* (cherry) and *kiku* (chrysanthemum), were also celebrated by the emperor with huge garden parties to which high officials and diplomats were invited with their ladies. I attended a number of them, which took place either in the modern, not very interesting gardens of Shinjiku or in the beautiful old Japanese park of Aoyama palace. The women guests wore their most beautiful kimonos, but the men had to wear Prince Albert coats and toppers, and, since most of the Japanese high officials owned these items in editions of thirty or forty years before, one saw some ridiculous sights. I suppose I offered a rather ridiculous sight myself. I had brought a silk hat, but the tropics did not agree with it, and it had twisted like a screw. I had therefore borrowed one that was so wide it fell over my face if I did not hold it, and it was shaped like a stovepipe.

When all the guests were assembled, the imperial court arrived and paraded before the guests, followed by the diplomatic corps. The present emperor, then crown prince, followed behind his mother, who was ruling for the sick emperor. She was a fine, noble-looking woman though somewhat hampered by her European dress and hat. I should have liked to see her in old court costume. The prince, looking very serious, wore a simple khaki uniform. As soon as the imperial party was seated in a special tent, a buffet was opened for the guests, and it was rushed in a most disgraceful way. Everybody scrambled for tea, cake, and sandwiches. High officials piled their plates with refreshments to be wrapped in the silken *furoshiki* and taken home to the children. Within a few minutes the mountains of food had disappeared like grass after a grasshopper invasion.

Many other little observations made while walking around the cities of Japan are worth reporting because everything has changed so much since. There was, for instance, the custom of tattooing the body, an elaborate art that one can still see on the stage and in old pictures. The government had forbidden it, but in hot summer when workingmen were almost naked one could still see beautiful examples. The champion was one workingman who exhibited on one of his well-rounded buttocks the fat face of the laughing Buddha, Hotei, and on the other the cheerful face of the god of luck, Daikoku, both beautifully designed pictures covering the whole of his behind. Then there was the amusing sight of ladies at streetcar stops taking leave of each other with innumerable deep bows and ceremonies while the streetcar waited patiently until they had finished their polite performance. There were the peasant women in town for a visit on a rainy day, who pulled their kimonos above their heads to protect their elaborate hairdresses from being soaked, not minding that they uncovered themselves below the waist. And there were the groups of six-foot-tall and immensely fat professional wrestlers, wearing the old Japanese pigtail on top of their heads and swaggering in an insolent way through the crowds. Fat men as well as women were otherwise unknown, and the only fat woman I saw was followed by everybody's smiles. But enough. Now I feel sorry I did not have a movie camera to record so many of the sights, which are bound to disappear if they have not done so already.

When I first came to Japan, in 1914, I did not know much of Japanese art beyond the woodcut prints that were collected in Europe. Realizing this gap I began to study the arts of painting, sculpture, lacquer work, and china, and have since derived infinite pleasure from my acquaintance with them. In my later visits I spent much time visiting private collections and had the pleasure of seeing some of the greatest national treasures not only in museums and temples, but in the houses of former daimyo and other lords as well as in the houses of newly rich collectors. Many an hour I also spent in the backrooms of the great curio dealers, where I could handle things that were kept from the eyes of the ordinary customer. During my first visit my lack of knowledge of the language was an impediment, but, when I returned later with some smattering of Japanese and a good background of art history, I was better prepared for an understanding of one of the great developments of the arts. But even from the beginning I was impressed with the perfection of Japanese arts and crafts. Every little article used by the Japanese was perfect in taste and workmanship, even if it was worth only a few cents. Unfortunately, however, these objects were not exported. For export they manufactured all those horrors that still fill Oriental stores all over the world: the gilt, overdecorated Satsuma china, the frightful embroidered kimonos, the ridiculous imitations of Western crafts, and all that stuff the Japanese call contemptuously *Yokohama muki* (treaty-port stuff), which no coolie would buy.

Also during my first stay I made the acquaintance of one of the greatest things genuine Japanese culture has to offer, the popular Kabuki theater. The Japanese stage has produced two very different types of dramatic art. One of these is the sophisticated, highly literary No play, frequented only by the admirers of the old— members of exclusive and highbrow literary societies. The No play is performed in a special building. There is no scenery on the stage, and the whole performance is more to be compared to a religious service than to a theatrical performance. The actors, members of old and famous families, wear the unbelievably gorgeous costumes made only for this purpose, and the wooden masks, if old and famous, are worth a fortune. The musical accompaniment is done with hand drums and a flute, and the lyrical verses are sung in a strange style called *utai,* very difficult to perform. Each movement is prescribed and must be executed as slowly as possible. Some of the famous classical plays are most fascinating provided one is able to appreciate a completely esoteric, hyperesthetic performance, and I enjoyed repeated invitations to attend No performances in a small and select audience of connoisseurs, mostly old people.

But the masses of the people do not attend such plays. Their theater is the popular Kabuki stage, where the classical dramas glorifying heroes and heroic deeds are performed. The plays themselves are not very good, but how they are performed! When I first visited Tokyo, the old *Kabuki-za* (theater) was still in existence, where the floor space was divided by elevated running-boards into boxes in which one sat squatting on the floor, a whole family in one little box. After this theater burned down it was replaced by one with seats and stalls in foreign style, an innovation anticipated by the Imperial Theater, also built in foreign style. My first visit to a Kabuki play was rather bewildering, but after I learned to appreciate the strange style of acting there was nothing more fascinating than a Kabuki play with famous actors in it, and the seven to eight hours of performance passed only too quickly. There is no actor in the world who can compare with the Japanese actor in mastery of his body. The acting is not realistic but strictly conventionalized. Each movement is prescribed and made for a definite effect. The spoken word is conventionalized and is pronounced in an unnatural voice, neither speaking nor singing. The acting is actually a combination of drama, opera, pantomime, and ballet. The actor may end or interrupt a dignified or passionate sentence with a pantomimic dance ending in a great dramatic and marvelously performed pose. The action is never hurried. An actor may take twenty minutes to write a letter and half an hour to commit hara-kiri (*seppuku* the Japanese call it), and every second of it is fascinating. Female roles are performed by men, and after I got over the first shock of the strained voices I never doubted for a moment that I was seeing the most graceful women on the stage. (Actually the occasional female performers—a concession to modern times—cannot compare with their male rivals.)

Some of the great dramatic scenes are extremely moving, and the Japanese audience raves with wild yells if the scene is of the heroic type, or the whole house rings with sobs if it is a sad scene. Among the many wonderful performances I saw, two scenes cling to my memory as superb beyond words. One is the famous scene at the frontier when the beaten hero Yoshitsune tries to escape in disguise. The guardian of the barrier has recognized him but wants to help him to escape, and this is accomplished after a long dialogue in which both measure their wits and hide their feelings. When finally the hero passes the gate into safety, it is a moment of unforgettable greatness. The other scene is the last scene in the great drama of the *Forty-seven Ronin*. After having avenged their master, the forty-seven heroes cross the bridge quietly in falling snow, without a word being spoken, marching toward self-destruction. It was difficult not to weep with the entire audience.

Among the really austere things I beheld in Japan, the tea ceremony ought to be mentioned. I do not mean the poor show staged for the benefit of tourists (and for their purses) by geishas in various places. I mean the ceremony as performed in private houses of conservative families who still cling to the ancient traditions in pure form. No foreigner is invited unless he is known to be a lover of old customs and ready to attend in the spirit of reverence and almost religious sentiment that the refined Japanese put into this esoteric ceremony. Many well-to-do families have in their gardens a small tea pavilion built after the strictest rules in prescribed size and equipment, and even the flagstone path leading there is laid out according to strict rules. Here they occasionally retire with good friends for the formal tea ceremony—an esthetic relief from the turmoil of everyday life. Every movement is quiet. The conversation is subdued, in the most polite form, and centers around philosophical or artistic subjects.

The tea ceremony proper is nothing but the preparation and drinking of powdered tea. The guests and hosts squat along the wall of the small simple room, imitating the style of a peasant's hut with the water kettle hanging down from the roof. But the studied simplicity barely hides the precious workmanship of the whole. The lady of the house, beautifully dressed, brings in the tea things, all of which are priceless. I have seen Japanese pay fifty thousand dollars for a bamboo ladle used in the ceremony by a famous medieval tea master. Setting the things around her, each at a prescribed place, in definite order, and with slow movements every detail of which is prescribed and requires not only schooling but also calmness of mind and mastery of the body, the lady proceeds, while the atmosphere of calmness, composure, and introspection spreads through the room. In the same slow way, the tea is prepared. The pot, the tea container in its brocade cover, usually a priceless piece of old pottery, the iron water kettle, the bamboo ladle, everything is moved around, taken up, deposited according to strictest rules. The finished tea is passed in primitive, thickly glazed pottery cups, again frequently priceless, and has to be drunk with prescribed movements and gulps. I repeatedly had the pleasure of attending the *cha no yu* in the most perfect setting with people who combined refinement and idealism with wealth. Since I happen to be afflicted with estheticism, I found the experience very similar to that of hearing an oratorio in an old cathedral.

Life swings like a pendulum from the highest to the lowest, and so a very different experience at the other end of the scale may now follow. During my first visit there was still an opportunity to see in its old condition the much-described red-light district of Tokyo, the Yoshiwara, which plays such a role in Japanese history, the stage, and the art of woodcut printing. Many a lady who decorates her boudoir with a charming print of a gorgeously dressed female does not realize that it is the portrait of a famous prostitute. The facts concerning the Yoshiwara and the sad fate of the women who were sold there by their parents are well known. Before the quarter, which was surrounded by walls, was destroyed in the earthquake of 1923 it was indeed a sight worth visiting. The houses were the largest and the most beautiful in Tokyo. On the ground floor there was a large room closed toward the street by a wooden lattice, so that it looked like a cage. Inside, up to a dozen girls, clad in gorgeous kimonos, wearing elaborate hairdresses and painted with thick layers of make-up, sat quietly in front of golden screens and waited for customers. The ordinary people considered this exhibition, which was later forbidden, quite natural, and one could see families with women and children walking through the quarter looking at the prostitutes on display.

There was one very interesting show that I was able to see in the Yoshiwara. At the time of my first visit to Tokyo, the owners of the brothels had revived the custom of the parade of the *oiran*, which is so frequently represented in old prints. Three of the "best" houses each selected one popular prostitute to parade with two little girls as attendants and a few male servants. The *oiran* was dressed in a heavy silken kimono beautifully embroidered with gold and held by an obi of the most valuable brocade. Her hair was done in the old style, with a circle of long, radiating, tortoise-shell pins, exactly as pictured in the old woodcuts. She walked on lacquered shoes with twelve-inch-high soles, in a strange ceremonial gait. I watched this parade from a teahouse and had the *oiran* come upstairs so that I could inspect her marvelous clothes. The poor thing was completely exhausted from the weight of her dress and the walk on stiltlike shoes and did not open her mouth.

Whenever I could get away from my work I took small trips out of Tokyo to see the famous sights. All of them I have since revisited many times. One trip may suffice as an example of travel in former times in the more untouched parts of the country. When I returned later to Japan for two years, I visited practically every region of the empire, much of it hiking, and I could fill a volume describing my experiences. But the most vivid impression was created on my first trip to remoter parts of the country, which I undertook toward the end of my first sojourn in Nippon. My friend Ishikawa intended to visit a remote region at the shore of the Japan Sea to study the strange biology of the luminous squids, and I thought this would be a good occasion to visit these parts in the best of company. Ishikawa went ahead, and as soon as my work permitted, in May, 1914, I followed with my pleasant assistant Takahashi.

When the train taking us west approached the popular summer resort of Kanazawa, completely empty at that season, I beheld the beautiful silhouette of the highest active volcano of Japan, Asamayama. I simply felt unable to pass such a beautiful mountain without visiting it, and when the train stopped we quickly decided to interrupt our trip for an ascent of Mount Asama. Rain was pouring down, but in order to make the high peak the following day we had to get as high up as possible before nightfall, climbing up to a pass where a teahouse was said to offer shelter. Thus we walked on over hills and valleys, and after five hours of climbing with a not too light knapsack we came out of the rain, the clouds parted, and we beheld the huge cone of the smoking volcano. We had not met a single person except a young peasant who told us that there was a police ban in effect against climbing Asama because the volcano had shown signs of an impending eruption. But he accepted the offer to make the ascent with us the next day as porter of my heavy knapsack. When we started upon the last ascent of the pass we met a strange sight. A man was leading a mare on whose back was strapped a kind of scaffolding with two seats level with the animal's belly, one occupied by an old man, the other by a girl. In between, a pile of household goods was heaped on the poor horse's back. A four-legged moving van combined with the family car!

It was already dark when our long march brought us to the *mine o chaya* (summit teahouse), a filthy straw-thatched hut in which an old man squatted near a fire. This did not look inviting, and we preferred to walk on for half an hour to another house, said to be more agreeable. At the second house, however, we were received with some restraint until Takahashi had succeeded in explaining our peaceful intentions. There was only one rather dirty large room in the house. Over a fire in the center the water kettle hung down from the roof, and this part of the house was plastered with mud. All around went a platform, and on it squatted an old woman, a girl, and a young man. The other half of the platform was somewhat separated by an incomplete paper wall, and here an old man was already sleeping in a bundle of rags on the floor. He was awakened to give the state quarters to the new guests. He peeled himself out of the covers, stark naked, and walked off with his rags to spread them somewhere else. The supper consisted of grayish rice and dried fish, both horrible looking, and afterward we slept in our clothes on the floor. Takahashi was almost murdered by hosts of fleas, but I am immune from those pests. Without regret—and incidentally without breakfast—we parted early in the morning after having paid the bill, twenty-five cents for both of us.

Returning to the *mine o chaya*, we found our porter and started the ascent. There was no great beauty in this climb. The steep ash cone was rather unpleasant, and as the day became very hot it was not much fun climbing the cinders past an old lava stream that led to an extinct crater. There, at the old crater, the cone began to be covered with huge boulders, each the size of a small room, which Asama had the ugly custom of throwing up. Some of them were quite fresh, and I certainly should not have liked to have been present when they were hailing down. Between these rocks we worked up the steep ash cone until, after about four hours of climbing, we reached the rim of the active crater, the approach to which was heralded by sulphur fumes and subterranean thunder. The very moment we arrived at the edge of the horrible-looking crater a dense cloud of white vapor was extruded with a hiss. Our porter, seeing this, cried out in terror and ran downhill as fast as he could. Unfortunately he carried my rucksack with him, and gone was my camera when it was most needed—and gone also was the lunch. Certainly the crater looked uglier than any other I have seen. The walls of the perfect funnel were very steep, incrusted with sulphur, and the hissing of the steam and the thundering below were really frightening.

After having a good look at the crater from different points of vantage, we walked, ran, and slid quickly down on the other side and after an hour found our heroic porter. I could not, however, eat the lunch of rice dumplings brought from the teahouse; the thought of their origin turned my stomach. Without a path, we climbed down, often rather uncomfortably, in the direction we wanted to take and finally struck a path farther down. For hours we continued our way through pretty forests of birch and finally came to a small village. Here I could fortunately buy a few eggs, my first food the whole strenuous day, and while I was drinking the raw eggs our porter told the assembled peasants all about his heroic deeds and the dangers from which he had escaped. He especially boasted that he had looked down the crater unafraid of the evil spirits therein.

A few more hours on the road brought us, rather fatigued after twelve hours of walking, to the small town of Komoro, where we found a nice little inn. When Odysseus came to the Phaeacians as a shipwrecked wanderer, Princess Nausicaä washed his tired feet. In Komoro it was only the maid of the inn who washed my tired feet with warm water before I entered the house, but it was a most pleasant feeling for the tired hiker. We were well taken care of, though I did not like the local delicacy, *sashimi* (raw meat) of carp. Though raw fish is one of the best dishes on the Japanese menu, this particular carp had been fed on silkworm pupae taken from the boiled cocoon after the silk was spun off. This is certainly a rich, fattening food, but the horrid odor of the silkworm grease is communicable to the flesh of the fat carp and does not appeal to everybody's palate. I was so ravenously hungry, however, that I emptied even this dish.

Our next goal was a visit to Nagano, a small provincial town right in the heart of Japan, beautifully located on a river surrounded by mountains, and rarely visited by foreign travelers. But the small town was an extremely busy one, for it was the seat of one of the holiest temples, Zenkoji, the central temple of the powerful Zen sect of Buddhism. Thousands of pilgrims came each year to visit the holy place, and approaching the town we met numerous special trains filled with pilgrims. The streets of Nagano were filled with groups of pilgrims, mostly peasants in white pilgrim's garb with a large straw hat, straw sandals, gaiters, and a string of beads around the neck. Frequently a man with a flag marched in front of a group of men and women of all ages, most of the women with children on their backs. The main streets of the town were lined with large hostels and stores selling trinkets relating to the temple. We put up at a beautiful inn, in a perfect Japanese room overlooking the valley and adorned with some fine works of art.

As always I enjoyed immensely the style of living in a good Japanese inn, especially one far away from Westernized towns. On arrival in the afternoon one undressed, aided by the chambermaid who folded up the clothes and put them away in a large bamboo basket, and then one put on a clean washable underkimono and a nice silken kimono, padded with silk in the cool season, both furnished by the hotel. At about five o'clock one was called to the bath, a large wooden trough or basin with steaming hot water in which all the guests bathed one after the other. In large places the trough was large enough for up to six bathers at a time; in small inns only one man could fold himself up into a barrel-like affair.

The ordinary Japanese bath was heated from the side by an attachment with a charcoal fire. In some out of the way places in western Japan, however, one still met with a terrible contraption— a barrel with an iron bottom directly heated by charcoal. On the surface of the water floated a wooden grate, which was supposed to be pushed down as one stepped in to protect the feet from the hot iron plate at the bottom. Not knowing this, the first time I used the contraption I took the grate off and stepped right into the barrel, but I certainly got out quickly enough. When I returned from my bath and told the story my Japanese companions burst out laughing.

Since everyone soaped himself thoroughly and soused himself with pails of hot water, it was perfectly all right to use the same tub over again. In large hotels an elderly man served as bathing master, soaped everyone's back, and watched that everyone was thoroughly clean before entering the frightfully hot tub. In out of the way places it was still the custom for the chambermaid to go with the guest to the bathroom and soap him down. In the smaller towns the sexes bathed together, and nobody took offense. The first use of the tub was offered to the guest of honor, and I always tried to arrive early in order not to miss this chance. After the bath a delicious dinner was served in the room, with the chambermaid attending all the time.

At sleeping time the quilts, more or less comfortable and beautiful according to the place, were spread on the floor, and in summertime a huge mosquito net was hung from the corners of the room. It frequently happened that at bedtime the landlady and all the maids would assemble in my room to watch the amazing sight of a tall foreigner going to bed. The quilts were always too short, and I had to add an extra pair to take care of my feet, producing unending laughter. The hard roll filled with rice husks used as a pillow by the Japanese was out of the question for me, and when I pushed a sitting cushion under my quilt for a pillow I was again a source of interminable giggling. Then I had to put on my pajamas in the presence of a crowd of giggling women and was finally stowed away for the night.

My greatest difficulty was always trying to get fresh air, since by order of the police the rooms had to be completely shut at night with heavy wooden shutters. At five o'clock in the morning the shutters were pushed open with a terrible noise, and soon the maid entered with tea and smoking utensils and, in old-fashioned places, a sour plum. Then one proceeded to the open general washing room, where men and women washed together in full sight of everybody. Soap, new wooden toothbrushes, and tooth powder were provided, but the guests brought their own towels. Breakfast was served back in one's room—*misoshiro* (sour bean soup) and rice, with fish, omelette, and other things added according to the rank of the place. It was *de rigueur* to eat three bowls of rice, the last one mixed with tea, and once I had learned to enjoy a breakfast without coffee and bread I took my three bowls with pleasure.

After we had bathed and dressed, we set out to see Nagano. The buildings of the Zenkoji temple covered a large area. Up to the high temple ground led a street flanked by the priests' houses and smaller shrines at which the pilgrims worshiped before reaching the main temple. Some of these shrines contained good works of art and were richly adorned. In one of the smaller shrines a priest blessed strings of beads and other souvenirs of the temple with incense and prayers and another sold them for twenty-five cents each to the pilgrims, who accepted them kneeling and pressing the sacred souvenirs against their foreheads. Each of these secondary shrines held a huge wooden chest that was constantly rattling with the coppers thrown by the pilgrims. At the end of the street the old and dignified main temple rose from a forest of stone lanterns and monuments. A beautiful thatched roof, four feet thick, adorned with wood carvings and figured tiles, was supported by immense wooden columns, each a single tree trunk. Inside there was a large columned hall. One part, the most sacred, was set apart by a net, and to pass through the pilgrims had to pay again. Before entering they rubbed with a piece of wood different parts of their body and the corresponding parts of a wooden image—this was supposed to free them from ailments in those parts.

High above the temple another small shrine was located on top of a hill, and every pilgrim had to worship there, too. The ascent in scorching heat was rather trying, and the shrine was not worth seeing. But the view over the valley and the whole town, with a famous battlefield in the background at the confluence of two rivers, was gorgeous.

Toward sunset we returned to our inn. Passing by the large pilgrims' hostels that flanked the main street, we beheld a picture that could probably not be duplicated anywhere. The stairways of the houses were arranged in front, leading from tier to tier, completely open toward the street. Here the hundreds of guests stood in line waiting for their turn in the bath. Men and children were stark naked, the women wore nothing but a red cloth around their loins, and everybody was talking and laughing and having a good time. Here, certainly, Western ideas had not yet penetrated.

The next morning we went to the temple early with the hosts of pilgrims to be present at a great service to be held by the head abbess, an imperial princess. With the other worshipers we first made the rounds of a narrow, completely dark, subterranean passage surrounding the sanctum. This passage secures forgiveness for many sins, a chance of which we gladly availed ourselves. Then we entered the inner sanctum of the temple hall and squatted on our heels. Near what corresponded to an altar a group of fine-looking old priests sang their prayers accompanied by drums; on the other side knelt the abbess in gorgeous attire with her seven disciples. I personally am sure that I atoned for all my sins for the rest of my days during the long services, for I had to sit ceremoniously upon my insteps, which hurt badly. Afterward I saw the solemn procession of the abbess returning to her quarters. She was a young woman with a round face and shaven head, who looked like a boy, wearing a beautiful purple silk robe with a large scarf of gold brocade. She was followed by a man holding a purple sunshade over her and by her seven disciples. She walked on immensely high wooden sandals with a solemn gait, and all the pilgrims knelt down with folded hands when she passed. With a white wisp very much like that used in the Roman Catholic service she touched the head of each pilgrim in a blessing.

A pleasant trip brought Takahashi and me from Nagano to our destination on the west coast of Japan. Since time immemorial the fishermen along a small strip of coast of the Japan Sea, between the little towns of Uodzu and Namerikawa, had known that each year at exactly the same time in May myriads of small squids appeared in the sea, approached the coast on a few dark nights to spawn, and disappeared as quickly as they had come. These squids were conspicuous by being beautifully luminescent. They were caught in large nets by the millions, dried, and sold in the Chinese markets. When the Japanese zoologists became aware of this phenomenon they found to their surprise that the luminous squid was an otherwise extremely rare deep-sea animal, known only from a few specimens obtained by deep-sea expeditions in the abysses of the oceans. Each year these animals left their haunts, reached the surface waters, and swam in huge schools to that strip of shore to lay their eggs. Afterward they were supposed to return to the deep seas. Since my friend Ishikawa was studying this phenomenon, I had arranged to meet him in Uodzu to see the unique sight. The days I spent there with my delightful companion are among my most pleasant memories, for I lived through a charming small-town idyl of a type still possible in Japan in 1914 in places far off the beaten tracks.

Every Japanese is a worshiper of the beauties of nature and loves to travel to places where something extraordinary can be seen. Such a place may be simply a group of old rocks or a promontory or a strangely formed tree or an area with an interesting type of fishing. Thus the luminous squids immediately attained commercial value as a tourist attraction. This led to bad jealousies between the two little towns, each of which wanted to get the tourist trade. Namerikawa claimed the right to advertise the squids because Professors Watase and Ishikawa had done their original work there. But Uodzu made the same claim because more squids were caught there. Finally a contract was made between the two "chambers of commerce." On the same coast a beautiful fata morgana (*shinkiro*) could also be observed. The exploitation of this was reserved for Uodzu, and the squids for Namerikawa. But now a terrible thing had happened: Professor Ishikawa, considered a kind of saint in those parts, had gone to Uodzu to study the squids because a small laboratory was made available there, and in addition he had brought the first foreign visitor, about whom the papers of the nearby provincial capital told all kinds of strange stories.

Of course the authorities of Uodzu were triumphant and treated me accordingly. When I arrived at the station I noticed a policeman who grinned knowingly when he saw me and disappeared. Later I learned that he had orders to report my arrival immediately to the mayor. I had, in fact, hardly arrived at the pleasant inn and met Ishikawa when the mayor called, and I had to go through all the ceremonies of politeness that were strictly observed in these parts. Ishikawa and I were enthroned on this occasion and on many subsequent ones upon beautiful silk cushions, one elbow resting on a lacquered armrest. In front of us stood our teacups upon high, candlesticklike saucers of gold lacquer, while the poor mayor, squatting upon an ordinary cushion, had to drink from an ordinary cup. To demonstrate his importance the mayor told us of his ancestry. His forebear who had first settled in this region had been a falconer at the shogun's court. One day he permitted a favorite bird to escape and fell into disgrace. He set out to find the falcon and finally spotted him in this region. He whistled, and the falcon was just about to obey when a bear appeared and drove him away. The falconer shot an arrow at the bear and followed it until he reached a river he could not ford. But the monkeys assisted him, forming a bridge across the river. Finally he found himself at the sacred mountain of Takeyama, where he became a monk.

We were, of course, much impressed with so noble an ancestry. From then on the mayor appeared at any time of the day and did his best to make our stay enjoyable. But he was outdistanced by the chief of the district, who appeared the first night and then called every morning at five and waited patiently until we were ready to receive him two hours later.

All these great happenings were duly reported in the daily paper of the provincial capital by a journalist who hardly ever left us. With deep sorrow these reports were read in Namerikawa, which was jealous of its birthright in regard to the luminous squids.

One day a delegation from that town appeared, clothed in beautiful Prince Albert coats, the latest style of thirty years before. The delegation consisted of the mayor, the director of fisheries, and three more notables. What a pity I do not have a film picturing this reception, which was held in strict traditional style just as if Japan had never been in contact with the rest of the world. Everything happened on the floor. The delegation entered and immediately went down, noses to the floor, and I did everything as they did. After a considerable time we sat up, and the delegates squatted in formal posture on their insteps. Everybody was introduced, and each delegate, politely crouching toward me on all fours, offered his visiting card. With every single one I exchanged greetings, which meant noses to the floor and sucking of breath. Afterward the important functions of each guest were explained, a new reason for noses to the floor. Finally the mayor presented an invitation to Ishikawa and me to come to Namerikawa as the guests of the city. The Namerikawans would show us that they could beat Uodzu. I told them—through Ishikawa—how greatly I was honored and that I should stay a day longer for this purpose (noses to the floor and much breath sucking). Triumphantly the delegates looked at each other and after many more noses to the floor departed, leaving me with a sore back but ready for one of the delicious sea-food dinners served out there. According to Japanese folklore each new dish tasted prolongs your life by seventy-five days. That day brought a longevity record. The menu was boiled tai (a delicious fish) in gravy, raw tai sliced, fried sole, fish soup with fish eyes swimming in it, dried abalone, deep-sea crabs, luminous squids boiled in gravy, and boiled as well as raw grated tendons of whale.

The following morning at five two reporters from the provincial capital appeared with a photographer. The interview was completely taken care of by Ishikawa, and, since he was full of fun and puns, I am sure he told them the most amusing inventions, which the province could read the next day as text to my picture in Japanese dress. Then we departed for Namerikawa. At the station we were received by the authorities, again all in heavy, hot Western suits, morning coats, or Prince Alberts instead of their comfortable and beautiful kimonos. The police commander even wore heavy white gloves. All of us boarded a special car of the local railway line. The director of the line and a special officer traveled along to insure our safety and comfort, and also a cook who was said to be able to prepare European dishes but was very much relieved when I explained that I greatly preferred Japanese food.

The train took us toward the mountains, which here were near the coast. At the last station a whole cavalcade of rickshas stood ready, and an especially strong fellow was selected to pull my 160 pounds. In a brisk trot the sturdy pullers started uphill into the foothills of the Japanese alps. The high peaks were still covered with snow, and a long range of these lofty peaks provided a beautiful background. In the center was the sacred mountain of Takeyama, which every male inhabitant of this region climbed when he reached his eighteenth year. The valleys were covered with rice fields in which the peasants used strong little ponies for plowing under water, man and beast behaving like amphibians. After some time we entered one of those romantic gorges that Oriental painters love to depict and reached the village of Oiwa, where we left our rickshas to climb to the famous Oiwa temple, visited by hosts of pilgrims for its miraculous waters. The best indication of its popularity was the number and size of teahouses surrounding the temple.

The temple, which was founded at the site of an old shrine of Fudo, the god of hell, by the family of Maeda, the former powerful daimyo of this region, specialized in cures for sterile women after a lady of the Maeda family had been cured by the priests. The cure consisted of worshiping a stone phallus, which was later shown to us by the head priest. It was a huge double phallus, wrapped around the middle with gold brocade and kept in a precious gilt cabinet. In addition, all kinds of diseases were cured with the sacred water, which was piped through four bamboo pipes from a nearby stream over a large natural rock that stood in one of the courtyards. The sick people stood there under the gushing water for a prescribed length of time. Formerly there had been no separation of the sexes, but after the introduction of Western ideas of decency, completely nonunderstandable to the average Japanese, two pipes were reserved for each sex and two separate cabins for undressing were erected. Then men and women walked stark naked the twenty steps to the waters, separated for decency's sake by a one-yard high bamboo railing and not at all near the pipes.

Still more powerful was the healing property of some of the waterfalls found in the numerous narrow gorges near the temple. Mental disorders especially were treated by holding the poor sick person under the thundering waterfall. At this place I was only told of the cure, but at another Fudo shrine in the mountains near Kamakura I later witnessed this brutal treatment, with the patient howling in terror like a wild animal.

The temple itself was built around an old giant rock carving of the horrible deity Fudo, separated from the temple hall by a wooden grate in front of which the pilgrims knelt and prayed in singsong. The notables of Namerikawa joined the crowd in their prayers. To think that an esoteric and philosophical religion like Buddhism has come to include the worship of such an ugly, flaming horror as Fudo, and that a police chief in gala uniform knelt and prayed to such an image, is one of the weirdest things imaginable. As so frequently when traveling in Japan outside the sphere of Western influence, I again was facing the strange duality of industrialized Japan with railways, airplanes, and battleships and the old culture and customs still as alive as ever though frequently hidden from the eyes of the casual observer.

The most beautiful part of the temple was the house of the head priest to which we had the honor of being invited. From the outside it was just a plain building at the edge of the courtyard; inside it was perfect in harmony and beauty. Quite unexpectedly it turned out that the rear of the house, perched on a rock high above the gorge, overlooked the waterfalls and the valley down to the sea—a wonderful place for rest and meditation. The fine-looking old priest in his white silken robe was an exquisite host and showed us all his treasures. Here, as so frequently before and after, I felt miserable when I had to write my name in his visitors' book. Calligraphy is considered the highest of arts in China and Japan, and cultured Japanese are able to write a sentence in Chinese characters with brush and ink that actually is a work of art in the harmony, perfection, and flourish of the strokes of the brush. To put in a book filled with such beautiful examples of picture writing a line in my—or any other Westerner's—handwriting is like hanging a ten-cent-store color print in the Sistine Chapel (or, as I have actually seen, an oil portrait of the king of Italy upon the glorious mosaic walls of the Capella Palatina in Palermo).

The great dinner our cook had prepared when we returned from the temple to the teahouse was indeed delicious. But the formalities observed outdid everything I had experienced or was to experience. Usually at a formal dinner, when I was the guest of honor, after I was seated in front of the *tokonoma* post, there was a little polite

135

squabbling among the other guests as to who should have the next important seat, everybody declining and pointing to somebody else as the most worthy. Of course everybody knew exactly where he belonged and after a sufficient show of modesty took the place fitting to his age and rank. Only the very young men staged a special show. When everybody was seated they squatted down at the end of the row but on the bare floor beside their sitting cushions. Only after the elders had repeatedly invited them would they finally sit upon the cushions, and even then they would hardly eat out of respect for the elders present. But, on the present occasion, Ishikawa and I had to sit all alone in a large room until dinner was served, and all the rest sat respectfully in an adjoining room. When dinner came only a few of our hosts, the big shots, dared to join us, and before sitting down they staged a very long fight for the least honorable seat. We dined and drank for fully two hours and wound up with a confection in the shape of the luminous squids.

Late at night we returned from a perfect day, and when we took leave of our pleasant hosts I assured them that I was now convinced that only Namerikawa was the proper place for viewing the luminous squids. Thereupon I was handed a poster printed in beautiful colors showing both squids and the fata morgana as attractions of Namerikawa. After all, they had put it over on Uodzu!

For me, of course, the greatest event in Uodzu was the night when it was dark enough to expect the arrival of the squids. Large nets had been set at the proper places, and toward midnight we rowed out on the quiet waters. While approaching the nets, we saw at a distance the bright sparkling of the animals. The squid, about three inches long, carries his main organs of light emission at the tips of two arms of about ten inches in length. These arms move around in the water, and thus the two small but very bright lights dance around each other in a strange way. With innumerable squids filling the water this was an unbelievable spectacle. The animals were present in such masses that one had only to put a hand into the water to catch one. Soon the fishermen's boats arrived and hauled in the nets from which a glowing stream of scintillating sparks flew over into the boats. The haul was about one hundred thousand squids, which the fishermen considered a poor catch. For weeks the whole town remained busy boiling down and afterward drying the animals for sale. I ate them boiled but did not like the sweetish taste.

I made many nice excursions from Uodzu, among them one to the famous gardens of Kanazawa, a classic example of Japanese landscape gardening and well worth its reputation. But I had really set my heart on a hike across the Japanese alps on my way back to Tokyo. I had mentioned this to the district officer and immediately he proceeded to find a proper companion for me, "proper" meaning a government official who would watch my doings, for the Japanese were suffering from an unbelievable spy hysteria. What could be spied in the lovely mountains of the Japanese alps I do not know, but I had to put up with this remnant of feudal times when, according to an old saying, one beheld ten enemies when leaving the gate of one's house.

As it happened, the young officer who was assigned to me, a very nice young man, later got into trouble on this account. By a strange twist of mind, the young man who was assigned to watch me became suspect of assisting me in spying—on what, I do not know—when later Japan entered the war, and he had a bad time of it. (Ten years later, however, I found him as a councilor in the ministry of education.) When I stayed in the United States during World War I, I told this little story to one of my colleagues, a famous professor at Harvard. After the United States entered the war this hysterical patriot denounced me, saying that I myself had told him that I had been in Japan as a spy! It is certainly sad to contemplate the thinness of the layer of reason that overlies the most primitive instincts even in so-called educated people.

The day of my departure the district officer arrived at five o'clock and waited patiently to take me to the station. He made the rickshas take a big detour in order to pass by his house, where the whole family and servants peeped out to see their master in such an important function. At the station the mayor said goodbye, and I left for the provincial capital Toyama. The young officer of the government who was to be my companion awaited me at the Toyama station. Below the waist he was dressed in native tourist garb—light white pants and straw sandals; above the waist he was European with coat, collar, and necktie. I wore heavy, hobnailed alpine boots, but I wished I could have walked in the native *waradji* (straw sandals), which were ideal for mountaineering. When you wore them out you could buy new ones in any hamlet for about three cents. They were light and gave the foot a perfect hold on any ground. But the fastening, which went between the first two toes, would have made a foreigner's foot sore within a few minutes.

I wanted to start immediately, but etiquette required first a visit to the vice-governor (in my hobnailed boots). He boasted in his house a so-called foreign-style room, one of those horrors with frightfully ugly furniture that Japanese of the higher classes sometimes added to their beautiful Japanese houses. Strangely enough their wonderful sureness of taste in Japanese things left them completely when foreign styles were involved. In this setting I was served with cocoa, which was considered utterly sophisticated or *haikara* ("high collar"), as the Japanese say.

Finally we could leave, and strong ricksha pullers trotted with us through the coastal plain toward the foot of the mountains. After two and a half hours we reached the bridge of Takasu where the pass road began. This road led into the valleys and was the only connection between towns and villages in those valleys. We walked into the slowly narrowing valley through which a foaming mountain stream flowed to the Japan Sea. There was a good deal of traffic of horse carts on which the ore from copper mines farther up was brought to the coast. Each horse was protected from sun and rain by a little roof made of matting and attached to the harness. The drivers looked with greatest amazement at my heavy alpine boots, which were unheard of in those regions, and during the whole trip they remained the greatest attraction wherever we went. At noon we rested at one of the numerous wayside booths and were served with excellent fresh salmon from the nearby stream. As my heavy rucksack was a great nuisance in the terrible moist heat I asked for a porter. Soon one arrived, but to my great surprise it was a nice young woman, very talkative, who took the heavy piece and carried it without the slightest strain the many hours of our afternoon march, talking all the time. Though I had always been rather proud of my athletic strength, I felt very meek around this tiny woman of the mountains.

The landscape became more and more beautiful. The road went up higher and higher, and far below thundered the stream between steep rocks. All the mountainsides were covered with a dense green virgin forest; innumerable waterfalls splashed over the rocks overhung by bizarrely shaped pines, which were frequently covered with the vines of wisteria in full bloom. Finally we reached the pass and descended into another gorgeous valley. At the bottom, where two mountain streams united in a beautiful gorge, we crossed the streams on a flimsy bridge and climbed up another valley, which quickly narrowed and was flanked by perpendicular walls, still covered with vegetation. Flowering magnolia trees covered the edges of the gorge, and the foaming stream down below was overhung by chestnut trees in bloom. The edge of the woods along the road was covered with small iris. The amount of water rushing down the slopes in foaming streams and waterfalls was hardly believable and seemed to constitute an inexhaustible source of power, not yet at all tapped. Wherever the rocks receded from the wild stream a little hamlet was found, and the smallest bit of ground was used for growing rice. In passing the villages I frequently noticed ink prints of two children's hands pasted to the wall of a barn. This meant that a child was sick and would recover when a thousand passers had seen the sign.

Toward evening we reached the village of Mozume, and, since we were anxious to reach before nightfall the only larger place of the region, Kusatsu, we accepted the offer of two strong-looking ricksha pullers to take us there. The little woman who had carried my rucksack cheerfully and indefatigably at once set out to retrace the long hike of the day. The two ricksha men got busy and performed the unbelievable feat of pulling us on the mountain road in a brisk trot uphill and down without a single rest for over two hours. People with weak nerves cannot be advised to take this ride along steep precipices that came uncomfortably close when our flimsy conveyances had to pass an oxcart. But finally we reached Kusatsu, a little mining town, where a decent inn was located. Before we entered, the polite ricksha men, still unfatigued, washed our feet with hot water brought by the landlady, and then the usual scenes were enacted. The bath, a rather small wooden box in which one had to sit in the steaming water, knees to the chin, was located in the courtyard, and all the maids of the hostel assembled to behold the rare view of a foreigner bathing. In the naïve way of country folks, far away from contact with the outer world, they wanted to see whether the *seiyojin* was made like other people and whether he was really white all over.

After a breakfast of rice and fish—the dinner, too, had been rice and fish—we continued on the old pass road and then later on a trail across the mountains. We passed densely wooded valleys, steep hills lying under a scorching sun, and mountain streams, bridged by slippery logs not very well suited to my large hobnailed boots. After six hot hours we reached a main road leading to the capital of the district, Takeyama. There we rode in a so-called bus, a kind of box on wheels, in which I hit the roof with my head when seated. There were five passengers and two youthful drivers, one of whom jumped down every few minutes to lead the horses at dangerous passages. An hour of torture brought us to the town, located in a beautiful valley surrounded by high mountains on all sides. At that time there was no possibility of reaching the town by railway or motorcar. As we had rather long distances awaiting us the next day, we decided to push on by ricksha to a village up the valley that would be a suitable starting point. We were promised two rickshas and went out to try to buy some canned food, as it was said that there was no inn in the village where we intended to stay overnight. When we returned the innkeeper informed us that the ricksha men declined to make the trip. We then went to police headquarters, where we were told that our arrival had been announced by the governor with orders to assist us if necessary. We sat down, sipped tea, and waited. For two hours the telephone rang incessantly, policemen came and went, conferences were held, and finally one ricksha was found. Meanwhile it had become too late for hiking, and we had to accept the offer of the police chief to show us a proper inn. The officer promised to find at least a porter for the next day and to make the arrangements personally.

Three hours later the police chief appeared, lighted his pipe, and entered into a very elaborate conference with my companion. When this was finished he informed me that he now realized that I actually wanted a porter. After another long conference he suggested consulting the innkeeper. Another very long conference followed with the innkeeper, who was overwhelmed by the honor of entertaining the chief of police and showed his gratitude by being so polite as to protract the conversation as long as possible. Finally the innkeeper left and returned after three minutes to inform us that the porter would be ready. This little scene was utterly characteristic, and I have gone through innumerable similar ones. It was considered simply bad taste to give an order and have it done. Time does not count, the rules of polite behavior have to be observed, and they require a three-hour palavar for what could be done in three minutes.

The next morning we worked our way up the valley and after five hours of hiking reached the highest hamlet, where we rested in a very poor wayside teahouse. For the first time we found a community where the people were too poor to eat pure rice but mixed it with barley. To improve the taste, tea was poured over the mixture. Not very much refreshed we started on the steep climb to the Hiraya Pass. The mountainside was covered with thin woods, and the trees, only two inches in diameter, were used for burning charcoal, one of the most important items of a Japanese household, for charcoal, which burns slowly, was used for all cooking as well as to heat the baths and warm the rooms. We frequently encountered a group of huts of charcoal burners. At the two ends of the hamlet a sacred rope with a few scraps of inscribed paper or cloth was strung across the way; the wanderer who passed beneath was cleansed of infectious diseases, which otherwise he might bring with him. Before we reached the pass we went by a regular alpine pasture with blockhouses and spotted cows. Some rich man bred the cattle there as a sport; cattle raising was still practically unknown except in a few outlying parts where the agricultural experiment stations fostered it.

The view from the pass was glorious. Deep down beneath our feet the village of Hiraya was seen amid wooded mountains. To our right rose steep, snow-clad Norikura (which has since been discovered by the skiers). Next to Norikura was the volcano Yogatake, covered with woods to the summit and emitting smoke at many places. Spring had just begun here at an altitude of eight thousand feet. The mountainsides were covered with bright green birches intermixed with chestnut and the Japanese maple. Azaleas and violets formed a dense carpet. Behind these green hills rose snow-covered Kasagadake, shaped like a workingman's hat. In good spirits we descended and reached the small *onsen* (hot springs) of Hiraya.

After donning kimonos we went to the public bathhouse. The pool was a large wooden structure the size of a drawing room, and many bathers were squatting in the terribly hot water, where they remained for hours. But as I knew that most of the visitors of such spas were syphilitics I refused to bathe there. Walking around a little, however, I found at some distance from the inn an old-style bath: out in the open fields a little roof had been erected over a wooden barrel into which the hot water ran through bamboo pipes directly from the hot springs. Here I started bathing, but after a few minutes a dozen peasants, women and children, had assembled to watch my antics with critical remarks which, unfortunately, I could not understand. After bathing we had dinner, but it was not a great success. There was nothing available except rice and the bulbs of the mountain lily, which may be great fare for poets but not for tired mountaineers. To increase our pleasure an itinerant entertainer amused our fellow guests in an adjoining room with songs and a *samisen* (lute), and as they did not have to climb the next day they enjoyed the racket until deep into the night.

The next morning we started at four in order to make the thirty-five miles across the central part of the alps. The whole day we passed through the most beautiful alpine landscape. First we had to climb a steep lumbermen's trail, frequently obstructed by cut timber, until we reached a wet strip of bottom overlooked by the whole great mass of Norikura. Another steep ascent through dense woods took us to the still snow-covered Abotoge Pass. Slowly we descended, frequently crossing snow-filled ravines. In front of us snow-clad Hodokoyama rose, called by the Japanese, not very appropriately, the Japanese Jungfrau. The path, constantly up and down, skirted deep gorges, and frequently the traverses were rather exposed with just a hold for one foot on not too solid ground. But fortunately we passed them without accident. From the distance I thought I heard the tinkling of cowbells, but it was the strange call of a species of cuckoo.

Slowly we returned into spring, with green birches, azaleas in bloom, and anemones forming a white carpet. Again we had to climb a short but steep and very hot pass. But a gorgeous view into a valley was our reward. Almost perpendicularly at our feet we beheld the roofs of another small spa, Shirahone. A short descent took us to the place, which was clothed in sulphurous vapor from the hot springs. The whole spa consisted of a single hotel, built in terraces against a steep hillside. The hot spring flowed right through the hotel, at the entrance of which the bathing pools had been erected. When we entered, hot and tired, and I took off my alpine boots, all the bathers, men and women, left the pool in the costume of Adam and Eve and surrounded us. Each one lifted my boots and exclaimed excitedly at their weight, the women of course with endless giggling. Finally we were able to repair to a room where we were first treated to a health potion—*kiri* root in sulphurous hot spring water. A good lunch of salmon and rice was very welcome. We were told that in the main season in September eight hundred patients, mostly syphilitics, came to take the waters. As it was a stiff and rather unpleasant walk of ten hours from the closest railway station, this was surprising. But Japanese, even healthy ones, love to visit the innumerable hot water resorts, for the prevalence of rheumatism and colds makes a cure pleasant even to the otherwise healthy visitors. I later visited numerous spas all over the country, and some of them, like Beppu on the shore of the southern island of Kyushu or Ikao in the mountains of central Japan, are most delightful places for a vacationer.

From Shirahone we descended for hours through a grand gorge in a typical alpine setting. But the wild character of the scenery was softened by the beautiful vegetation, which grew even upon the precipitous rocks. Waterfalls and small ravines were crossed on single trees put across the precipices. Everywhere wisteria and large camellia trees were in bloom. I remember as an unusually beautiful sight a rock rising out of the foaming mountain stream and completely overhung with wisteria. The valley widened, and the rocky walls over which the path led were almost perpendicular. Finally, after an eleven-hour march, we reached a small hamlet with a road leading to the next railway station and fortunately found a horsecar that took us to the station just in time for the night train. The end of this beautiful hike was rather funny. The railway car was one with long side benches. Tired, I lay down and started sleeping. I noticed that at another station another passenger did the same, his head toward my feet, which I pulled in a little. Then I dreamed that I was shut in a cave and somebody closed the entrance with a huge rock. Frightened, I tried with all my strength to remove the rock by pushing with my feet. I succeeded and woke with the noise of the falling rock. I had kicked my fellow passenger off the bench. Fortunately I had taken off my hobnailed boots.

Among the many beautiful trips and hikes that led me to lovely and extremely interesting parts of the country a few deserve to be mentioned since not many foreigners have had a chance to visit these places. One trip took me to Gifu to see the famous fishing with cormorants. The river near which this provincial town is located abounded with a small trout about six inches long called *aiyu*, regarded, and justly so, as a great delicacy. On this river the fishing right belonged to the imperial household and was exercised by fishing the old Chinese way, using tame cormorants to catch the fish. The Japanese, who are great gourmets, believe that *aiyu* caught by this bird and showing the slashes cut by the bird's beak are superior in taste, and they pay huge prices for them.

While I was traveling to Gifu, the emperor was returning from worshiping at the tomb of his father, and all along the road the tracks were lined with school children, officials, and priests. When the imperial train approached a conductor came and asked us to shut all windows and shades and not look out. When the train passed on the other track all the Japanese passengers stood at attention, bending their backs, their eyes fixed to the floor, but with their backs turned toward the windows. This was a custom surviving from the time when nobody was permitted to look into the sacred face of the emperor.

Ishikawa, who had done much to improve Japanese fisheries, had announced my arrival in Gifu, and an officer of the Gifu fisheries took me in his boat at nine at night to watch the interesting procedure. With difficulty our oarsman pushed the boat upstream through shallow water. On the right, large teahouses with lighted windows flanked the stream; on the left, the dark silhouette of a high, wooded hill stood against the starlit sky, crowned by the ruins of a castle of the medieval hero Ota Nobunaga. Soon other boats appeared, filled with merrymakers drinking sake in the company of geishas, and there was even a boat selling food, drink, and souvenirs. At the bend of the swift river we stopped and waited until in the distance the flaming torches set in the hull of a fishing craft became visible. Soon the boats appeared, drifting down river. In front of each, hanging from a bamboo pole, was an iron basket filled with burning logs. Next to this stood the head fisherman in medieval garb, indigo-blue clothes, a short skirt of straw, and an elaborately arranged headcloth. In his left hand he held twelve strings to which twelve cormorants were harnessed. Another man handling six birds was in the rear, and behind him was an oarsman.

The birds swimming alongside were set to work with cries sounding like "Hoo, hoo, hoo." They dove repeatedly, swam under water with great speed, and reappeared after they had caught the *aiyu,* which were attracted by the torchlight. Then the fish were swallowed and disappeared into the baglike crop but could not be swallowed completely because of a ligature at the end of the bird's long neck. How the fisherman succeeded in keeping his strings in order while a dozen birds crisscrossed through the waters was a riddle, but he did. When a bird had gorged himself to capacity, the fisherman quickly lifted him into the boat and stripped the whole catch out of the bird's crop into a basin.

Rowing along with the leader's boat—there were twelve boats —I wondered which to admire more, the cleverness and agility of the birds or the skill and quick work of the men. The catch that night consisted of about one thousand *aiyu.* It was interesting to watch the greed of the birds and the storage capacity of their necks. After they had landed, a fisherman fed a whole basket of fish to one of the birds, and when let loose the creature swallowed the contents of another. The harness that kept the bird from actually eating the fish and simultaneously held it at leash was made from tough cypress fibers. A flexible rod extended along the back of the bird and was continued into the leash. Two short strings made up the ligature, which was tight enough to prevent larger fish from passing through but allowed very small fish to reach the cormorant's stomach. Two longer strings were pulled under the wings as harness and fixed to the rod near the shoulder.

The next day we paid a special call to the fishermen's huts to see the birds in daytime. They rested peacefully—but smelling horrible—each in a not too large basket. They belonged to three different types, two said to be different races, Shimozu and a yellow-breasted Kowozu, the other, Hikamaiu, said to be a hybrid of both. Their training started when they were caught as young birds. The oldest fellow of the flock was twenty-three years old, and the fishermen said that he always led and watched jealously over his prerogatives.

Only one more of the beautiful trips away from the tourist attractions that I had the good fortune to make will be reported. The most sacred of all sacred places in Japan were the temples of Ise, dedicated to the sun goddess Amaterasu, the ancestress of the imperial family. At the temples of Ise the mythical mirror of the goddess was kept, and there the emperor worshiped regularly. It was inconceivable that there could be a state official who had not worshiped there, and on historic occasions or on the eve of great decisions the ministers of state proceeded first to Ise to worship. I have visited and revisited Ise, and I must confess that in all my wanderings I have seen only one other sacred place that could compare with Ise in the breath-taking impression of holiness. I mean the dark, mystical, lower church of Assisi. But the overwhelming effect of the Ise temples has a very different basis from the physical and dramatic splendor of a Roman Catholic church filled with incense, the sounds of the organ, and the recitation of the Mass, which transport both the believer and the unbelieving esthete into the realms of mystical contemplation. Shinto shrines are remnants of an old animistic religion, nature worship. The temples themselves are as plainly built as possible though using beautiful lumber and perfect workmanship.

In Ise the temples themselves were not accessible to the public, and only the emperor and his delegates and, of course, the priests could enter the sacred precincts. But, even so, the visitor entering the temple grounds was immediately impressed with the great holiness of the place. Crossing an ancient camel-back bridge one entered a forest of immense old cryptomerias with trunks rising perpendicularly like the columns of a cathedral. A river meandered through the forest in which the pilgrims washed their hands. The closer one approached to the temple buildings, the higher the trees and the more impressive became the silence and holiness. When one finally arrived at the bamboo fence surrounding the main temple, Naiku, one was permitted to stand at the right side of the gate for a short look into the enclosure.

When July came it was time to think of my departure. My work had been finished successfully. A package containing the precious eggs of the *Lymantria* races and their hybrids which I had bred had been dispatched via Siberia to Berlin. (Fortunately it arrived before war broke out.) A duplicate set was ready to be taken home via the United States. It was only two weeks before the outbreak of World War I, but neither I nor anybody in my surroundings had the slightest idea that the tragedy was near at hand.

I was frequently the table guest of the German ambassador, Count Rex, one of the strangest types of diplomat I have ever met. A *grand seigneur,* said to be a linear descendant of August the Strong, King of Saxony and Poland, he had made his career without any merit but his descent. He did not care much for work

146

Women stevedores coaling a steamer, Nagasaki, 1914

The author (*third from left*), Karl Muck (*fourth from left*), and others interned
at Fort Oglethorpe, 1918

Breeding caterpillars in Tokyo laboratory, 1925

"Coffee break" with laboratory assistants, Tokyo, 1925

and did not take his responsible position very seriously. His main interest was good living, and he thoroughly enjoyed the masterpieces produced by his French cook. I had made myself popular with him by acclaiming a wonderful dessert served at a luncheon at which, as I remember now with a certain amusement, the other guests were the future wife of Herr von Ribbentrop and her amusing and charming parents, with whom I had made friends some time before. Two weeks before the outbreak of the war, Count Rex gave a farewell party before leaving for his summer residence in the mountains. The only worry he showed in his conversation was whether a donkey he had bought would arrive safely to carry the delicacies needed for his cuisine at the mountain resort.

Actually, as I learned later, the ambassador remained in the mountains even after war broke out, an event that did not seem important enough to interrupt his vacation. He came back to Tokyo only when the Japanese government made him return to hand him the declaration of war and his passport. Even then, his only concern was that he was forced to leave the country on a steamer with second-rate accommodations. A day before I myself was to leave Japan, a week before the declaration of war, I called at the embassy, for rumors of a crisis were already at hand. In case of war it would be my duty as a reservist in the army to report for service in the colony of Tsingtao. The embassy told me to proceed on my trip, for they had no reason to assume that a war was near!

At the farewell party given by Count Rex the only guest who mentioned the possibility of war was the naval attaché. With a very clever professor of law and me, he discussed the situation. As an officer, he was in favor of war. He was sure that France would be beaten in a few weeks. As for England, he believed that she would stay out and, if not, that the German navy would settle her. Russia did not worry him—"We leave it to Austria to finish off that tottering empire." The professor of law warned him against underestimating the strength of Russia, but the attaché did not take this seriously.

It is worthwhile to follow the fate of this officer, since it is quite characteristic of the times. He came from an officer's family, his father was a favorite of the Kaiser, and he was set for a splendid career. During the war he became one of the naval heroes who performed a much-heralded feat in eastern waters. After the peace of Versailles, however, he found himself without a job or a future and returned to Japan to try his luck in business. Perhaps it was only natural that he became a violent enemy of the democratic German government and took part from a distance in all plots. At the time of the Kapp *Putsch* he considered himself already the ambassador to Japan. At that time, and for many years after, the excellent ambassador Wilhelm Solf had to be on guard constantly against the intrigues of this dissatisfied officer, a man of great energy and brutality, who worked hand in hand with the secret reactionary organizations in Germany that were later included among Hitler's followers. One of the great tenets of these groups, taken over by Hitler, was a violent anti-Semitism, and the former naval man became extremely rabid. Needless to say, to him and so many like him, Hitler was the great liberator. All the former officers who had lost caste in their own eyes by condescending to work in business were now able to return to the old glory. This explains largely why the army and navy were behind Hitler.

Life is sometimes strange, though, and I record the following only as a study in human psychology. Years after the war when I was again in Japan and could observe the pernicious activities of this man as well as his rabid anti-Semitism, we happened to live in the same small hotel. One night he knocked at my door and asked me to have a glass of wine with him in his room. I accepted, and after a short time—he had drunk very little—he suddenly began to spread before me all his worries, all his secret sufferings, and bared his soul to me as completely as if I had been his father confessor. I have never revealed his confidences, and I never will. But the thing to think about, the real human element, is that the violent Jew-baiter wept on the shoulders of a Jew when for some reason or other he needed this relief. This little episode always appears to me a sign that human nature after all might be improved one day.

My last official activity in Tokyo was a lecture on my work presented to a large audience at the university. Afterward a dinner party, attended by both Japanese and Germans, was held in my honor. An old professor and a representative of the government spoke, and the German ambassador Count Rex presented me as the typical representative of German science. His toast was to the collaboration of the scientists of both countries. How many times have I attended similar functions in my honor, with German diplomats extolling my person and foreign officials and outstanding men greeting me as the welcome representative of my country. And then came Hitler—who deprived me of my citizenship.

My last day in Japan I spent with a former student in a charming beach resort at Sagami Bay, with the glorious pyramid of Fuji-no-Yama in front of us. On July 27, 1914, the *Shinyo Maru* sailed for Hawaii. It was my intention to stay two months in the Hawaiian Islands to study whether any of the endemic animals, which play such a role in evolutionary discussions, might be used for experimental breeding, an idea that even now after more than forty years has not yet been taken up by my profession. In October I was to be back in Berlin in time for the solemn opening of our institute by the Kaiser. Actually one of the rooms, I was informed, had not yet been separated by a wall from the adjoining large library in order to leave more space for the great ceremony. But I was to return only five years later, and no Kaiser was there to keep my wall from being finished or to lead the opening ceremonies of a great laboratory.

7: I COME TO AMERICA

The sixteen days aboard the
Shinyo Maru, a Japanese steamer with Japanese crew but officered
by Americans, were the most exciting ones I ever had on a sea
voyage. The day after we left Yokohama the wireless announced
Austria's ultimatum to Serbia, and each day brought worse news,
up to the declaration of war. The effect of the news upon the passengers was tremendous. There was only one other German aboard,
a young and refined manufacturer who had been sent on the
grand tour. From the very first moment, we two were morally
isolated, for everybody at once took a stand hostile to Germany.
This, at the time, was incomprehensible to me. Certainly all the
Japanese, American, and English passengers were perfectly polite.
All day long we played deck games with them or walked around
in polite conversation. I was under a terrible strain, for I longed
to talk about what was foremost in my mind. But I had to keep
up appearances, not show my excitement and worry, and make
believe that a good score in shuffleboard was all I cared about. So
I played my games smilingly with a charming English consul;
with an American medical officer, Dr. Victor Heiser, who never
failed at a shot; and with a Scotch engineer who never spoke
a word except when somebody scored ten, whereupon he said in his
brogue: "Tem-po-ra-ri-ly"!

Only at night after almost everybody had retired could we two
Germans drop the mask as we waited in the smoking room for the
wireless news which arrived between twelve and two and was
terribly exciting, though mostly wrong, as it turned out later.
Our companion at these night sessions was a young man who was
traveling with his father, the owner or editor of one of the big
New York dailies. The old man was certainly one of the most
disagreeable fellow passengers I have ever traveled with. Unctuous
and bumptious, he had appointed himself "most distinguished passenger," strutted around like a peacock, made all the speeches
that were required in a greasy, conceited way, and was certainly a
thoroughly ridiculous fellow. His son, a nice boy who served as
his secretary and was treated like a slave, had to sit at his type-

writer below deck all day and half of the night. He joined us at night and, as he had access to the wireless operator, gave us all the news when it arrived. It usually was too exciting to permit sleep for the rest of the night, and the next day the smiling mask had to be worn again.

When the news came that Germany had declared war on Russia, a New York banker offered to bet me five thousand dollars that this was not true. Germany, he said, had such huge investments in Russia that a war was unthinkable. I mention this because we have learned since how utterly wrong the economic tenets of bankers and economists turned out to be. Everything they believed to be impossible happened: a long war, an inflation of currency to less than one-billionth of its value, breakdown of the banking system, abolition of the gold standard, and what not, and yet the nations survived and were able to wage a still more terrible war.

After ten anxious days we finally arrived in Honolulu on August 4, 1914. The first news that greeted us was England's declaration of war. We two Germans went immediately to the German consulate to get advice whether to return to Tsingtao or to continue on our way to Germany. The titular consul, a fine businessman, advised against Tsingtao (which as it turned out would no longer have been possible anyway because of Japan's entry into the war), and so we decided not to stop in the islands but to proceed immediately to San Francisco. My greatest worry was, of course, my family. I knew that they were spending the summer near the Swiss frontier, and I imagined that the French army would invade Germany at this point. I tried to wire them to move to Berlin (which as it turned out they had already done), but a few minutes before the steamer sailed a messenger came to inform me that the German cable had been cut. A friendly American who noticed my worry offered his car and took me to Cook's where I spent a small fortune on telegrams to my friends in neutral countries, to be forwarded to my wife. None of them arrived, and the considerable sum for a prepaid answer was also lost. But fortunately I had, during the day, done a little quick thinking and cashed all the balance of my letter of credit. A few days later the letter would have been a scrap of paper.

The rest of the trip was worse than the first part. There was now the certainty of the war, the uncertainty of how to get home, the uncertainty about my family, and, in addition, the daily sensational news spread by British propaganda: Russian army nearing Berlin; 100,000 Germans killed; and so on. In addition the hostility on board increased after England had entered the war, which, nobody doubted, had been started by the Kaiser just for the fun of it. The bumptious publisher installed himself as an oracle though his information on European politics was just as poor as that of any sailor. His most glorious day came when the news of the death of President Wilson's wife arrived. He arranged a ceremony at which he delivered a sermon unctuous and hypocritical to the limit, and I was glad to notice that even the American passengers left the hall with ironical expressions on their faces.

I think I judged the situation at that moment rather correctly and much better than the German statesmen, who had not reckoned with England's entry into the war and its consequences. In a letter to my wife, which was never mailed but which I kept, I wrote: "But the worst is that I do not know when we shall ever be united again. I feel sure that England will immediately start blockading Germany, and by the time I reach the United States the road to Germany will probably be blocked. And for how long?"

Upon arriving in San Francisco, without even noticing the beauty of the Golden Gate, the first thing I did was go to the German consulate to find out how I could best reach Germany. The consul, von Schack, a rather unsympathetic *Junker* type, unfriendly and conceited (later to be jailed for a childish conspiracy), knew only that the British blockade was already in effect, that all Germans were being taken even from neutral ships as prisoners, and that it would be wisest therefore to wait. My German fellow passenger did not believe it, went ahead, and found himself only a week later in a Canadian prison camp where he had to stay for five long years. In San Francisco, two weeks after the outbreak of the war, the anti-German feeling already ran high. In Market Street a newspaper flashed the news nightly in huge luminous letters. Though I knew that the news was colored, I could not help going there. All day long extras were sold with huge headlines, always about German defeats and German atrocities. Though I tried not to read them I could not help glancing at the headlines and thus kept myself in a continuous state of excitement and worry. Needless to say, I was a patriotic German and believed strongly that Germany had been attacked, and therefore

I could not understand the violent feeling against Germany. Many things became clear to me later.

At that time, however, I certainly suffered intensely from what I believed to be the misrepresentation of Germany. Still worse was the fact that I was without news from Elsa and the children. After a short time of walking around aimlessly trying to soothe my agitation, I decided that I must occupy myself until I could see my way clear to go home. I remembered that an old colleague, Professor Kofoid, with whom I had had friendly associations when he visited Germany, was professor at the University of California in Berkeley, and I called on him. I was well received, and he did everything in his power to settle me comfortably in Berkeley and to make the institutions of the university accessible to me. If I had dreamed then, in my cheerless hotel room in Berkeley, that twenty-two years later I would succeed the same colleague in his chair, myself driven by brutal criminals from my fatherland for which I now suffered agonies, and that I should find a refuge from persecution in this most congenial and charming of all universities on earth, I certainly would have refused to believe that such a dream could ever come true.

I decided to make use of my time by improving my English. Brought up with the British pronunciation, I had difficulty at first understanding American speech. I therefore audited a number of lecture courses in different departments and also attended seminars. All my colleagues were extremely friendly and helpful, tried to comfort me, and took me to their homes and clubs or on hikes and helped me to become acquainted with the American way of living. I am glad to say that I made many friends then who still today are my friends (or were during their lifetime) and that I felt as happy as circumstances permitted. When the following year the University of California offered me a temporary appointment, which circumstances prevented me from accepting, I considered it a proof that I had succeeded in making friends during those hectic weeks.

Thus I lived for two months. The consulate, which I visited occasionally, advised me to wait since the war would certainly be over by Christmas. But I was too nervous to wait—there was still no news from my family—and I decided to go east, hoping that in New York I might find some way to return to Germany. Though I was certainly no militarist I felt like an outcast for not sharing the fate of my compatriots, and I was anxious to join the colors. Therefore, I said good-bye to California and traveled east, visiting on my way important scientific institutions, always received by my colleagues in the most charming and hospitable manner. Though my mind was not set for pleasure, I enjoyed my first sight of the great desert of Arizona during a few days' stay at Tucson with my charming host Professor McDougal, and I stood breathless at the rim of the Grand Canyon, one of the most overwhelming sights I have ever beheld. It was even greater than the expectations I had held since my boyhood.

After a few very instructive weeks I arrived in New York. About that time my funds began to run low, and there was no possibility of getting money from Germany. I had a wealthy uncle in New York, but when I arrived I found out that he had died. Fortunately his son kindly offered to lend me the necessary funds until the end of the war, and he kept his word, at least until the United States entered the war and he went to serve as a major in the French army. Thus I was relieved from the necessity of finding employment outside of my profession, and, since I soon found out that for the time being there was no chance to return to Germany, I made up my mind to settle down to work. I was foolish enough to believe that the war would not last long, and I thought that here would be a good chance for me to learn a new technique that had interested me for some time, the technique of tissue culture. At Columbia University I consulted with E. B. Wilson, whom I had met in Germany, and he introduced me to Theodore H. Morgan. Both suggested that I go to Yale University and work in the laboratory of R. G. Harrison, the discoverer of this technique. Morgan kindly wrote to Harrison, and soon a friendly answer was received saying that I would be welcome. I went to Yale University in November, 1914.

At Yale I was given the status of a visiting professor, and a fine laboratory made it possible to settle down to work. I soon entered fully into all the scientific and social activities of the group and made many pleasant acquaintances. I was introduced to a group of delightful professors who, on Saturday afternoons, took long cross-country hikes, which I enjoyed thoroughly both for the congenial company and for the beautiful New England landscape. The most precious fruit of this time was my friendship with Professor Harrison, who had been known to me as a great scientist and turned out to be also a great personality and a great man. Because he had considerable knowledge of European affairs he was not easily swayed by propaganda and sentiment, and he looked at the happenings in Europe in an objective and scientific way. I could, therefore, discuss things with him frankly, and even where we disagreed in our judgments we could put opinion against opinion in a friendly spirit. This was a great relief to me, for I felt rather unhappy in an otherwise hostile surrounding. I could not simply remain quiet and smile. I felt strongly that my fatherland was being maligned, and I had to say so—and this was not cautious or wise. But I did not think that honesty in discussions was damnable. I have learned much since.

Before Christmas I finally had news from my family, and thus I was relieved of a great worry. I worked hard at my problem, spermatogenesis in tissue culture, and was successful in my work. To keep my mind occupied I read a good deal in other fields, especially in biochemistry, and I greatly enjoyed trying to elaborate my ideas about the physiology of heredity. These thoughts, which I was nursing in connection with some experimental results, were to come to fruition only decades later. In addition I started writing a popular science book with the thought that I might fulfill a patriotic duty by contributing to the education of the masses of my country for which I was not able to fight. How strange all these things look today! The book was later finished, had a great success, and was actually used throughout Germany for the purposes for which it was written, until the Nazi government forbade its further sale. (It was translated into many languages, including Russian, and ten years later, when I required the assistance of a Soviet commissar on a trans-Siberian train, he recognized my name as the author of *Ascaris*.)

All in all my days were well occupied, but the long evenings were hard. To escape from my depressing boardinghouse room, I visited the silly movies and vaudeville shows from which, at least, I acquired a knowledge of slang. Occasional conversations with a very friendly professor of music and organist, Professor Jepson, who lived at the same boardinghouse, led me to take up the violin again. With a borrowed instrument and a music stand, a Christmas gift of the kind organist, I started practicing, took lessons again, and in the following years got much pleasure and comfort from playing duets, quartets, and in a string orchestra. But the same boardinghouse where I met a number of fine people also held a constant torment for me. A group of young language instructors and professors took their meals in the dining room, and they always talked in very loud voices about the war, venting their extreme anti-German sentiments. When they learned who I was, they made a point of shouting from the door of the room as they entered phrases like, "Fifty thousand Huns killed, hurrah!" A mean-looking instructor of French particularly enjoyed tormenting me in such a manner and did not stop even after his attention had been called to his meanness. I finally could not stand it any longer and moved to another place.

In the new boardinghouse there was a very pleasant group of men and women from all walks of life, and everybody was nice and helpful. With one man, a young engineer, I associated quite a bit. One night after dinner he, a young girl, and I went for a walk in the starlit night. We walked through Prospect Street, which looked down into a valley where the big Winchester plant was located. The whole plant was brightly lit and was working at full capacity to make arms and munitions for the Allies. The lights, bustle, and noise, the glowing vapors rising to the dark sky, the contrast of the starlit skies over the beautiful valley and the men beneath forging weapons for destruction, possibly for the destruction of my own kin and friends, overwhelmed me so that I said, "How terrible! I wish this thing would be blown up right now." Years later I found out that either the engineer or the girl had been hysterical enough to report this utterance to the police!

Spring approached, and the war did not end, and I had to think of saving the results of my work in Japan. I had brought the precious living material with me for further experimental analysis. After hibernation the caterpillars would hatch in spring and they must be bred or all my earlier work would be lost. Fortunately a duplicate set was in Berlin, and since my assistant there, Dr. Seiler, was a Swiss he could work in spite of the war and could also receive my instructions via Switzerland. But this was not the same as doing the work myself, and I had to prepare to do so.

Here a very unexpected difficulty turned up. I had brought with me from Japan the egg batches of *Lymantria* sealed in a tin for hibernation. When I came east I asked a colleague in an experiment station, my lifelong friend G. H. Shull, for permission to hibernate my material in his laboratory. He asked me if *Lymantria* was not the same thing as the gypsy moth. Upon my affirmative answer, he was horrified and told me what I had not known, that this moth, introduced from France by a Mr. Trouvelot in the eighties, had turned out a terrible pest in this country and that it was against the law to have such materials around. He frightened me with the prospect that I would have to destroy my precious egg collections.

Immediately I wrote to the United States Department of Agriculture, explained the whole situation, and asked for orders. The very friendly answer requested that I hand over my material immediately to the director of the gypsy moth work in Massachusetts and follow his orders. This gentleman was good enough to take care of my material over the winter and gave me permission to breed it in an already infested area in Massachusetts. The entomological department of the Bussey Institute of Harvard University was assigned to me—actually the whole area swarmed with gypsy moths. I moved there in the spring of 1915 for my breeding work and spent a most pleasant and scientifically successful summer in that now-defunct research laboratory. Decisive facts were found that permitted me to establish the new phenomenon I called intersexuality and to derive from it a general conception of sex determination. In addition, important foundations for my work on geographic variation and evolution were laid.

There were a number of fine and interesting scholars at the Bussey Institute and at Forest Hills—Theobold Smith, E. B. Castle, W. M. Wheeler, Ed East; graduate students Sewall Wright, Otto Glaser, Edmund Sinnott; and others—and I had many friendly associations both scientifically and socially. Again the only unpleasantness was derived from the violent anti-German attitude of most of my colleagues. I remember vividly two scenes in connection with this situation. One took place in the house of W. M. Wheeler, a great scholar and man of unusual erudition though highly emotional and going easily to extremes in all his general attitudes. He was violently anti-German and loved discussion. Once we had debated all evening, with me defending the German cause. When I left I was asked to inscribe my name in the guest book, which I did, and I added my address in Berlin with the remark that I wanted my host to know where to write when, after the war, he realized his error. Unfortunately, he became more violent in his views as the war progressed and did not even refrain from maligning me personally. The moment I had foreseen when

I gave my address never arrived. But I am sure that he, like so many other fine Americans, later felt sorry for having been swayed by mass hysteria.

One other friend actually expressed his sorrow later. One day when I came to the laboratory I met the geneticist E. M. East, with whom I was on very friendly terms. We played tennis regularly and occasionally went together for a glass of beer. East passed without looking at me. I soon learned what was the matter: the *Lusitania* had been sunk. For weeks East did not talk to me and looked at me with a most hostile expression. Of course I had not sunk the *Lusitania*, and I did not condone the crime. But such were the feelings that all logical thinking was forgotten. It happened that I met East again many years after the war. When we were alone he told me that he had waited for a long time for this moment to come, to tell me how sorry he had always been for hurting me and for having been rude to me when I could not defend myself, and that he regretted his wartime hysteria. This I think was a truly American attitude.

During the summer I had tried to persuade my family to come to the United States, for there was no end to the war in sight and no prospect of my return to Germany. The submarine warfare had started, and I assumed that soon transatlantic traffic would be closed. To my deep disappointment a cable informed me that my family's arrangements to come had been cancelled. I later learned that my mother had dissuaded my wife from exposing the children to the dangers of a sea voyage through mined and submarine-infested waters. The same cable contained the sad news of my father's death.

In low spirits I wound up my work in Forest Hills and proceeded to Woods Hole, Massachusetts, to stay for some time at the famous marine biological laboratory to which so many American biologists repair during the summer. I found a very friendly reception and had the privilege of meeting and making friends with many of the outstanding scientists of this country. I especially enjoyed walks and discussions with the great physiologist, Jacques Loeb, a man of genius and a great personality, full of benignity though violent in his judgment of scientific and political adversaries. He was the only one who understood the significance of my work in trying to bring dynamic viewpoints into genetics. The geneticists, with whom I discussed the matter frequently, were not interested, and when, in a lecture on intersexuality and its explanation by the balance of sex genes, I submitted the results of my experimental work, they did not show any understanding. But Loeb saw at once the importance of my new ideas.

Woods Hole at that time was an ideal place. There were not too many people, and there were hardly any motorcars. Hikes, beach picnics, sailing, canoeing, and swimming were the simple pleasures in between sessions of intensive laboratory work. Everybody knew everybody else, and the atmosphere was friendly. Of course it happened frequently that conversation stopped when I approached, and little disagreeable situations often arose. For instance, there were two Belgian refugee professors whom I had known for a long time. They did not greet me, and I was willing to understand their feelings. And once a visiting French colleague, Professor Caullery, still today one of my friends, met me unexpectedly in the room of an American scholar. He turned pale and stepped back, then extended his hand, shook mine, and turned away. When I had left he said to the American scholar, "Goldschmidt was my friend and I shake hands with him, but I cannot talk to him." Fifteen years later he was my most charming host when I lectured at the Sorbonne in Paris, and during World War II we both became victims of the same criminals.

Toward the end of summer I felt so unhappy that I decided to investigate once more the possibility of running the blockade and returning to Germany. It was not only the longing for my family but also the feeling that my country was going through its greatest time in history without my sharing the experience of my fellow countrymen. It seemed to me that it would be hardly possible for me to look into the faces of my friends after the war if I had not taken part in their sufferings and their exaltations. Thus I went to New York to see the only man who might be able to help me, the German military attaché, von Papen. High up in a skyscraper on Broadway this young officer had an office where he hatched his childish plots, which had no effect whatsoever on American aid to the Allies, did great harm to German's reputation, and landed in prison a few silly young men who fell in with his schemes.

I had been told that von Papen had some safe routes to Germany, supposedly with neutral passports, and I wanted to be sent home in such a way. The distinguished but unintelligent-looking young officer who received me was not interested at all and dismissed me politely. I might have expected it; he obviously needed his false passports for his own agents or those of the German government and could not waste them upon a homesick professor of very doubtful military value. I certainly could not imagine that this rather uninteresting officer would one day become German chancellor and influence my own fate decisively though indirectly: it was the same von Papen, the insipid plotter of 1915, the archplotter of twenty years later, who deceived senile, honest Hindenburg into handing over the government to Hitler.

After this unsuccessful visit I had lunch with a physician of German extraction and told him my story. It turned out that he knew the address of a Norwegian ship chandler who, for three hundred dollars, would arrange a passage on a Norwegian boat as coal trimmer or steward with a neutral passport. I went to see the man, and he promised to inform me as soon as a chance offered itself. After a few weeks he wrote that the moment had come and that I would be hired as a coal trimmer on the steamer *Stavangerfjord*. It happened, however, that on the same day a cable arrived from Copenhagen informing me that my wife and children had left Germany and would arrive at Christmas aboard a neutral steamer. This was actually their last chance to come over, for soon afterward even German women and children could not pass the blockade any more. Naturally I cancelled my arrangements with the skipper, and I later learned how fortunate I had been. The whole thing was a bad racket. Another young homesick German took my place, and for his three hundred dollars he landed in an English internment camp. The crew of the steamer made their own share by selling the unfortunate stowaway to the British at Kirkwall.

I returned to the friendly and congenial surroundings of Yale University and continued my work. Two days after Christmas, 1915, I stood in an icy gale at the open pier in Hoboken. Slowly the Danish ship *United States*, covered all over with ice, moved in after a horrible three-week-long passage including search by the British and wild gales. On deck stood my wife, Elsa, and my children, Ruth and Hans, from whom I had been separated for two eventful years.

The rest of the winter was spent pleasantly in New Haven where everybody was exceedingly nice to my family. In spring I had to transfer my work again to Massachusetts because of the gypsy moth danger, and, with the permission of the United States

Department of Agriculture, I settled for this purpose at Woods Hole. An attic in the laboratory was fixed for my purposes, my cousin furnished funds for buying the equipment and hiring a helper, and thus all my problems were solved most pleasantly. My children attended the wonderful biological summer school and played with the youngsters of our friends. A good deal of music was played, and especially enjoyable was a regular quartet with Mrs. Theodore H. Morgan and the pathologist Pappenheimer at the violins, the pathologist Woglom as cellist, while I tried my hand at the viola, an instrument I had recently taken up. Of course the war feeling was running higher and higher, and it separated us from our friends. Everybody was very nice about it, but the fact that conversation with us completely evaded the subject of the war showed us that we were practically alone in hostile surroundings. But only rarely did disagreeable things happen. Fortunately the children were not made to suffer at all and had a most happy time, and we all enjoyed the simple rustic and scholarly atmosphere of Woods Hole.

The winter of 1916–17 was again spent at Yale University. We rented half of a house from a pleasant and jolly Irishman, Mr. Dinneen, who inhabited the other half, and we lived peacefully. The children went to school, quickly became completely Americanized, and had a wonderful time. I worked hard and began writing two books, which were to appear only four years later. In one I applied my new insight into the problem of sex determination to the whole field; in the other I tried to bring together my ideas on the physiology of heredity and on evolution derived from my experimental work of the foregoing years. I was completely absorbed in this work, and I still believe that this small book in the form of four essays is the best book I have succeeded in writing, and that it was far ahead of its time. Between the work I enjoyed practicing violin and viola, took lessons from a former student of Joachim (Professor Troostwyk), and played in a string orchestra. To keep fit I took up gymnastics, in which I had excelled as a boy, and went daily to the Yale gymnasium for a workout and a swim. I was rather proud that at the age of thirty-six I was again able to perform all the difficult tricks that I had mastered in my youth.

In the fall of 1916 Woodrow Wilson was re-elected with the slogan, "He kept us out of war." (All my friends at Yale had voted for Hughes.) It is well-known history that during the winter of 1916–17 British propaganda along with the interventionists worked hard to drag America into the war. It soon became apparent that the President himself was inclining toward this course. The tone of his utterances changed, and when he made a speech in which he adopted the British version of the Berlin-to-Baghdad scare we became apprehensive. Anti-German feeling was now worked up by systematic organization in the press, in speeches, in lectures by war correspondents and propagandists, and even from the pulpit. One preacher in New Haven, a member of the Yale faculty, went so far as to preach savage hatred of the Germans every Sunday in church.

War began to be in the air. Certainly stupid German diplomacy did its best to antagonize American public opinion. But I do not think that Woodrow Wilson was influenced by this. I do not believe either that pressure from financial interests and munitions makers who wanted to safeguard their investments made any impression upon him. If the Allies had been sure of winning or even of coming to a draw, he would have kept America out. But when in 1917 the danger arose that Germany might beat the Allies, and when Balfour came personally to Washington to explain the situation, Wilson made his decision according to his deepest conviction: namely that German autocracy, as he conceived it, must not destroy English and French democracy, for this would be dangerous to American democracy.

Wilson's later catchword, "To make the world safe for democracy," was not, as so frequently claimed, cant or the unworldly dream of a professor. It was the expression of the same belief every American was to hold again in World War II, namely, that England is the rampart of American freedom. Whatever has been written about America's entry into World War I, I hold the belief, based on careful observation of the actual developments in 1916–17, that in the last analysis it happened as I said. The frantic efforts of those who opposed America's entry into the war were doomed to failure after Wilson had made up his mind. Whatever opposition there was he easily silenced when, at the last moment, he published that masterpiece of German diplomatic stupidity, the Zimmermann Note to Mexico. One night the newsboys raced screaming through the quiet streets of the town. War had been declared, and we had become "enemy aliens."

My wife and I had frequently discussed whether it would not be wiser to go to Central or South America in case of war, for the growing war hysteria, especially among women who accepted any propaganda story at its face value, frightened us. Immediately after the war declaration, however, the President published a declaration in which he promised the protection of the law to every German who continued his work and behaved loyally. Pointing to this declaration our friends ridiculed the idea of our leaving and told us that nothing could ever happen to us who had never dabbled in politics, had associated exclusively with good Americans, and had led the retiring life of scholars. Needless to say, we immediately stopped talking about the war, retired as much as possible from social intercourse, did not show ourselves much in public, and kept to ourselves in general. Actually there was not much war spirit among the majority of the American people, and it took about a year to work up public feeling to the boiling point.

I even dared to go again to Woods Hole for my summer work, after having secured, as a matter of precaution, the consent of the authorities. We realized that things might be more unpleasant in a small community where everybody knew us as Germans, but I was anxious to continue my experimental work. Actually the summer passed not unpleasantly. Everybody was as nice to us as we could possibly expect. I recall one professor of physiology who was almost out of his mind with hatred of the Germans. But whenever he passed me on the other side of the street he came over and shook hands. I noticed how much it cost him to do it, and I respected him for it. There were, of course, small unpleasantnesses, and we had to keep mostly to ourselves, but all our friends and acquaintances behaved admirably, and the international spirit of science prevailed over national chauvinism. We were especially grateful that the children were not made victims of hostility, as would certainly have been the case with American children in a similar situation in Germany. But not all grownups behaved as fairly as the children, as I soon was to find out.

When we returned to New Haven in the fall of 1917 things became more unpleasant. The drive for war enthusiasm had begun. The papers were full of spy stories; all Germans were registered and fingerprinted; and patriotic societies, especially those with a membership of society ladies, established themselves as vigilantes. It would have been wiser for me to live in a big city where people did not know each other. In New Haven everybody knew me, and people began to ask themselves why I lived there, where my money came from, and so on. I noticed that the bank teller was embarrassed when I cashed a check. Later I learned that the bank was watching my account and reporting to the authorities. Denunciations were sent to Washington by a professional stool pigeon, a young professor in Yale's biology department; by former colleagues; and probably also by hysterical women in the neighborhood. The Department of Justice made an investigation—as I later learned—but accepted President Hadley's guarantee for my good behavior. All this was unknown to me at the time, but it was not difficult to read in people's faces what was happening.

There were also some tragicomic situations. A very unmilitary colleague in another department donned a uniform and strutted around in it. When he was in civilian clothes he greeted me, but in uniform he cut me. Another colleague, an old friend of mine who is still a friend today, was swept completely off his feet. In a staff meeting he seriously proposed to paint on the flat roof of the laboratory in huge letters: "Here works Goldschmidt," in order to prevent German fliers from bombing the building.

One Sunday afternoon a German-American whom we knew only as a neighbor called on us unexpectedly, for the first time, saying that he had intended to do so for years. Immediately he started talking about the war and called President Wilson all kinds of names for having entered it. I realized at once that the fellow had been sent as an *agent provocateur* and answered him that he had better be cautious as his remarks might land him in prison. I wondered what he reported to his superiors. After the war I met this man on the street. He walked up to me and asked me to forget what had happened. He had been down and out, he said, and this was the only job he could find. I am afraid that the majority of the host of secret agents were of the down-and-out type, and that their work was done accordingly.

It was a rather unfortunate coincidence that the laboratory where I worked harbored two more enemy aliens. One, a lady scientist, was a perfectly harmless woman who had worked there for many years. But since she was of the aggressive spinster type she had made many enemies who now were set against her and watched her suspiciously. I suppose that the professional stool pigeon, an assistant professor, made glowing reports on her. The other foreigner, an Austrian, was a poor psychopath who suffered from a persecution complex and acted very strangely. Everybody was afraid of him because he had once threatened his wife with a knife, and now everybody believed that he must be a plotter or worse. Actually he was a harmless lunatic. But this combination of three enemy aliens was a great thing for the denouncers, and the atmosphere in the laboratory became charged with tension though outwardly I went in and out and did my work without interference. I still went daily to the gymnasium (having asked the university for permission), but even there things were changing. A professor of geology who always exercised at the same time ostentatiously stopped greeting me. Clearly something was going on.

The winter of 1917–18 had not been very successful for the Allies, and it was necessary to speed up American efforts. This involved also bringing the war nearer to the masses of Americans. One of the methods of doing this was to increase hatred for Germany and the Germans, and the victims of this campaign, which was systematically waged by the Department of Justice in spite of President Wilson's pledge, were the Germans within the country. The papers began to report arrests of some dangerous Germans, and privately one heard of others.

One day in April, 1918, big headlines brought the news of the arrest of Karl Muck, the great conductor of the Boston Symphony. The wildest stories were told. I read with my own eyes that Muck had been found to have in his house a wireless set with which he communicated with the Kaiser. In order to hide his terrible doings he always went to the basement to chop wood while he was wirelessing on the roof! Another paper told us that Muck had distributed infected prostitutes among the army camps. And this was not the worst of such stories. It was later explained that his internment was for his own safety, which was endangered by his pro-German feelings. Be this as it may, it certainly brought near to me the danger of my own situation. If Muck, the uncrowned king of Boston, the idol of a whole nation, was treated like a criminal while the most shameless lies were spread and left uncontradicted, there was not much hope for me. Later, when I became friends with Muck, I learned some of the details. What had hurt this great and noble artist most was that he was arrested on Good Friday just before he was to conduct the *Passion of St. Matthew* from the unabridged score. This was to be a great event, for which he had studied and rehearsed. When the secret agent who arrested him saw the score on Muck's desk, he read the title and asked, "Isn't this fellow Bach"—he pronounced it "batch" —"a German?" When told that Bach was a German, the agent asked, "Where does he live?" He even took with him the priceless annotated score, and for a long time Muck was worried that he might never see it again.

On the first day of May I went to the laboratory as usual. About eleven o'clock I was called to the director's room to meet somebody. When I entered I found my colleague, the German lady, and two unpleasant-looking men, obviously police agents. While Harrison, who had been informed, looked uncomfortably away, one of the agents told us to come with him to the Hotel Taft, where a federal officer wanted to talk to us. A taxi waited at the door, and when we had entered with the agents two more tough fellows appeared and stood on the running board. We certainly felt well protected. Arriving at the hotel we were taken to different rooms. An official appeared and told me that he had orders from the Department of Justice to take me into custody. I asked him for the reason but did not receive any answer. Then he called the local marshal and gave me into his custody. The marshal—a nice man who disliked the job, knowing that injustice was being done—told me that he had to take me to the Hartford jail because on former occasions arrested Germans had been too well treated in the New Haven jail. I asked him to take me first to my house to say good-bye and get my night things, but this he could not grant. Finally he permitted me to telephone and have a satchel brought downtown. Then he took me for lunch to a restaurant, where I realized that I did not have a cent on my person and had no possibility of getting money. The marshal then took me to Hartford and was nice to me all the time for he felt ashamed of his job.

In Hartford I was brought before a judge who took down my personalia in a perfectly friendly manner. When he was through I asked him whether there was any charge against me. He answered no. My marshal then took me to a photographer to be photographed for the rogues' gallery. While walking through the unpleasant streets of the ugly town of Hartford I noticed in a curio shop the most beautiful colonial silver service I had ever seen, and I thought that I should like to return and bargain for it. But I soon had to forget about silver coffeepots.

At the jail the tone changed quickly. A brutal-looking young guard ordered me to empty my pockets and suitcase. When it appeared that I had no money he showered invectives upon me. When I answered that I had been arrested in the laboratory without any cause and contrary to the law of the country as well as the President's proclamation, he told me that a university professor who was sent to jail without bail must be an uncommonly low individual. Then he took away my pajamas—"Such things are not worn here," he said—and my razor and shoved me through an iron gate into a hall where he opened what looked like a small cage for wild animals and locked me in.

The feelings of a cultured man suddenly locked into a cage can hardly be described. Claustrophobia is only a word, and the actual sensation is overwhelmingly horrible. For years this cage was to appear in dreams that filled me with horror. When at last I calmed down, I looked around. In front of me the high hall, oppressively hot and stuffy and lighted all through the night and day, was occupied by a towerlike structure with many tiers surrounded by iron gangways. In each tier, rows of iron-gated doors indicated the individual prisoners' cells. It was after curfew, and there was complete silence. After some time a decent-looking young man tiptoed to my cage and introduced himself as a trusty who did some chores in the hall. He asked me if I had eaten. I had not had anything since lunch, and he brought me some bread, milk, and horrible-looking corned beef. He told me, whispering, about the conditions in the place and the types of inmates.

The next morning I was taken from my steel cage and put into one of the cells in the tower. This cell was simply ghastly: a vaulted niche about seven feet long and three to four feet wide. One wall contained a bunk, which could be folded against the wall in day-time; opened out it practically filled the cell. The rest of the furniture was a stool and a pail with cover, which represented the sanitary arrangement, emptied only once a day.

The idea that I would have to spend an unknown time here was certainly crushing. I had not the slightest idea what was in store for me, and nobody told me. Actually I was to be interned, and it would have sufficed to order me to report to the internment camp at such and such a date, an order I should certainly have followed. But, as I later found out, the complete disorganization of the Department of Justice, together with lack of cooperation with local authorities, caused innocent people to be put into jail and kept there sometimes for many months until somebody succeeded in organizing a transport to the camp. But all this was unknown to me, and I think it was especially cruel not to tell me what was going on. I began to imagine that some stool pigeon or agent had sent in a false denunciation in order to show his zeal, and that consequently I might have to stay for a long time in my cage.

After the first shock had subsided I decided to prepare for a long siege and to keep myself bodily and intellectually fit. I devised a complete set of strenuous exercises, which I at once started doing three times a day. I decided to write a work of fiction as soon as I could secure paper, and I began to think out a plot. Thus the day passed slowly. At noon and at night the guard pushed under the grate, next to the pail, a metal plate filled with evil-smelling cabbage and corned beef. But I did not succeed in swallowing it. At nine in the evening an automatically moved heavy steel bar was pushed with much noise against the locked grate, thus increasing the ugly feeling of being locked up. Then I tried to sleep, unwashed, unshaven, in my day things, on the hard bunk.

Early the next morning suddenly all the grates opened with a bang. Doing what I saw the others do, I stepped out to the gallery, pail in hand, and fell in with the line quickly moving down the iron stairs. At the bottom the prison guards stood in two lines, armed with canes, between which we had to run, like running the gantlet. In front of me ran a giant Negro, a killer as I learned later, and each of the guards hit him with his cane. In this pleasant way we reached the lavatory, where we had about a minute to wash our hands and faces in a filthy sink. There was of course no shaving or brushing of teeth. With the same speed the line moved on, each of us grabbing a fresh pail and a tin cup filled with so-called coffee, and after a few minutes we were again locked in our cages.

Toward noon I was taken out of the cell and brought to a steel grill downstairs. On the other side stood poor Elsa. She had brought some bananas (on which I lived for the next day or so), and she reported that my American friends were busy trying to get me out of the place. Only later I learned how nobly they had acted in the face of personal danger. Two of them had gone to Washington and tried to argue with the Department of Justice, actually endangering themselves seriously. The press, which at that time had reached an unbelievably low level, had told the story of "the arrest of an extremely dangerous German" with glowing headlines and the most ridiculous lies, and simultaneously my friends were also attacked and actually had to fear mob violence. Their noble actions

brought many unpleasant experiences upon them during the following year, but I am glad to know that after the war, when people
began to feel ashamed of their hysteria, everybody respected them
for their upright Americanism.

Every day my wife made the difficult trip to Hartford to see me
for a few minutes at the grill in the presence of an ugly guard.
She brought me a book, one of my favorite novels by George Eliot,
and some much-cherished writing paper. She did not tell me of
her own worries. I had been receiving our means of subsistence in
the form of a loan from my wealthy cousin who sent a monthly
check. This American-born cousin had been raised in France and
was violently anti-German. Even before America's entry into the
war, he had volunteered for the French army and served as a major
in France. During his absence his lawyer sent the checks. It happened, however, that the lawyer had not yet mailed my monthly
check when on May 1 the headlines of the morning paper informed
him what a dangerous criminal I was. He decided it might be harm-
ful to his client to support me further, and he simply did not send
the check. Thus my wife found herself penniless in addition to
everything else. A visit to the lawyer was unsuccessful, and my
other cousins, all wealthy people, were too cowardly even to see her.
Fortunately our American friends and acquaintances behaved dif-
ferently. Every single one offered his help. A violently anti-German
scholar, himself a poor man, came and offered money, and so did
many others. The market with which we traded told my wife to
order her things and not to worry about payment for the war
would be over one day. My wife had kept the children out of
school when the newspaper sensation started. The next day the
teacher, Miss Joslyn, came with a kitten for the children and asked
them to return to school. When they came the next day the whole
class rose and cheered. We have ever since been grateful that the
real American spirit was still alive in spite of the ravings of a
rotten press and the war dances of the Department of Justice. There
was also occasionally a bit of humor. One day a New Haven paper
published a highly colored, detailed description of how I, together
with a gangster, had tried to break jail. We were, according to the
account, already sitting astride the prison wall when a guard shot us
down!

Meanwhile I continued my observations of jail life. In the afternoon we were brought downstairs into a place that looked like a
huge cage of the type used in circuses for wild animal shows. In

the center stood the guards with cudgels, and the prisoners had to march crisply around in a circle. This was called exercise and was felt to be a special humiliation. Here I first saw my fellow prisoners, many of them decent-looking young men but all looking sullen and resentful. One day one of my friends, a Yale professor, came for a visit. He had been in Washington on government business, and when he returned he received the news of my treatment. He at once proceeded to Hartford to see what he could do for me. Of course this was immediately reported in the papers and caused him many difficulties and worries at the hands of the 150 per cent home fighters. I had meanwhile learned from the trusty that the jail contained a sickroom supposed to be heaven in comparison with the cells. Thus I asked my friend to use political pull to get me into that sickroom, for my cell was really ghastly. Fortunately the Republican party was in power in Connecticut, and Governor Baldwin himself kindly interfered and did something even better for me.

The next day I was brought into the hospital cell to the great dismay of that brutal guard who had received me so pleasantly and continued to show me his spite. Here was a real room with six real beds, and it was possible to forget the presence of the steel grates over the windows and doors. Four of the beds were already occupied. There was a very nice young Swedish workingman who was sentenced because he refused to give alimony to his wife, who had deceived him. He declared that he would rather spend his life in prison than give a cent to the hussy. There was a young Italian with a social disease who was booked for a minor offense. The third was a huge Negro who sat on his bed stripped to the waist and showing his herculean muscles. He had killed or almost killed somebody in a quarrel. I thought it wise to keep him friendly by giving him my food, which I could not swallow. The fourth inhabitant was a drunkard with delirium tremens. He lay on his bed in a stupor, fastened to the bed with heavy chains. During the nights he roared and shook his chains—not very pleasant night music. But nevertheless it was a fine place compared with the cell.

I did not hide my story from these companions. Only later I heard that this might have been unwise. A German businessman who was arrested in New York to be interned was brought to the Tombs. There the jailer told him: "I'll have to put you in a cell with two murderers. Don't tell them you're a German, as it might prove dangerous." After the cell was locked the murderers addressed the businessman with the usual question: "What are you in for?" "I killed my wife," he answered and was well received.

The following morning I was suddenly told to get ready to be moved. A marshal, again a nice man, came and took me out of the jail. He told me he had orders to take me to the state prison. I was horrified because I thought I was to go there for the rest of the war, which might last for years. I did not know that Governor Baldwin had arranged for my transfer because state prisons were much more humane than county jails.

Again an iron grill closed behind me. But then the pleasant surprise came. I was brought to the warden, a fine-looking cultured gentleman who told me that he had been given orders to treat me as well as circumstances permitted. A guard took me to my room in this new "hotel." It was again a cell in a tower within a large hall, but this steel cage was the size of a small steamer cabin and contained a little washbasin with running water, a toilet, and a small table. A new mattress was put on the bunk along with some real bedsheets, and I was permitted to shave—a heavenly happiness after many days of untidiness. I was even permitted to take a shower, and I felt as though I were living at the Ritz Hotel.

Soon another surprise came. I was taken to the guards' dining room, I sat down at a table with a white cloth, and a waiter in white jacket—a murderer serving a life sentence—served me a delectable breakfast, the first thing I had eaten for days except bananas. Here I took all my meals, and I was kept away from the prisoners. I saw them only twice, once during a very dignified Sunday service and once when I attended their hour of exercise in the courtyard, where they played baseball. There were many "lifers" recognizable by a mark on their uniforms. I did not have to wear a uniform at all.

The greatest privilege granted to me was permission to work in the prison's library. The warden suggested that I make a catalogue of the really excellent library with short book reviews attached to each entry. I was brought every morning to the library and stayed there until it was time to return to my cell.

Thus I lived rather pleasantly for a week or so, and then one morning I was called to the warden and told to be ready to move again. Again a friendly marshal appeared, and I took leave, with many thanks to the humane warden. The marshal told me he had orders to bring me to New York and to hand me over to the military. Here again was a bit of unintentional cruelty derived from interstate red tape. If the marshal had been told that I was to be interned he would have told me and I would have felt as much at ease as circumstances permitted. But he knew nothing except that his orders were to deliver me to the military authorities, and nervous as I was the words "shot at sunrise" rushed through my mind. In wartime anything might happen. Thus I entreated the good-natured marshal, a sensible man, to let me telephone to New Haven and have my wife and children come to the station while the train stopped. This he did, and I was able to say good-bye to my dear ones, not knowing where I was going.

8: THE INTERNMENT CAMP

Arriving in New York we at once crossed to Governors Island and there the marshal handed me over to an army sergeant. The sergeant conducted me to the office of a young officer, obviously a reserve officer, who, looking at me with a grave expression, stated that he had received a telegram from Washington ordering him to transport me directly to Georgia. He obviously considered this a sign that I was an especially dangerous criminal. What actually had happened was that my friends at Yale University had appealed to the Department of Justice to intern me quickly if I was to be interned and to bestow upon me the special favor of being brought alone to the camp instead of waiting in prison for the assembly of a mass transport. But the military mind interpreted this special favor as a special precaution, and thus the officer spoke to the sergeant with dramatic accentuation: "Now you take that fellow and deliver him to the commander at Fort Oglethorpe and, if you can't deliver him, deliver his body" (great accent on "body"!). Having spoken thus, he opened a drawer and handed the sergeant a pair of handcuffs, new and shiny.

The sergeant took me to his barracks where we were joined by a private. While I sat on a bunk and watched their antics the sergeant took his huge gun, loaded it, and put it into his belt. Then he took a small revolver, loaded it, and put it into his pocket. Another pocket he filled with a handful of extra cartridges. The private brought his rifle and loaded it with a frame, and then he loaded a revolver, put it into his pocket, and added a few frames of cartridges. After these preparations for a major battle the two took me between them and we marched to the ferry. Before we boarded I was handcuffed. Arriving in New York we traveled on the elevated to about Thirtieth Street, and then the pleasantest part came. On a Saturday afternoon, between five and six, I marched handcuffed between two heavily armed soldiers through the crowded city to Pennsylvania Station. The private, who marched slightly behind me, held his rifle ready for action at all times.

As a matter of fact, we were now four. Already on the ferry we had been joined by a nice-looking young girl in military uniform. It turned out that she was in charge of the transport and had to take us to Pennsylvania Station, buy the tickets, and see to it that we got under way. While we were marching through the streets she kept at a little distance but joined us at the station. Here she found out that the train would not leave until eleven o'clock. I was standing with my guards in the main hall, stared at by the public. Since I had had no food since five in the morning, I asked the girl to give me something to eat. She agreed, and we marched to a small eating place on Thirty-third Street. Before a staring crowd, the sergeant took off my handcuffs before we entered the place. If a single hysterical woman had shouted, "German spy!" I wonder what would have happened. But the crowd was silent and dispersed after the restaurant owner pulled the shades behind our table.

During dinner I began to talk to the girl soldier and explained to her what had happened and how ridiculous it was to handcuff a harmless scholar who was to be interned for no other reason than the place of his birth. The girl was sensible, and when we left the place she ordered the soldiers to refrain from handcuffing me. The sergeant, who had already seen service in France and was not afraid of an unarmed professor, agreed, but the private did not trust me and kept his rifle ready. Then we saw the young girl home rather peacefully. I am sorry that I never learned her name—she was Canadian—for I should have loved to send her flowers after the war. Toward midnight we departed.

When we had passed through New Haven, my wife had handed me twenty dollars, which she had borrowed from a friend. I was able, therefore, to take my guards to the diner next morning, the first experience in a diner for both of them, and after they had finished a stack of hot cakes things looked brighter. The sergeant put away his gun and told me of his experiences in France. "Next time," he said, "we shall fight with the Germans against the French, who do nothing but cheat and rob the American soldiers." But the private did not like this fraternizing. He still held his rifle in his hands, and when I went to the toilet he put his foot in the door and gripped his rifle tighter. The other passengers looked on in amazement but were decent and tactful.

Late in the night we arrived in Chattanooga and drove in a buggy to Fort Oglethorpe. Here I was handed over to the guard, and my sergeant took friendly leave. But one more shock was in store. I was not brought into the camp but was locked up in a cage in the guardhouse. Fortunately this turned out to be only for the rest of the night. The next morning a huge transport of "prisoners of war" arrived from the Midwest, and with these fellow victims of hysteria and poor organization I marched into the stockade while the prisoners already there stood at the inner barbed wire and sang, *"Schon wieder eine Seele vom Alkohol geret-tet-tet"* ("Again a soul saved from alcohol").

The camp, erected in a completely bare hot plain, was not a very cheerful sight. It was surrounded by a high barbed-wire fence interspersed with towers upon which machine guns were mounted and from which powerful searchlights worked at night. A strip of no man's land separated the outer fence from an inner one, and touching the inner fence meant being shot at by the guards. A very strange feature in the camp, which housed toward the end of my stay four to five thousand prisoners, was the existence of a small extra camp within the main camp where prisoners of higher social standing, about one hundred of them, were separated from the rest. These special prisoners were permitted to buy their own food; to subdivide their barracks into small cabins, thus achieving a kind of privacy; and to engage other prisoners for kitchen work and cleaning. The other prisoners called this the millionaire's camp and hated such a "capitalistic institution." It was even rumored that the inmates had bacon and eggs for breakfast! Actually the millionaires spent twenty dollars a month on their food and service. The obvious reason for this establishment was not to make social distinctions but to deprive the mass of the internees of possible leaders in case of trouble. But the effect was a very pleasant one for those concerned. I soon found out that the Swiss embassy would furnish money to those properly qualified but without funds, and after application I received an allowance of thirty-five dollars monthly, which qualified me as a millionaire.

If it had not been for the barbed wire and the separation from my family, life in camp might have been called an extremely interesting experience. Some of my friends who had lived formerly only among their own set claimed that it was the most interesting time of their lives. The prisoners had laid out some football and volleyball fields, and many hours a day were spent in games. During the summer the Department of Justice did us the favor of interning the entire army band from the German colony of Tsingtao.

They brought their instruments and scores, and the energetic band-master Witte, a very good musician, increased his band with amateurs into a full-fledged symphony orchestra. I was able to borrow a violin and happily spent hours each day at rehearsals. Later the two conductors Karl Muck and Ernst Kunwald consented to conduct some concerts. Thus I had the wonderful experience, otherwise unattainable by an amateur, of playing the *Eroica* under Muck's baton. A huge hall, erected by the Y.M.C.A., was filled with three thousand men, many of them in the most unbelievable garb, many of them tough and untractable fellows. When Muck raised his baton one could have heard a mouse running. The whole performance was unforgettable. I do not think that a symphony ever created a more profound impression than this upon thousands who had probably never before heard classical music. The American officers who attended said it was the greatest revelation they had experienced. I still have the score my friend Muck wrote out for me, in notes that look like engraving, because I could not read the rough handwriting of the military band's music sheets.

Another remarkable institution run by the prisoners was the camp university. A young high school teacher who had fought in France and had escaped from the horrors of a French prison camp, only to be interned again when America entered the war, built up what amounted to a small university. Teachers for practically everything could be found among the internees. There were elementary classes for those less educated in English, commercial letter-writing, bookkeeping, shorthand, and similar subjects. In great favor were the language courses, especially Spanish and Russian, given mostly by businessmen. But one could also study Hebrew and Swahili with a former missionary to Africa, Sanskrit and Hindu with a professor of Indology, or Chinese and Japanese with an engineer who had acquired these difficult languages and scripts as a hobby. There were splendid courses in physics given by a prominent physicist, the great radio specialist Zenneck; chemistry by industrial chemists; various engineering subjects by specialists in the field; European and American history by historians. I had the pleasure of giving a class in biology attended by four hundred men from all walks of life. There were, of course, no books available since a military edict forbade the receiving of books except if sent directly from the publishers, and we had no money to buy books from publishers. But the relief committee in New York at least sent language textbooks. In the other fields we had to rely upon our memories. I must say that I never before or afterward had a more attentive and grateful audience, and this made teaching a real pleasure. For my own edification I studied Spanish and Chinese and enjoyed them thoroughly.

Thus time passed with sport, study, music, and many good conversations with intelligent and highly educated people. It was possible to build a little furniture for one's cabin with scraps left over from the construction of the barracks, nails collected from the ground, and tools borrowed from some happy owners. Some of us tended little gardens and grew flowers and salad greens; others built ship models or carved in wood or made some kind of gadget; others drew, painted, or wrote. A group of young artists started a literary magazine, edited by the well-known German novelist Hanns Heinz Ewers and a young Bohemian writer. A painter of considerable talent, which he otherwise unfortunately wasted, made woodcuts for the magazine, cutting them with a pocket knife in cigar-box wood. A chemist with an artistic vein produced linoleum cuts. Many of us contributed articles and poetry. The printing was done by a merchant marine wireless operator with a small hand press formerly used for printing menus aboard some steamer. Where the miserable paper came from I do not remember. Copy had to be handed to the censor, who usually passed it. A favorite game was to inject some political joke into a poem in such a form that the censor did not understand it and passed it. I have presented a copy of this rare magazine to the Hoover War Library in Stanford University.

Life in the camp was not always so idyllic. A constant thorn in our flesh was the censor, one of the ugliest fellows I have ever met. A teacher of German in some college, dry and pedantic to the bone, this man considered his office a means of inflicting mental torture on the prisoners. There was, of course, no sense in censoring letters to and from relatives living in the United States. Since we were permitted to have newspapers we learned of everything that was happening. But the censor made a point of cutting parts out of both incoming and outgoing mail, and he left letters in his office for weeks before delivering them. Even in urgent cases, like sickness in the family, he told inquirers he had no letter when he was actually holding one for belated delivery. This man was unanimously hated, and everybody was glad when it became known that about a year after the peace of Versailles he was recognized by some sailors walking through the city of Hamburg and badly beaten up.

A bad time came when the terrible epidemic of Spanish influenza paid a visit to the camp. Almost half of the internees fell sick. The authorities did everything in their power, but the hospital facilities were not prepared for such an onrush. The number of fatal cases was fortunately low. When I caught the flu, knowing of the hospital conditions, I preferred to cure myself in my little cubicle. As this was not permitted I had to get up every morning and stand in line for the roll call. Afterward I could quietly nurse my fever for twenty-four hours without being noticed.

But the worst came later. For weeks and weeks I did not receive any news from my wife and children, and I knew from the papers that the epidemic was especially bad in New Haven. The censor was adamant in not permitting me to make any inquiries beyond the permissible number of letters. Finally I went to the camp chaplain, an exceedingly fine gentleman, who was ready to forget about the strict rules and send a private telegram to New Haven. The next day he told me that he had received a reassuring answer. Only much later I learned what had happened. My wife and little boy Hans had both been dangerously stricken and taken to a hospital, while my little girl Ruth escaped and was taken into the home of one of the most prominent New England families, the Woolseys, an act of noble-mindedness I shall never forget. In the hospital, however, the war fever was running so high that my wife could not take the risk of writing to an interned husband. Only after her return home with Hans, who had been in serious danger, did she dare write to me again.

Needless to say, all this time I and many others tried to be released, for our internment was completely unwarranted and contrary to the solemn promises made by President Wilson. But the Department of Justice politely replied, "Your being at large would be incompatible with the best interests of the United States." The interests of Germans in the United States were in the hands of the Swiss legation, and we asked them to interfere in our favor. One day the chargé d'affaires appeared in the camp to hear our complaints. He barely escaped being beaten up when he told us that he was going to do nothing whatsoever. We certainly were angered by his cynical remarks and his rude manners. But, after all, what could a second-rate Swiss diplomat do when the Department of Justice preferred to be deaf? Soon afterward the Swedish chargé appeared to take care of the Austrian internees. He was able to do just as little, but the aristocratic and charming Swedish baron said this in such a way that everybody liked him nevertheless.

Slowly the extremely hot summer passed. The days were sometimes unbearable with an intense heat against which there was no protection, so that we looked forward to the night when it was possible to walk along the only path in our camp, humorously called the *Chemin des Dames*. Autumn approached, and the newspapers began to bring stories of revolution in Germany. A cafe society litterateur was said to have deposed the king of Bavaria without a single officer's drawing a sword in defense. All this was true, but behind the barbed wire we did not believe a word. We had a religious belief in Germany, and if any seer had told us what would become of Germany fifteen years later he would have been burned at the stake. Most rabid were the sea captains. Anybody saying in their presence that there might be something behind this news after all exposed himself to danger. Excitement was running high, changing from depression to defiance.

Then like a thunderbolt came Ludendorff's request for an armistice. When the Allies' conditions were published we laughed at the idea that they could be accepted. During the night the answer had to come, and if Germany accepted the sirens in all the factories were to whistle the death knell of Imperial Germany. Sleepless we lay in our bunks, still hoping that the night would pass quietly. Then suddenly the whistles began screaming. Afterward there was deep silence. Then suppressed sobs were heard from different corners of the huge barracks. Silence again. A world had broken down for every German. Had I known what was in store for me fifteen years later I would have had reasons to rejoice. But I was, and had every reason to be, a patriot who believed in Germany and who would have declined to accept as even the remotest possibility that the Germans, or at least a majority of the Germans, could turn one day into the scum of humanity under the leadership of a mad monster and his hand-picked gang of criminals.

But at that time only one idea was in everybody's mind: to get out from behind the barbed wire. Unfortunately it took up to a year before the last prisoner was dismissed. I had better luck. Immediately after the armistice I wrote to the Department of Justice that I did not think there was any sense in continuing my unjustified internment. It was a great moment when a favorable reply came. I hoped to be back with my family at Christmas, but the formalities dragged on so that I could leave only the day after Christmas. And the release brought one last humiliation. I was brought to the station in a military truck escorted by armed soldiers. While we were waiting for the train to arrive the soldiers, arms ready for shooting, surrounded me, and I heard a man nearby saying to his wife, "A spy to be shot." Only when the train arrived was I left alone. But it took a long time before I could get rid of the prisoner's phobia. When a pleasant lady sitting next to me in the train started a conversation I did not answer for fear she might discover where I came from.

I arrived in New York on a Saturday morning and went to see the agent of the Department of Justice to whom I was to report. He told me my papers had not yet arrived from Washington and that I would have to stay in New York over the week end. Now I lost my temper. A few miles away my family waited for me in New Haven. I told the agent that it was bad enough that a harmless scholar who had quietly attended to his research work as an involuntary guest of a country where he had been stranded against his will was being treated like a criminal. But now when I was finally released I wanted to go home and not wait for the bureaucrats. It was his duty to call Washington and clear things up. The agent got angry in his turn, told me that he did not think it was his place to telephone Washington, and left slamming the door. But after half an hour I was called again. He had, after all, called Washington, and he told me to go home and return after the week end.

When I returned on Monday I was disgusted to learn that my release was on parole and that I had to find a citizen of good standing who would put up two thousand dollars for me. Not knowing how to find such a man, I went to see my colleagues at Columbia University, who felt rather ashamed when I told them my story. Professor Morgan, the great biologist, immediately told me not to worry, went straight downtown with me, and, after we had fortified ourselves with a glass of beer (my first in eight months), he deposited the required sum. Only three months later was I actually released and the money returned.

The next half year was not pleasant. I tried to get passage back to Germany but, with the peace not yet signed, was refused permission to leave. I could not ask to be given facilities for work in the university after all that had happened. In addition I had no money except what little was given by the Swiss legation, and that might stop any day in view of conditions in Germany. Nor was there the possibility of a job. I kept away from friends in order to save them embarrassment.

One little anecdote is worth recording because it shows how a man may get innocently into trouble in excited times. It turned out that my manuscripts had been taken away from the laboratory by the Secret Service. Obviously they could not do much with records of genetical experiments, and they left everything with the police. The papers had been kept in a little strongbox together with a few valuables. When I went to the police station to receive them it turned out that the manuscripts were intact, but that someone had appropriated a bag of pearls that I myself had fished for in Japan. When I was ready to leave with my box, the police officer opened a drawer, took out the envelope of an old letter addressed to me, and asked, "It this yours?"

"Yes, it is."

Then he turned it over, pointed to pencil scribblings on the back, and asked, "Did you write this?" It was my handwriting. "Is this not a code? It looks like a code." I stared at the thing, and fortunately the origin of the scribblings came back to my memory. Four years before I had had a literary discussion with my friend E. M. East at Harvard University. We were discussing Edgar Allan Poe, and this led East to enlarge upon Poe's interest in code deciphering. This again led us to the topic of codes, and I told him that as high school boys we had used a code taken from one of Jules Verne's novels to communicate with each other in class. I took out of my pocket a letter I happened to be carrying and wrote on the back of the envelope "Edward East" and the translation in the childish code. Later I told East that as a boy I had enjoyed learning strange scripts like hieroglyphics and runes. One of them was the old script of the Shetland Islands, called ogam, and on the same envelope I drew an old Nordic tombstone with the inscription "Edward East" in ogam characters. This letter happened to be among some old letters in my box. Fortunately the war was over, and the police officer smiled at my explanation—of which he certainly did not believe a word.

The winter dragged on, and I had not enough work to fill the long days. I wasted my time making longhand copies of four books that I had written and intended to publish in Germany. Actually

I had ready for publication what amounted to a small library: a big monograph on my work on intersexuality; a theoretical book, *The Quantitative Basis of Heredity and Evolution;* a comprehensive book on the mechanism and physiology of sex determination; a popular science book, *Ascaris: An Introduction to the Science of Life for Everybody;* and a small book on Mendelism for students of agriculture. But when all the copies had been made I was too restless to start something new.

Spring came, and nothing happened. One day I learned from the always helpful relief committee in New York that a transport was being prepared to take thousands of interned sailors and other "prisoners" from Fort Oglethorpe back to Germany. Since I did not have the money for the outrageous passage rates prevailing at that time, I applied for permission for me and my family to join this transport of prisoners of war, and my request was granted. The transport was to sail from Charleston, South Carolina, in July. We therefore began to sell or give away unnecessary things and to buy clothing and nonperishable food in anticipation of the conditions awaiting us in Germany. Finally the day came to leave the charming town of New Haven, our simple small apartment at 610 Orange Street, and the many dear friends who had stood by us in hard times, actually to the point of endangering themselves. We shall never forget what these real Americans did in a time when hysteria and mob spirit spread a smoke screen over all American ideals.

Up to the last minute little difficulties furnished excitement. On our way to Charleston with innumerable pieces of luggage we stopped for a few hours in New York. About an hour before the train was to leave from Pennsylvania Station it flashed through my mind that it might be safer to check to see if my priceless baggage—hams and lard and everything—had been transferred from Grand Central Station. The baggage had not arrived. I raced in a taxi to Grand Central where I learned that a porters' strike was on. All incoming baggage had been dumped into a huge hall where it was left at anybody's mercy in an indescribable chaos of thousands of trunks. I must have reckoned with such a thing in my subconscious, because before leaving New Haven I had painted in white paint upon three sides of each trunk the Chinese characters for "East" and "West" in huge script. This saved the hour. Though my dozen or so trunks were scattered over the entire immense hall I was able to pick them out in a short time and collected them all in one spot. Near the station strikebreakers with horse carts were lingering, and I got hold of an evil-looking fellow with a ramshackle cart and a bony horse. With his not very powerful assistance I hoisted the heavy trunks upon the cart and seated myself on top. Then we drove to Pennsylvania Station and reached it in time.

When we arrived in Charleston we received the unpleasant news that our sailing had been postponed a week. The hotel was expensive, and our purse consumptive. The heat was the worst I had experienced in all my travelings. By chance, though, we found a delightful boardinghouse in the nearby Isle of Palms and spent the last week near and in the grandiose breakers of the Atlantic in a peaceful spot—our last rest in peace and plenty for a long time to come.

Finally an old Austrian liner, now a United States army transport, the *Martha Washington,* arrived. As we entered the pier we became voluntary prisoners of war. Aboard we found Commodore Ruser, former commander of the *Vaterland-Leviathan,* busy preparing accommodations for the prisoners. In one of the holds with room for four to five hundred men quarters were established for the ship's officers and other quiet elements, far away from the space allotted to the anarchist I.W.W. group, which had been a rather desperate group in the internment camp. These men had practically been deported, and they did not hide their intention of joining the Spartacist revolution in Germany at once. Their harsh treatment in the special stockade in the camp had made the men still tougher, and thus there was always trouble in their quarters, which were guarded by marines.

While the men were treated like prisoners on a transport, the women and children had fine staterooms on the upper deck and dined in state in the first-class dining room with the officers. Most of the sailors were enlisted college boys, probably homesick for their own families, and the children had a grand time with them. A rather amusing situation arose daily when we filed past the windows of the dining room on our way to receive our rations and saw our families enjoying a well-served meal while we were drenched by the waves rolling over the gangway on which we lined up. But I also had my comfort when after ladling out my tin cup with good

183

nourishing food I sat on a coil of rope and lighted one of the delicious Havana cigars with which the untiring director of the relief committee, Mr. Boschwitz, had presented me.

After twelve days we landed in Rotterdam. We were now under guard by Dutch soldiers and were taken care of by the Red Cross. We were herded into a big warehouse, which nobody could leave— the Dutch did not want anybody to stay in Holland where things were scarce—and sitting on our suitcases we lunched on milk and sandwiches. Looking out toward the pier I saw the sailors unloading our baggage: trunks were simply thrown overboard to the pier. Half of my trunks were broken but kept miraculously together until I was able later to tie them with ropes. Soon we were entrained and rolled through the fertile plains of Holland. In Utrecht the train was received with music and flags, and coffee and cake—the last for a long time to come—were distributed. Toward evening we arrived at the frontier city of Wesel. We were again free men on German soil.

9: *GERMANY AFTER THE WAR*

For years we had anticipated this great moment. Now that it arrived we were deeply disillusioned. We were prepared to find conditions bad in a Germany beaten to the dust. We had not, however, imagined that such a complete disorganization would be possible. The streets were filthy, the shop windows empty; nothing was for sale in the food stores. Service in the hotel, if any, was sullen. Breakfast consisted of ersatz coffee (toasted barley) with saccharin. Since we did not yet have any bread cards there was nothing for us to eat. At the station nobody knew when a train was to leave or if one was to leave at all. We looked for our precious baggage and found it strewn over the tracks, but at least it was there and had not yet been pilfered, which we later learned amounted to a miracle. Probably the population did not expect prisoners of war to return with hams and sides of bacon. Finally word went around that a certain baggage car was to go to Berlin—sooner or later—so we rolled the car to a suitable place and all helped load it. I certainly got my exercise that morning on an empty stomach.

Since I had learned from the papers that there was still street fighting in Berlin, I decided to take my family first to my home town of Frankfurt and then explore Berlin alone. Finally the good news came that a train would be put together to take everybody east. But what a sad sight this train was to a German accustomed to cleanliness and efficiency: filthy, antediluvian fourth-class cars, with every piece of metal, leather, and cloth removed, leaking roofs and squeaking axles, moving at the speed of a snail. It was a typical sign of the material and moral breakdown. At noon we stopped at Hagen and were treated to soup from a military kitchen. Here I learned that a regular train to Frankfurt was soon to pass, and we succeeded in boarding it. Sitting on our suitcases in the overcrowded train we continued our journey, listening to the talk of the passengers, which was anything but cheerful.

The next day I proceeded alone to Berlin. To my great surprise I found our house intact in spite of the fact that it had been unguarded during the revolution. Life in Berlin went on though there was still some fighting in the workingmen's quarters. I wired my family to come up, and normal life began again—or what passed for normal in those days of misery. Though almost a year had passed since the armistice, Germany was still blockaded and starving. For us the beginning was difficult. Nobody could live upon the official rations. But in the course of years of starvation everybody had made some connections with farmers or underground dealers and was able to supplement his meager fare somehow. We were completely ignorant of these things and had to live upon our rations. Thus we had to think of helping ourselves.

We bought a couple of goats, which we kept in the basement until I built a stable in the backyard. My wife became an expert milker and devoted much time and energy to taking care of this source of strength for our children. Occasionally we even had a little milk for the neighbors' children. Soon chickens followed the goats, but from then on I had to sleep with a gun at my bedside, for edible animals, including dogs, were freebooty to nightly pilferers. Only slowly did a few edibles of unbelievably poor quality appear in the markets. Bread was available, but the black sticky substance called bread was hard on the system and upset my digestion for years to come.

I shall never forget the day when word went round our suburb that for the first time in years fish could be bought in open market. The housewives rushed to the market and each triumphantly brought home a cod. When it was cooked the whole house smelled of ammonia, for the fish was half rotten, but we all ate it. After this meal one of our neighbor's undernourished children, a little boy who had known only war and starvation in his short life, said, "I never thought that the world could be as beautiful as that."

Though peace had been concluded, this condition lasted for four more years. All this time the first thing in everyone's mind was food. When the telephone rang, it was as often as not a friend who had found out that in some place one could get half a pound of margarine or sausage, or flour without a card, or who had received an underground shipment from somewhere and let us have a share. For years I took a knapsack to work in case I should hear of some source of victuals, which I would tap without delay. Occasionally the fat butcher's wife—*she* had meat—called up to say that we might have a leg of lamb. It was actually a leg of old goat and smelled like old goat, but we ate it as mutton. Another delicatessen

186

store suddenly sold sliced smoked beef. It was horse, and we knew it, but we ate it as a delicacy.

Nevertheless, there were moments of happiness unknown to the well-fed citizen. There was a package sent by American friends containing ham, cocoa, bacon, sugar, and similar unheard-of delicacies. But the real laurel belongs to my Russian colleagues. One day in 1921 they sent what was called in an accompanying letter "vitamin-rich caviar," and we gorged ourselves with this millionaire's dish. There was an extra joke to this. The parcel contained two identical five-pound tins, and since the first contained caviar we assumed the second to be the same. For a long time we kept it carefully in the icebox, waiting to open it for some festive occasion. When we finally opened it we found that it contained butter, completely rotted into a smelly, black substance.

Bad as was the lack of proper food, of soap, of good clothing material, of metal and leather, of efficient transportation, and a thousand other comforts, the most oppressive feature was the psychic condition of my fellow countrymen after all their sufferings. The most widespread characteristic was plain and simple *Futterneid* ("food envy"). A fairly well-dressed man was insulted wherever he went as *"Schieber"* (profiteer). People who had the bad luck to grow fat had a hard time. Riders on horseback were stoned. Bitter envy and hate separated people, and the workingmen were rabid in their feelings against the white-collar men, considered indiscriminately as profiteers.

One of the results of this moral breakdown, based after all on the lack of everyday necessities, was the new rise of anti-Semitism. It started with the uprooted young men who could not fit themselves into society any longer and banded together into so-called free corps, organizations of ruffians who, hiding their toughness behind ultranationalistic phrases, fought, whenever there was an opportunity, in the Baltic states, in Upper Silesia, in Saxony. They introduced the swastika as their symbol and anti-Semitism as their major creed. Many of the later Nazi leaders hailed from these circles.

Unfortunately, the agrarians and *Junker* and many former army officers, grumbling under the loss of caste, also joined the chorus. They would not recognize their own guilt for the breakdown, and they needed a scapegoat. Led by the already mentally unbalanced General Ludendorff and his rabid wife Mathilde, they made the Jews the always available scapegoat. Not the army but the Jews had lost the war; not the exasperated and starved workingmen and soldiers but the Jews had made the revolution. It is now history how this movement culminated in the murder of the foreign minister Rathenau by the lowest type of uprooted youngsters and how the circles that stood behind it glorified the deed. (One of the participants was later to be sent to San Francisco as Hitler's consul general!) It is also history how an unknown corporal wrested the leadership of this movement from the conceited general and, using ultranationalism and anti-Semitism as battering rams, mustered all the disillusioned toughs in the country under his ugly banner and rose to the position of dictator.

But let me return to the summer of 1919 when I set foot on my native soil after five and one-half years of absence. When I had left the happy and powerful German empire, I had planned to return in less than a year to a newly erected research laboratory, the best of its kind in the world, provided with ample means and all the requisites for successful work. In spite of the war the laboratory had been built and my staff had started work, on my written instructions, with the material I had sent back from Japan. Of course I was impatient to see the laboratory, which I knew only from the original plans. I had already heard that the Kaiser's favorite, the tyrannical court architect Ihne, had changed our plans to suit his so-called architecture and had produced an example of very poor taste.

The first impression was, indeed, anything but pleasant. Opposite the laboratory building had been established a military motor park filled with the most unbelievable wrecks of cars and a crowd of undisciplined soldiers who looked to me more dangerous than the dreaded Spartacists. The soldiers occupied some rooms on the first floor of the laboratory and filled the whole building with noise and evil smells. Mounting the staircases one encountered a machine gun at each window, protecting the auto park from Spartacist attack—though I cannot imagine what the revolutionaries could have done with those cars.

In my department I found first that all my ducks, which I had brought from Munich after years of breeding experiments, were gone. For some time they had been saved by a poster: "Experimental animals inoculated with dangerous germs." But when food became unavailable they had finally disappeared into the frying pan. No better was the condition of my other material. My assistant, J. Seiler, had carried on as long as he could, but when conditions became impossible he had returned to Switzerland. My rooms were there as planned, but the purchasing of equipment had been postponed until my return, and now instruments and equipment were practically unavailable. Thus the beginnings were difficult. But my colleagues helped out with this or that, and slowly the work got under way. My friend Ishikawa in Tokyo immediately sent replacements for some of the lost breeding stocks, and the work was gradually built up. The Kaiser Wilhelm Society, which financed the institute, was losing its endowment because of inflation, and some of the men who had supported the society when the sun of imperial grace shone upon them left the sinking ship. But the immense energy of Adolf von Harnack and the fervor of the republican government to promote science even in times of need helped to keep the society and the laboratories above water and to lead them, later on, to a new flowering.

So life went on, and we almost forgot how it felt to lead a normal existence in a happy country. The majority of Germans were captives of the low rate of exchange and could not leave the confines of their prison. Foreigners began to come again, many of them Americans, who seemed to be all millionaires and were treated like kings. Many of the foreign visitors came on charitable business, especially the American Quakers, who did wonderful work among the undernourished children. But the speculators came also, and many a man I knew as rather mediocre became fabulously rich by working with foreign speculators.

In one respect I was better off than my countrymen. The prison doors opened for me repeatedly when invitations to lecture abroad took me across the frontier. I was one of the first German scholars invited to England, in 1923, and thus had the chance to help repair the broken threads of scientific solidarity. I went first to Liverpool to visit with Professor Dakin, who had translated my recent book on sex determination and who became a lifelong friend. Afterward I lectured at Oxford, Cambridge, and Edinburgh. I was received everywhere with courtesy and was able to renew old acquaintances and make new friends. A meeting of the Genetics Society was convoked at Tring, the country seat of Lord Rothschild, to hear me present a paper on my recent work. At the buffet lunch before the meeting, champagne and other delicacies were served. A very noble-looking butler offered me some whiskey and, when I declined, said in a grand style, "Sir, think it over; you have never tasted such a whiskey, and you will never taste such again."

As I had not been in England before I greatly enjoyed my first acquaintance with the charming customs of the modern Middle Ages in the amazing university towns of Oxford and Cambridge. Another new experience was the Englishman's training to live in cold houses, where even the baby was washed in an ice-cold room and survived. In all my experiences, including skiing in the high mountains, I was never so miserably cold as in those unheated houses of England in late winter. I remember being the guest of a very rich shipowner in Liverpool. When I entered his house I saw the radiators of a central heating system and looked forward to my first warm room. But it remained ice cold, and the beds felt like iceboxes. The lady of the house, my charming hostess, said, "We had such a warm winter this year that we did not even need to start the central heating."

My visit in Liverpool led to a unique experience that is worth remembering. Young Marco Pallis (later to become known as a mountaineer and explorer) was a student and collaborator of Arnold Dolmetsch, the remarkable Swiss-Englishman who was prominent in reawakening the interest in old music. He was not only a great expert in the understanding and analysis of this music but in addition an expert builder of all the instruments and a fine performer on them, as were his wife and son. Pallis gave me enthusiastic descriptions of this family and told me that I must meet them. He gave me a letter of introduction, but in the rush of meeting with innumerable interesting people I had completely forgotten about the letter in my pocket.

One day I was driving with relatives through the English countryside when I noticed that we were entering the little town of Haslemere. I suddenly remembered that this was where Dolmetsch lived, and fortunately I had the letter in my pocket. I went to see him and was most charmingly received. For hours Dolmetsch and his family performed for me, playing their favorites and also allowing me to choose.

The same year brought an invitation to Norway and Sweden, and the nice Scandinavians extended their invitation to my wife. We went by ferry from Sassnitz to Trelleborg, a four-hour trip, during a terrific storm. In all my travelings over the seven seas I have never been so seasick. I was actually in the condition described by the old joke, "afraid the boat would not sink." In

Lund, our first stop, we were regally treated by the great geneticist Nilsson-Ehle, an old friend of mine. (He unfortunately later isolated himself by outspoken Nazi sympathies. I know, however, that this was nothing but a misguided love for the old German culture and complete political naïveté.) As a matter of fact we were so weakened by the lean German diet that the rich meals and the huge quantities of liquor we were served did not agree with us. In Stockholm the feasting continued, and although we enjoyed the beautiful town and our indescribably hospitable hosts, the Bonniers, we were glad to learn that our next hosts in Oslo, O. L. and Tove Mohr, were teetotalers.

Another trip took us to Holland. The Dutch students had and may still have an organization completely run by the students themselves. They arranged for lectures by foreign scientists who traveled as guests of the students from university to university all over the country, which harbored within its small area four famous universities and one agricultural school of university standing. Again we enjoyed ourselves immensely and met with the most charming hospitality.

Strange situations occurred occasionally as a result of the way the students handled the arrangements. As our German money was worthless, and foreign exchange not available in Germany, we were penniless as soon as we passed the frontier. At the station we were met by a student delegation that took care of us until we left at the same station. This meant that whenever we went for a meal a student kept us company and paid the bill, sometimes without participating in the meal. When we left our hotel a student came to pay the bill. But it happened that the inexperienced young man forgot about tips, which in Holland were larger and more eagerly solicited than in any other European country. Our exit between the rows of waiters, chambermaids, and porters, who certainly did not hide their feelings, was almost like running the gantlet.

In Amsterdam I had to lecture under the hardest conditions I remember. The lecture was scheduled for eight o'clock, and at six we were taken to dinner by Professor Stomps to one of the famous places in town. After an hour new hors d'œuvres were still being served, followed by many delicious courses. Each dish was accompanied by the proper wine, ending with champagne and French brandy. The clock struck eight o'clock while the last drop was being swallowed, and I was rushed to a car and raced to the audi-

191

torium. When I reached the desk and looked over the large hall filled with students everything turned around me, and my brain was completely empty. Looking down I saw a telegram on my desk. The great Dutch botanist Hugo de Vries, living in retirement in his advanced age, welcomed me to his old lecture hall. This charming gesture helped me to recover my senses and to start with the lecture. But the greatest event in Amsterdam was certainly my first acquaintance with the Rijks Museum and its glorious Rembrandts and Halses.

The students of Switzerland ran an institution similar to that of their Dutch comrades, and an invitation brought me to some of the Swiss universities. Again I experienced the feeling of having left a prison when I crossed the border from unhappy, hungry, neglected Germany into the plenty of Switzerland with her clean whitewashed homes and prosperous-looking, proud, and aggressive citizens. There was no oil for paint in Germany, and all the houses looked filthy and dilapidated; a few steps beyond the border every house was spick and span. There were no metals in Germany, and copper and brass had disappeared from public sight. In Switzerland, however, the doorknobs sparkled like gold, and the railway cars had real brass handles. There was no material in Germany to replace the few completely worn-out railway cars that the victors had not carried away, and traveling meant uncomfortable, unclean, and ramshackle old-fashioned cars. Here brandnew, comfortable trains were running with dining cars that served real coffee or chocolate and fresh white bread. The stores contained good merchandise, and one could buy what one wanted. Again I had a fine and interesting time as always before and always afterward in my numerous visits to this remarkable country. A rather strange experience was a lecture in Basel which took place in the same medieval hall in which the Council of Basel had met about five hundred years before. The spirits of the cardinals, bishops, and princes hovering around the place must have wondered not only at the devilish contraption of a lantern, but also at the heresies a scientist could pronounce in that godly town without being burned at the stake.

Another lecture trip took me to Czechoslovakia, the newly founded state which, at that time, had not yet outgrown the travail of its origin. The formalities at the frontier were exceedingly severe as the Czechs hated everything German most heartily. In Prague I arrived at a station named after the liberator Woodrow

Wilson. The town was as beautiful as ever in its charming baroque setting. But I still felt everywhere the war psychology. The considerable German element in the city lived completely separated from the Czechs. Street fights and broken windows were a daily occurrence. The German and the Czech professors did not talk to one another, and, since I was a guest of the German group, I could not greet my Czech colleagues and none of them could attend my lectures. The general picture I received of this country then was very distressing, but when I returned later the antagonism had become much milder and would have eventually disappeared if it had not been kept aflame from the outside.

The only countries accessible to a German traveling with his own money were those with a still more broken-down currency like Austria and for some time Yugoslavia. Special arrangements with these countries permitted a German traveler to buy a certain amount of their exchange, and thus vacation trips took us to these countries, in winter for skiing, in fall or spring toward the warm southern sun.

In unhappy Austria one could study the ravages of inflation outside one's own den. Vienna was a pale shadow of its former glory. The misery and gloom of this happy-go-lucky city were appalling. Here had lived the most cultured aristocracy, the same families whose ancestors had first played Beethoven's quartets. Here the music-, art-, and literature-loving bourgeoisie, considerably mixed with Jewish blood, had made Vienna one of the most cultured and gayest towns of the world, much more charming than its western rival Paris. Now everybody was impoverished and, though keeping up appearances, unable to enjoy life. The political and social hatreds were even worse than in Germany, though a great deal of the natural, good-natured Viennese *laisser-aller* hid the underlying sadness.

Outside of Vienna, which had been deprived of its hinterland by the breaking up of the empire, conditions were better. In the mountain resorts of Tyrol, in the charming episcopal city of Salzburg, in the small cities along the Danube, people actually lived better than in Germany. Visiting with my friend Hans Kupelwieser on his beautiful estate in lower Austria, I could observe the condition of a land owner who was left with a chateau and an immense hunting estate staffed with deer and chamois, but who had no money to run the property. On one of these visits I joined him on a trip to Mondsee in the Salzburg Alps where he

193

was to buy for the Kaiser Wilhelm Gesellschaft a site for a fresh-water biological station. I had just received a good fee for a new edition of my genetics textbook, and I so liked the charming lake at the foot of a high mountain that I bought a piece of land adjacent to the future station grounds and ordered to be built on it a mountain lodge for which I paid in advance. I mention this little incident as an apt illustration of conditions in inflation times. When after a few months the lodge should have been finished and nothing had yet been heard from the lumber company in charge of the building, I inquired and found out that the company had gone into bankruptcy. But I was assured that my money would be returned, and it was, after some months. Meanwhile, however, inflation had progressed, and the sum that had purchased a summer home now purchased exactly one loaf of bread.

But this anticipates the rolling wave of inflation that dragged first Austria and, a little later, Germany downhill. The year 1923 was the craziest I have lived through. At the time Poincaré started his occupation of the Ruhr, the German mark (equal to about twenty-five cents in gold) had kept for some time a level of depreciation of about twelve hundred marks to the dollar. Now the downward slide began gathering more and more momentum until in the fall of 1923 the lowest level was hit—4,000,000,000,000 marks to the dollar! Nobody knows whether the German government, at that time a highly responsible democratic government, helped this decline in order to lead the Allied greed and spite *ad absurdum* or whether they actually were unable to stem the tide. The value of the money decreased daily by leaps and bounds, and the printing press could hardly follow, turning out today ten-thousand-mark bills representing the value of a dime and tomorrow million-mark bills with the same purchasing power. Salaries had to be increased every few days and became worthless with increasing ciphers. Our whole life became a crazy merry-go-round. I remember seeing, before the beginning of this time, a piece of furniture I liked very much, but the price of 1,200 marks was too high for me. Some time after the tumble started I came to the same store and found that the piece was still there but now cost 15,000 marks. Now it was really cheap and I could buy it!

When the dollar par of the mark was in the millions, and doubled almost daily, salaries were paid out twice a week. Since I was in the civil service as director of our laboratory I had to travel downtown twice a week on the overcrowded, neglected, and filthy subway and elevated cars, a briefcase in my hand and a knapsack on my back. At the payroll office I stood in line for a long time until a huge pile of paper bills in denominations of millions and billions was shoved over the counter. I packed the bills into my briefcase without counting them. Then the mad race began. At noon the new exchange rate was made public. Usually the mark had again slipped down to half its value. My millions, which before noon might have bought half a pound of sausage or oleomargarine, now bought only a quarter of a pound. Thus everyone raced from the payroll office to the shopping district to beat the downward race of the mark and was victor' when he reached the store before noon. This did not mean too much, though. No store sold any single customer more than half a pound of sausage or meat and a quarter of a pound of oleomargarine or lean cheese. But when you arrived after noon either they sold nothing at all or you got half the amount for your money. For a long time I kept a receipt of over 1,200,000,000,000 marks for a pair of gloves, which I was happy to obtain. At that time my salary, one of the highest paid to professional men, had a gold value of $180 a year.

One of the natural consequences of such conditions was the rush upon the stock market. Everybody speculated—if one could call it that. What we did was buy, for whatever money we had, stocks of completely unknown companies that nobody had ever seen. A great many of them probably did not exist at all or had nothing behind them. But we gave our orders in the overcrowded banks (which had to employ ten times the number of their regular employees) and assumed that they bought what we wanted and kept it for us. When we needed cash a few days later we sold our stocks and got, say, six times the price we had paid. Meanwhile the mark had depreciated ten times and our profit of 600 per cent was in fact a loss of two-fifths of our money. But we had saved at least three-fifths, which otherwise would have melted down to one-tenth. Speculation thus actually meant keeping a fraction of our money for later purchases instead of seeing it dwindling to nothing in our hands. There was of course a difference in stocks: some would rise constantly with the fall of the mark and others would not. So we had to know what to buy. As a scholar who had been completely innocent of such things and who had not even known the difference between stocks and bonds,

I had to follow advice. Thus every night I had to call up friends who worked in trade or manufacturing and get their tips on what to buy and sell. I did as I was told without even knowing what the company whose stocks I bought manufactured, or even if it really existed.

It is amusing to remember how the first thing I did in the morning when I reached the laboratory was go upstairs and see my colleague Otto Warburg and exchange with him information about the stock market. Work could begin only after this important business was attended to. Of course, we were miserable amateurs and were happy when we kept up part of the purchasing power of our salaries this way. There were others who understood the game and made money, which though actually worthless bought goods like houses and real estate. But even with my childish gambling I did not succeed in making ends meet, and I had to sell a considerable part of my collections of Japanese art, prints, sword guards, and the like in order to buy clothing and household goods. The real uncrowned king of Germany at that time was the dollar. To own dollars was unbelievable happiness, and every American was considered a billionaire: with a few hundred dollars he could buy what he wanted. At one time I actually owned $180. I had succeeded in selling in the United States for that sum a beautiful set of Japanese prints worth $2,000 (today probably $8,000). I felt very rich and kept the bills in a safe in the laboratory for eventual emergencies. Fortunately these emergencies did not come, and when the German exchange was restored in 1924 this capital of almost two million billion marks shrank again to 750 marks.

With all these crazy goings on, life went ahead. We worked and played, visited with friends, and listened to music. We hiked on Sundays and went for a swim to the lakes. We were even able to make a summer trip to the seashore or a skiing trip to the Austrian Alps. And during these years my work went on, too, but reached a point where progress became difficult. Whatever could be done with the material I had sent home from Japan, as well as the new material that Ishikawa had sent from Japan after the war, had been done. But to finish my work on intersexuality and on geographical variation and evolution required a thorough field survey and breeding work in Japan where I had discovered the strange races of the moth I was analyzing. There was, of course, no possibility of traveling with inflated money, and my efforts to get a traveling grant from a more fortunate country did not succeed.

About this time a former vice-minister in the Japanese ministry of education, Mr. Sawayanagi, came to Berlin. He brought a large sum of money given by his friend the banker Mochizuki Kintaro to be used on behalf of German science, which had suffered so badly from the depression. Mr. Sawayanagi asked my advice, and an arrangement was made for the establishment of the Mochizuki Foundation to grant fellowships to young scholars. I was a trustee of that foundation until I left Germany. During these conversations I made friends with Mr. Sawayanagi, one of the finest personalities I ever met, an idealist to the core, who had left his exalted governmental position to start a school based upon his educational ideas. Needless to say, I spoke to this man about my plans for returning to Japan in the interest of my research work. He became interested immediately, for he had a little plan of his own. It had worried him while he was in charge of his country's universities that so many Japanese professors stopped active research work once they reached a full professorship and devoted so much of their time to unnecessary things—conferences, visitors, bureaucratic pursuits. Thus he thought that it might be helpful to demonstrate how a German scientist worked even after he had attained all there was in the way of promotion. At that time Ishikawa was to retire from his chair and he, a great idealist and an admirer of German science, had a similar idea in mind. When Sawayanagi returned to Japan he and Ishikawa took things into their hands and succeeded in inducing the ministry of education to appoint me as Ishikawa's successor for two years, certainly much against the wishes of the faculty, who could not see why a foreigner should be sent for when enough Japanese were available. I personally was not interested in the position, and two years was much longer than I wanted to stay away. But as I could not see any other way to get there and accomplish my work I accepted for the autumn of 1924.

Meanwhile inflation had come to an end, and German money could be used abroad again. This made possible a very fine arrangement. The Prussian ministry of education and the Kaiser Wilhelm Society were broadminded enough to permit me to take part of my budget with me in order to buy equipment and pay for assistance, and in addition they sent with me my splendid preparator, Michael Aigner, who had participated in my work for ten years and who could supervise the technical side of my experiments, the large scale of which would require a considerable staff of helpers to be trained for that type of work. I received in addition a leave of absence with full pay—such was the regard for scientific work in republican Germany—and thus I did not have to worry about my family. When finally everything was settled, only a short time was left for me to get to Tokyo in time for the winter term.

Shipping at that time was still suffering from the depredations of war, and the few steamers that took passengers to Japan were booked for a long time ahead. Finally I secured a berth—actually the so-called luxury cabin—on the S.S. *Carl Legien* of a new steamship line that the inflation profiteer Hugo Stinnes had started. My wife accompanied me to Bozen, and we spent a few pleasant days in the mountains and valleys of southern Tyrol. Unfortunately I caught a bad intestinal infection with high fever and left for Naples in a very low condition. The trip through Italy in August was frightfully hot, and, since I had starved for three days, I arrived in Naples in a completely exhausted condition. I decided upon a horse cure, dragged myself to a small restaurant facing the bay, and ordered huge platters of macaroni and *frittura di pesce*. These I swallowed together with two liters of red Capri wine. The next day I felt fine, and I was able to enjoy a couple of pleasant days and nights with friends, carousing at night in lovely *trattorie* overlooking the bay and the surrounding mountains, with Vesuvius in the background.

When I boarded my steamer the surprise was certainly not a pleasant one. Stinnes had taken a very old freighter of about six thousand tons and put on top a kind of passenger arrangement. The staterooms had their doors open to the promenade deck and were exposed on all sides to the tropical sun without a chance of ventilation. They became unbearable as soon as the Suez Canal was passed, and the passengers, of whom there was only a handful, had to sleep in cots on deck. The captain was a gruff old sea dog who suffered in bad weather from seasickness and therefore always predicted storms, of which we had plenty, including a typhoon. The crew was of the postwar type, undisciplined and difficult to handle. The boat was supposed to make ten knots, but with the poor coal used it could not manage more than seven to eight against the heavy monsoon, and thus it took us six and a half weeks to crawl to Japan.

10: MY SECOND VISIT TO JAPAN

A colleague had been sent to receive me in Nagasaki, and we traveled together the day's ride to Toyko. Halfway there, my old friend Ishikawa boarded the train, and in Tokyo Sawayanagi and a number of the leading Japanese scholars met me. Tokyo had completely changed since my last visit ten years before. The old stations had disappeared, and I arrived in the new large central station. Next to it was a new quarter, completely Americanized, with skyscrapers and paved streets, both unheard of a few years earlier. The old wooden Imperial Hotel had been replaced by Frank Lloyd Wright's building, an amazing piece of architecture, immensely interesting as an artistic experiment but certainly not very homelike.

I found it impossible to secure a suitable Japanese house but had the good luck to share with a friend a house located within walking distance of my laboratory in a quiet park, the former estate of a feudal lord. I had made a point of going to Tokyo in the fall though my own research would not begin until the following spring when my experimental animals would hatch and be bred. I wanted first to get completely settled and to make all my preparations in time. This turned out to be wise planning, for my laboratory in the agricultural college, way out of town, was anything but perfect. The college had indeed done its best. In the old ramshackle building, which had suffered badly from the earthquake, a room had been cleaned, whitewashed, and furnished with new furniture. It even contained that rarity, an iron stove, though this was of a rather prehistoric type and, with approaching winter, became my sworn enemy. The monstrous thing, which looked like a barrel, was heated with a native coal that neither looked nor acted like coal. When lighted with charcoal it burned in a way, and even produced some heat, but it did not continue unless constantly cajoled and lighted over and over again. Thus I had to fight the monster with very little success all winter long, and sometimes envied the janitors who sat all day long in their lodge warming their fingers at a *hibachi* and sipping tea. As far as I could discover this was their only work. Of course I, too, had all my tea things around, for each visitor—and there were scores—had to be served with tea, and I acquired quite an experience in the preparation of *bancha* (light green tea). My other worry was the cleaning of the dusty room. The Japanese are, as is well known, exceptionally clean people in their own homes. But a Western room was not considered "inside" because it was entered with the shoes on, and therefore nobody could understand why I wanted this room cleaned. Finally I engaged a boy to do daily cleaning and dusting, but I am sure that my colleagues considered me crazy.

It was certainly not easy to prepare my work, though the university did everything to help me. But there is a long way from the appropriation of money for battery jars to the actual delivery of the jars, and this was even longer in the Orient than in the Occident, and even longer than the way through the purchasing department of an American state university. Another difficulty was that the Japanese professor considered it incompatible with his dignity to have anything to do with menial tasks. The design of a shelf, for example, he would never tackle, and if it was explained to him he would not even try to understand. This was the business of somebody else. Thus I ran my head against walls trying to get such things done until my friend Miyake, who knew my difficulties, took me directly to the carpenter or glassmaker, to whom I could explain my specifications. Again, I think, I earned the reputation of being undignified, rash, impolite, and generally insane.

My appointment was as a regular professor, and my duty was to give a large number of classes. I think my contract mentioned twenty-five hours a week. Though the term had already started when I arrived and I was ready to begin my classes, I was told not to hurry. The beginning was postponed and postponed, and it was November before I was encouraged to begin a class of two hours a week. It soon became clear that the faculty or whoever ran the thing did not want me to do any real work for them. They simply sabotaged the plan of the government in inviting me. I found out that even the one class I gave was being given simultaneously by somebody else, and that only his course was obligatory. I had also expected that many graduate students would come to do research work under me, but they were not encouraged. I never could find out whether this was sabotage against the foreigner or the result of an intrafaculty feud between the great

Ishikawa, my friend and sponsor, and his bureaucratic enemies among the faculty politicians. Though I did all the teaching I was asked to do, I do not think I gave more than a hundred single lectures during those two years—so that each lecture was rather expensive for the government.

When I realized what was going on I stopped being zealous to do my duty and concentrated upon my own research and the writing of one of my favorite books, which I had had in mind for some time, *The Physiological Theory of Heredity*. I also did some extramural work. Many scientific societies and other organizations invited me to lecture as did even the popular societies, where my friend Miyake had to do the translating (otherwise I spoke either English or German, and once French). All the other imperial universities, and some other schools, invited me for guest lectures. Quite a bit of lecturing was also done in the foreign colony, especially for the German Asiatic Society. Thus I was able, after all, to deliver some of the goods that had been expected.

I had hardly started, however, when the long New Year's vacation began. It was part of my program to visit as much as possible of the regions surrounding Japan proper in order to check upon the natural limits of distribution of the moth I was studying, a point of considerable importance in evolutionary discussions. The form had been described as occurring in the subtropical island of Formosa, and this seemed incredible to me. (Actually I could prove that an error was involved.) Thus I decided to make my first field trip to Formosa during the long holiday, and fortunately my friend Miyake decided to come with me and to make the necessary preparations.

The weeks Miyake and I spent in Formosa belong to my most pleasant memories, memorable especially now when the events of subsequent history have changed the island completely and made it a storm center in international politics. The coastal towns were typical southern Chinese towns, but they bore the stamp of a very progressive colonial administration. Though I am sure that this administration was of the police type it certainly had accomplished much. The cities were clean, and sanitation was up-to-date. Beautiful parks and government buildings made Taipei, the capital, a most attractive subtropical town. There was a university (later an imperial university) with a medical faculty that was successfully combating tropical diseases. I delivered a lecture to the students at this university who turned out more than a thousand strong, mostly Chinese but including a few aborigines. Afterward the university presented me with a large amount of the delicious oolong tea grown in Formosa and some excellent cigars produced for export by the government monopoly.

In the capital there was even a Western-style hotel, the only one on the island. But in all the other towns there were excellent Japanese inns, even in the smallest inland cities, for the Japanese colonial administrators liked to travel in comfort. Needless to say, where there were hotels there were also geisha entertainers. Wherever we went I was proudly shown schools, hospitals, and agricultural experiment stations, and I received the impression that here was a flourishing colony in which the Chinese inhabitants also shared in the wealth, even though big business was exclusively in Japanese hands.

The most interesting parts of our sojourn were repeated trips into the wild, mountainous interior. The high mountains, up to sixteen thousand feet, form a kind of backbone of the island, and the high valleys between the mountain ranges offer some of the most beautiful scenery in the world. Traveling by pushcar, which amounted at times to a not undangerous tobogganing along precipices over insecurely fixed little rails, was at that time the only way of getting into the interior. The pushcar lines ended at the sugar plantations located in the high valleys or at military outposts near the mountains. From there we had to climb on steep paths into the territory of the natives.

The story of the natives in Formosa is the story of the camphor tree. When the Chinese began colonizing the island—a kind of outcast group, the Hakkas, came first—it was inhabited by Malay tribes akin to those of the Philippines. The Hakkas took away the fertile coastal plains and pushed the aborigines into the mountains of the interior. Then a second wave of Chinese immigrants from southern China took possession of the rich agricultural coastal plain, and it was now the turn of the Hakkas to be pushed into the foothills. Here they worked mainly as woodsmen exploiting the valuable camphor wood. The mountains of Formosa abound in giant camphor trees, which do not form forests but stand isolated within the virgin forest. A lumberman would pick out such a tree and erect nearby a primitive still. The tree was cut and chopped slowly into chips, which were distilled for the precious camphor, and a single tree might keep a family busy for a year.

But the search for camphor brought the Hakkas into conflict with the natives who claimed the forests. All these tribes were head-hunters, as so many Malay tribes are, and for centuries the fight went on, with innumerable heads being taken by the aborigines and reprisals following. Even at the time I visited, there were still untamed head-hunting tribes in the mountain fastnesses, kept in check by Japanese militarized police. No chance was given us to visit these wild tribes, for their very existence was a sore point to the colonial government; not even information about them could be obtained. The tribes we visited were of the semi-pacified type, living high up in the mountains in primitive villages surrounded by unfinished clearings where yams were cultivated. Nearby police posts kept an eye on the natives, and we were not allowed to visit their villages without police escort. But we spent interesting hours among them after much arduous climbing.

In one colony, Musha, the natives put on a drunken orgy for our benefit. The old women of the tribe did all the dancing and most of the drinking, and it was rather disgusting to us. A few years later I learned that the small tribe had revolted because of some real or assumed injustice and had murdered their Japanese "teachers." A military expedition sent to the place killed or drove into the mountains all the males of the tribe, and all the females fled into the woods and committed suicide there. Thus my photographs preserve the last traces of this tribe.

Soon after my return to Tokyo, the experimental work began with the breeding season of the gypsy moth. My faithful preparator, Michael Aigner, arrived from Berlin to start with the technical preparations and the training of my crew. To breed about sixty thousand moths in two to three hundred different genetic lines requires a factorylike organization that we had worked out through years of experience. It is necessary to have a large number of helpers who must work smoothly hand in hand and be careful not to commit errors. Miyake had connections with a progressive girls' school run by a Mrs. Hani on a highly idealistic basis including Christian training and the use of Western methods of living and work. The girls in this modern school—the building had been designed by Frank Lloyd Wright—were carefully selected, and from its graduates Miyake picked a group of fine, intellectual, and eager girls to serve as my technical assistants.

They did splendid work under very difficult conditions, laughing and giggling from morning to night. A deserted laboratory, half wrecked by the earthquake of 1923, was rigged up for my purposes. It was a dangerous place—half of the ceiling had already come down in the earthquake—but no other large room was available. Actually one day the rest of the ceiling crashed down; fortunately nobody was in the room at the time. Only a few broods were ruined. The hot summer went on with much work and frequent excitement when different cogs in the machine broke down, but finally we were able to celebrate the successful end of the summer's work with a big *Kaffeeklatsch,* for which the girls discarded their ugly sailor suits and appeared in beautiful kimonos.

During the breeding season I could not leave the laboratory very much except for an occasional Sunday at the beach or a hike in the hills. But usually I was free in the late afternoon and could devote some hours to my hobbies. By good chance the gentleman with whom I shared my house owned a beautiful Amati violin. The noble tone of this instrument induced me to practice again, and I spent many a pleasant hour with the instrument. Frequently musical friends from the German and American colonies dropped in at night, and duets or trios were performed. It might be surprising to know that there was a considerable musical life both within and outside the foreign colony in Tokyo. There was, of course, much music among the Germans, especially at the embassy where musicals were a regular feature. But also the Japanese were developing an immense interest in Western music, a situation I could not really understand since Japanese music is as different from Western as day from night.

The Japanese musical tradition was also very much alive when I was there. There was the strange recitative of the *utai,* the classical singing of the No play with its forced voice and the accompaniment of hand drum and flute. At first utterly incomprehensible to a Westerner, this music, which might be compared to the liturgy of the Greek Orthodox Church, grows on one. There was the more popular ballad singing, represented in the singing of the commentator of the classical puppet play of Osaka, one of the most amazing and thrilling performances imaginable. There were, too, the jolly or sentimental or romantic or satirical songs of the geisha with the samisen obbligato, and the funny duets of samisen and drum. There was the old Korean court music played by orchestras of harps, lutes, Chinese violins, flutes, and drums, which I often heard played by the imperial palace orchestra, a real antiquarian type of music in Oriental scales.

With all these and other types of strictly Oriental music constantly played, the people nevertheless enjoyed Western music with its completely different musical scale and instrumentation. There were of course some sophistication and silly imitation: Western college songs sung by students, and made-up "folk songs" based upon Western melodies. And there were also the daughters of rich families, who performed upon the piano for guests. But the same daughter who rattled out a Beethoven sonata like a player piano had also learned to play the koto—the long Japanese zither —or to sing and dance to the samisen. How the same mind could work with and enjoy both Oriental and Western types of music I could not understand. But I found there was a considerable gift for Western music. My friends who taught at the imperial conservatory extolled the gifts of their pupils, and I frequently heard very creditable performances on the piano and violin and singing by Japanese students. A symphony orchestra led by Prince Konoye, the brother of the statesman, gave good performances of Western music, and the Japanese public filled the huge concert hall to the limit.

It seemed that in the field of music the Japanese did not suffer from the feeling of uncertainty with which they faced other forms of Western art. At the large art shows held yearly in Tokyo, just as in Paris or Munich, there were exhibited innumerable pictures painted in Western style, which meant imitating exactly the style of some French or German school. But the majority of the paintings kept up the classical Japanese tradition with only a few concessions made to Western influence in perspective, color, and subject. The public in general cared only for the traditional style of painting. In the many houses of well-to-do or rich people that I visited I found only old Japanese or Chinese paintings, including many priceless ones by the great masters, for which Japanese collectors paid prices equal to those paid abroad for Rembrandts or Dürers. Only in a single house of an old aristocrat did I find a collection of modern European paintings. Obviously the Western style of painting was in general neither cherished nor understood, and a Japanese connoisseur who raved about a Sesshu or an Ogata Korin was helpless in front of a Botticelli.

Needless to say, I spent a good deal of my spare time studying Eastern art. Before coming to Japan this time, I had prepared myself by acquiring the necessary historical knowledge. Thus I could start out to learn by experience.

After a few chance purchases, I became especially interested in those charming pottery statuettes of men, women, horses, riders, and the like, which the Chinese put into their tombs from the beginning of our era to the early Middle Ages. These figurines had come to light only recently, and not much had been found out about their history, dating, and meaning. Thus I was attracted not only by the esthetic beauty of the little works of art, but also by the historical and cultural problems connected with them. I began to read, with the assistance of a teacher, the Oriental literature upon the subject and the old annals of the great Chinese dynasties that had been translated. In the course of the years I was able to see and handle many thousands of pieces in the hands of dealers and collectors in both China and Japan and also in the remarkable museums of Tokyo, Kyoto, Peking, and of Manchuria, Korea, and India. I enjoyed immensely bringing together the material for a monograph on the subject. My own collection grew to be a rather complete one and has given me much pleasure through the years—and also much work when twice I had to pack the brittle things for long transport.

In connection with my work there were also field trips to northeastern China to check upon the distribution of my moth and to secure breeding material. These trips could be pleasantly combined with a visit to China for purely cultural purposes. I decided, therefore, to forego during the summer vacation the rest in a mountain resort which foreigners and Japanese alike think necessary in the hot season. Instead I made plans for a trip into the summer heat of northern China. A small Japanese boat took me from Shimonoseki to the former German colony of Tsingtao where I intended to spend a week at the beautiful beach, at the same time looking for my moth. Tsingtao was a strange-looking place, built after the model of a small German town with clean concrete streets and comfortable houses, an incongruous setting for a Chinese population. The bare hills surrounding the town had been reforested by the Germans and offered a charming sight. Unfortunately, I immediately caught an intestinal trouble locally called the "Tsingtao frog," which hardly any newcomer escapes, and I had to spend my week in bed instead of swimming and hiking.

By chance I heard of a Franciscan monk in nearby Kiaochou who was known as a naturalist. I got in touch with him, and he took me at once to a place in the woods where I found numerous females of the coveted moth in the act of egg-laying, thus saving me the time of searching for them. I was able then to proceed on my way to the old capital of Shantung province.

The day's trip on what was formerly the German Shantung Railway with its neat station buildings gave me the rare chance to observe from close by one of the worst of the war lords under whose oppression China seethed in those years. My traveling companion in the train's only first-class compartment was the ill-famed "General" Chang Chung Chan, a former coolie and robber, then master of life and death in the beautiful, rich province of Shantung. The brutal-looking fellow stood about six feet six in his boots. He was surrounded by a group of young men in uniform, and all around stood desperate-looking men with submachine guns. The general talked for about two hours without interruption in a raucous bellow, moistening his throat with innumerable cups of tea. Finally he got tired, took off his coat, and lay down to sleep with half-open eyes, looking like an evil animal. His guards stood by with their guns, eyeing me with not very friendly glances. At every station a guard of honor was posted along the tracks, and a band played martial tunes. Sometimes the great man got up and saluted in his undershirt; sometimes he continued sleeping. I was glad when he disembarked after half a day's ride; he certainly looked exactly as he was pictured in the numerous tales of his energy, cruelty, and voluptuousness.

In Tsinan I spent a few interesting days seeing the old-fashioned life of a medieval walled town that probably had not changed for centuries except for the foreign colony outside the gate. The noise was deafening by day and night. Much of it came from the huge, one-man-power wheelbarrows that served as trucks as well as taxis. The axles were not greased and squeaked miserably—this was done on purpose, I was told, to allow the cart to show its soul. The town was formerly a center of the apricot kernel and hairnet trades, both in the hands of foreign firms. The hairnet industry had done much for the rural population since old and young women were able to earn a little cash in their spare time by making nets from bleached and cured Chinese hair. Unfortunately, the bobbed hair craze that had appeared in America in the twenties wrecked the trade just at the time I was visiting and brought misery to many a peasant household.

Tsinan was filled with the soldiers of the war lord Chang Tso Lin preparing for some phase of the eternal civil war. Along the sidewalks were strung ropes to which the small Mongolian ponies of the cavalry were hitched. Recruits were drilling everywhere. The noncoms carried leather straps, which went whistling down upon the backs of the recruits, who made up for it by beating up ricksha men and other civilians. In front of each troop marched the executioner with a huge, broad, old-fashioned sword, and executions were carried out on the spot. All around misery was visible. I remember one empty lot where people had dug holes and hung a rag in front, and there entire families lived.

Leaving Tsinan, I took the famous Blue Express, which was to bring me to Peking. The express was not a very cheerful sight, though. Machine guns were mounted on all the platforms, and tough-looking soldiers patrolled the cars. The express had been held up by bandits the night before, and some passengers had been killed. But this time nothing happened, and in the morning I arrived at Peking station, overshadowed by the glorious Chien-men gate.

The month I spent in Peking was overwhelmingly beautiful. All the foreigners had fled from the summer heat, and the city was purely Chinese. In spite of electric lights, streetcars, and a few Western buildings, one dived immediately into the early Middle Ages by entering the gigantic walls and gates of the Tartar city. I never wearied of roaming around the streets crowded with all kinds of vehicles from the modern automobile to the primitive camel car. There was always something going on—a wedding, a funeral procession with all its historical weirdness, a camel caravan arriving from Mongolia. The shops were filled with the most interesting things from fake curios to priceless works of ancient art. And the overwhelming grandeur of the Forbidden City— then accessible—with its huge gates and porticoes, innumerable courtyards, and grandiose yellow-tiled roofs is never to be forgotten.

I was under way from early morning to late at night, taking in all I could. I had hired for a month a ricksha puller who was always there when I wanted to go out and who knew the town thoroughly. He had once served in some humble capacity in the British legation and had learned a little pidgin English, which made him a priceless acquisition. He knew this and tried to behave like a guide. Wherever I went, he went in with me, clad in nothing but a pair of torn shorts, and acted as if he were my pal. The Chinese looked rather horrified at my escort and frequently tried to stop him from entering a palace or temple with me. But he always managed to slip through, and I was greatly amused at the consternation of the public when I sat down with the fellow in a tea garden.

This man was a big scoundrel and a rather wild fellow. When I occasionally rode in the company of a Chinese friend he ran so fast that the other ricksha could not follow. When we arrived, with him breathless and the other puller exhausted, he would say triumphantly, "Him big boy no good." He could not stand to let another vehicle pass him, and he would outrun it at a dangerous speed. Once a coach with two horses passed him nevertheless. He heaped upon the driver a whole avalanche of the obscene insults in which the Chinese language is said to be especially rich. But after a few hundred steps the coachman doubled upon his tracks and, as he passed us again, spat squarely in the eyes of my puller, at the same time returning some of the compliments. Every day I had similar experiences and paid with embarrassing situations for the efficient legs of my man. The day before I left he asked me in passing whether I had a daughter. When I paid him off the next day he produced a little box with the queer artificial flower ornaments that the women of the lower classes wore in their hair and presented them to me with the injunction to take them to my daughter. This was certainly a gracious thing to do and was a lesson to me.

Only too fast the time flew with sightseeing, study of old art, excursions to the West Hills with their old temples, and association with pleasant people, both Western and Chinese. Of the numerous small incidents that make up the spice of foreign travel two may be related. A wealthy American friend had asked me to look for a special size of antique Chinese rug, which he wanted very much. I made it known that I was in the market for such a piece, and after a time a prosperous-looking Chinese clad in beautiful silk called and told me he had what I wanted. I went with him, and after a breathless race between his ricksha man and mine we entered the courtyard of a beautiful mansion. Servants brought a large rug and spread it on the lawn. It was a magnificent rug, blue and yellow with a cutout golden background. My host told me that it had been taken from one of the palaces of the Forbidden City when it was occupied by General Chang Tso Lin. One end of the rug had the mark of the palace woven in Chinese characters. The rug was indeed all a sophisticated collector could want, but the price was fifteen thousand Chinese dollars. I looked it over carefully and noticed that the yellow color looked more like aniline dye than old mineral dye. Finally I went away to look for an expert to consult.

When I told this story to a German collector who had lived in Peking for a long time and knew any good piece in the market, he laughed and told me the story of the rug. He, himself, had seen it on the loom two years before when it was made for the man who tried to sell it to me. When it was finished this man had a gang of barefoot men trample on it for months in order to achieve the mellowness of antiquity, and he had succeeded remarkably well. I at once asked a Chinese friend to call up the crook and tell him in good Chinese what I thought of his and his ancestors' morals.

A few days later I was called up by a Swedish dealer who offered me a rug for fifteen hundred dollars. I asked him to describe it, and it was the same rug. This would have been a proper price for the beautiful piece, but my friend wanted an old one, and so I did not succeed in fulfilling my mission.

My other anecdote has a certain curiosity value. I was of course looking for my gypsy moth eggs but did not find any in the surroundings of Peking. I told this by chance to the German chargé d'affaires when I was having dinner with him. He volunteered to collect some eggs for me at his summer place at Peitaho where the diplomatic corps used to spend the hot season, and I furnished the necessary instructions. After my return to Japan I received one day a package with perfectly good moth eggs from that locality. Not many scientists, I think, have used their country's diplomats as field collectors!

The enchanted days in Peking finally came to an end, and a steamer from Tientsin took me back to Japan, where my wife was to arrive for a prolonged visit. There were still summer vacations to come, and I was able to show her many of the famous sights, including those every traveler visits like the temple town of Nikko

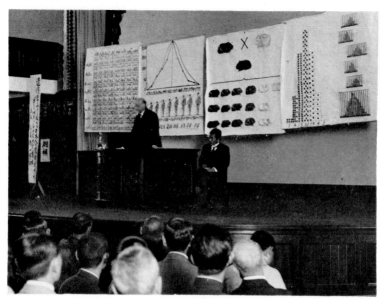

The author lecturing in Tokyo, 1925

Peking art dealer, 1925

Members of the Tsu tribe, central Formosa, view their first
white man, 1925

Women of Musha, Formosa, 1925, members of a tribe no longer
in existence

and the old residence of Kamakura and the romantic fishermen's island of Enoshima. Other trips involved beautiful hikes like the crossing of the Ten Provinces pass, with its glorious view of Mount Fuji-no-Yama, into the Japanese "riviera" of Atami; and the visit to the *solfataras* in the Hakone mountains. A week was spent in the picturesque mountain resort of Ikao, aglow with the autumnal tints of the *momiji* (small-leafed maple) and a center for beautiful hikes into the mountains. Between excursions, sojourns in Tokyo gave us a chance to get acquainted with Japanese hospitality and home life, to meet the foreign colony, and to enjoy the unending fascination of the Japanese theater.

In October, I was to give a course of lectures in the Imperial University of Sapporo, located on the northernmost island of Hokkaido. On our way we had a charming visit, with the inevitable lecture, at Sendai University, which gave us a chance to see the famous sight of Matsushima, the thousand-times painted rock islands sprinkled over a blue sea and crowned by a few bizarre-looking pine trees. For my wife this trip gave the first experience, too, of living in a Japanese inn with all its unusual features: the transparent room partitions, sleeping on the floor, the general bathroom, the giggling maids, the delicious native meals, the nightly noise of pipes knocked against the brazier by the guests taking a whiff between sleeping, the infernal noise of the closing and early opening of the wooden shutters. A typical teahouse party with all the traditional formalities and geisha performers was another novel experience for her.

In Hokkaido, which we reached in six to eight hours by a fine modern ferryboat (the same that capsized thirty years later) from the northernmost city of Aomori on the main island, it was already cold, and the rather wild landscape looked gloomy. Toward evening our train stopped suddenly in the mountains. The conductor came and talked excitedly. It turned out that a long tunnel that we were about to enter had caved in. The train backed to the last station, the name of which, Kuromatsunai, has stuck ominously in our memories ever since. We went with the other passengers to the village inn and sat shivering on the floor of the unheated, untidy, draughty room. At night a meal of gray, unappetizing rice with evil-smelling dried fish was served, and then we stretched on the floor to try to sleep.

Toward morning the innkeeper informed us that we could continue our journey. The train returned to the entrance of the tunnel. From there the railroad men had built, overnight, a path around the mountain. The whole length of it—about a twenty-minute walk—was covered with straw mats spread over the deep mud, and in precipitous places ropes had been stretched to hold on to. Railway men carried the baggage and escorted us around the mountain to the other end of the tunnel, where another train waited. We certainly admired the efficiency and considerate action of the railway administration.

In Sapporo we were well received by our friends, who had not been informed of what had happened and were worried. Unfortunately this intermezzo had an unpleasant aftermath. I had contracted from the food in Kuromatsunai a bad infection that kept me in bed with high fever for over a week, and my wife brought as a souvenir from the draughty inn an agonizing rheumatism of the worst type, which completely paralyzed her. In addition, the otherwise beautiful Japanese inn where we stayed in bed nursing each other was unheated, and the sanitary facilities were in another wing of the big house. My colleagues did their best to help us, and finally we both recovered and I was able to deliver my postponed series of lectures.

On our way back to Tokyo an incident occurred that is typical of some Japanese scholars of that time. When we arrived at Hakodate to take the ferry to Aomori we were accosted at the station by a gentleman who looked just like those small, bespectacled, morning-coated, serious scientists so well known in European and American universities a generation ago. He introduced himself as a professor of medicine in a local college and offered to show us the sights during our stopover of a few hours. He took us around in his car, and we had a pleasant time. When we were ready to embark, he declared that he would keep us company on the ferry, a trip of about six hours. I grew curious to know what it was all about. An hour after we had put out to sea, he suddenly took out of his pocket a typewritten manuscript on some physiological subject and asked me to read it. Now I understood. He wanted me to make suggestions and to brush up his German. What could I do? Instead of looking at the sea and the islands all around, I had to sit in the drawing room and correct his paper. But at least somebody got pleasure out of this performance. A week later the mail brought to my wife a beautiful fox fur with the clever physician's compliments.

The fall term passed with the usual work, and again Christmas vacation came. I had planned to spend it in the beautiful south-west area in order to show Elsa some of the sights and the great works of early Japanese art accumulated in that region and well known to me from repeated visits. We first spent interesting days among the sacred temples and cryptomeria groves of Ise and then in Nara, the first capital of the early Japanese state roughly between A.D. 500 and 1000. Though the landscape around Nara could not compare in beauty with many other regions of Japan, it was the place to study the greatest period of Japanese wooden architecture and sculpture.

The temples of Nara were filled with great works of art, the finest of which had, fortunately, been put into a fireproof museum. The huge hall of the giant image of Buddha is one of the treasures of architecture. Still more beautiful things were to be seen in the neighborhood of Nara, rarely visited by the casual traveler. Here was found the oldest edifice in Japan, the Horiuji temple dating back to the seventh century. It still contained some of the greatest pieces of Japanese sculpture of the Tempyo era, probably made by Chinese and Korean sculptors in collaboration with their Japanese pupils. Some of them belong among the greatest masterpieces of the world. The finest, in our opinion, was a gilt statue of Kwannon (Kuan Yin) made in what I call the pre-Raphaelite style that characterizes the earliest Korean sculpture. This breath-taking work of art was found in a small nunnery, Chuguji, near Horiuji, and could then be seen only in the presence of the abbess who lifted the brocaded curtain in front of it. Later it was represented on a postage stamp!

From Nara we proceeded to Kyoto, the medieval capital, visited by all travelers. I had been there many times and could serve as a guide for my wife through all the palaces, temples, and ancient gardens with which this pleasant and easygoing town abounds. The surroundings offered beautiful excursions and hikes, many of which we made: to Mount Hieisan, famous in Japanese history for its bellicose monasteries destroyed by Oda Nobunaga, overlooking charming Lake Biwa; the ancient temples and bridges of Ishigome and Miidera at the shore of this lake with their lore centering around the strong man Benkei; the Uji Valley, strewn with very old temples and monasteries, the home of the best tea; Momoyama, the tomb of the great emperor Mutsuhito, a simple

213

tumulus above a huge staircase of the most impressive grandeur. Only too quickly time passed, each day full of lasting impressions, and then we had to return to Tokyo, for Elsa had to sail home in January.

After a winter full of work—I was writing a book that required great concentration and two other less technical ones—spring vacation came before the new breeding season was to start. This time I decided upon a trip to the Ryukyu (or Loochoo) Islands, those small coral islands, including Okinawa, stretching from the southern tip of Japan to Formosa. These islands had been rather rarely visited—one early visitor was Commodore Perry—except by naturalists interested in the remarkable fauna and flora, which are related to the Indian zone. My interest was in the first of these—to establish the southern limit of the moth with which I was working. This professional interest combined pleasantly with the wish to study the entire civilization of the islands, which were known to preserve many of the characteristics of the ancient ancestors of the present-day Japanese. The trip turned out to be most interesting, and I collected many data of general human as well as historical interest, all reported in detail in my book *Neu Japan*. Today most of what I saw has disappeared, and Okinawa has lost all its esthetic or historic attraction. I am glad that I explored the lovely island while it had still been untouched for centuries.

The small steamer on which Miyake and I traveled went through some rather rough weather. We were the only cabin passengers. In steerage a huge hold was covered with mats upon which the passengers squatted in the daytime and slept at night. A large number of natives of the islands were returning home from Brazil, where they had worked on plantations. The poverty of the islands forced a considerable part of the population to go out and then return with their savings after a few years of hard work. One of these migrants was very anxious to make conversation with me. This was a difficult task, since his language was Ryukyu, and in addition he knew a few words of Japanese and some terribly corrupt Portuguese. But with some good will and imagination I could decipher the sense of his lingo, and I answered in a similar ragout of Japanese and personally invented Portuguese concocted from Spanish, Italian, and Latin. The marvel was that we understood each other, and I still remember the story of his life, which culminated in the statement that all his savings from Brazil were six children and so he would have to return to his slaving in South America.

We spent all our time on the largest island of Okinawa with headquarters in the main city of Naha, from which other parts of the island were easily reached on foot, by horse cart, or even in a miniature horse train, which tipped dangerously when I stepped onto the rear platform. The coral foundation of the island gave an excellent roadbed so that the roads were actually much better than any found in Japan at that time. There was also a single motorcar on the island, belonging to the Japanese governor, who kindly put it at our disposition for longer excursions. But these rides were dubious pleasures. The children in the villages through which we passed had never seen a motorcar before and, for unknown reasons, would run toward the moving car and try to put their hands between the spokes of the wheels. We suffered agonies, but fortunately nothing happened. In out-of-the-way places the children collected when we appeared and enjoyed thoroughly their first sight of a white man; they actually gaped with open mouth, not moving from the spot as long as we stood there.

Needless to say, the local authorities treated us here, as everywhere in my travelings, with many courtesies including dinner parties. One such party given by the governor is worth mentioning for its rather unusual setting. The dinner was served in Japanese style in a large room of old Japanese character, but the cooking was Chinese of the most elaborate kind with innumerable delicious courses. One of them was a local and rather unusual treat. The sea around the islands swarmed with a very venomous sea snake. This was killed and dried, and the stiff dry bodies, as sold in the stores, looked like burnt sticks. The meat was considered a delicacy —I suspect it was assumed to be an aphrodisiac—and at our party sea snake was served as a stew together with fat pork. It was tough and without taste. On entering the restaurant where the party took place, I was surprised by a kind of cheap luxury not usual in Japanese teahouses, and my suspicions were raised further by the dresses of the pretty girls who served at table. I inquired cautiously and found out that the governor's party was taking place in a brothel, the only place in town capable of serving a large and elaborate dinner party!

There was a scion of the family that had ruled the islands before annexation to Japan living in Naha under the name of Count

Sho. He was related by marriage to one of the former ruling families of Japan, and a member of that family, a charming countess with whom I had a friendly acquaintance, introduced me to him. Thus we were invited to his beautiful old mansion surrounded by flower gardens, which were his hobby. We were shown fine examples of the old art of the islands, which was completely under Chinese influence. The dinner consisted exclusively of native dishes, all new to me and all delicious, a kind of modified Chinese cuisine. But the most interesting part was the drink. The rice wine, called *awamori,* was prepared with a different kind of fermentation from the Japanese sake and was thus very different in taste. I found it at the same time highly repulsive and very attractive, but the latter sensation won out. *Awamori* improved with time, and, since time did not count very much in these islands, good *awamori* was at least a hundred years old. Count Sho served us with a three-hundred-year-old vintage, in porcelain cups the size of a thimble. The taste was excellent, and the experience, with the entire setting and company, a unique one. The next day I found in my room a present of some bottles of *awamori* "only" one hundred years old.

The mansion of Count Sho was in the old capital of the islands, Shuri, located on a high coral bluff and now, unfortunately, completely destroyed. The main sight was the old castle of the rulers, built in Chinese style and situated in a pleasant park. Nearby were the strange old tombs of the family, which were opened for me and which I was allowed to photograph, I assume for the first time. These were to serve as bunkers during World War II. Shuri was a very picturesque place with its narrow streets and high walled properties, and heavy tiled roofs and old doorways, and the costumes and hairdresses of the women, like those of Japan in the early Middle Ages.

Shuri was also the center of the old arts and crafts, and I succeeded in collecting some of the old pottery, which as late as the last century was still inspired by the classical Chinese Sung ware. The art of weaving cloth from banana fiber and patterning it with beautiful colors in a kind of batik technique, in which a paste made of rice hulls replaced wax, was also disappearing. I visited a lady who owned some beautiful old costumes and asked her to don one so that I could take a photograph. When she was ready her husband suddenly appeared on the scene, clad only in an imported union suit, and expostulated wildly with his wife and with us. He was protesting against my taking the photograph because anybody who saw the picture might think the islanders were barbarians who still wore that type of clothing. After much asking we finally found a small workshop where an old man still did some of this *sarasa* technique, but only for souvenirs.

Among the many institutions preserved in the Ryukyu Islands in a condition that represented a stage through which Japan had passed more than one thousand years before, probably the most interesting was an animistic cult that still used the symbols typical of ancient Japan and Korea. I had the rare opportunity to visit in northern Okinawa an old site of the cult that preserved to that day the animistic rites of an otherwise long-past epoch. The sacred ground, the scene of a yearly religious festival, was located on top of a mountain overlooking the sea, and the spirits of mountain and sea were here worshiped simultaneously.

Nearby lived a strange relic of earliest times, the priestess called *Noro,* who was in charge of the rites. We found the kindly old lady working around her house. Her house opened toward the sea when the shutters were removed. One room was her living room. The other was the sanctum, in the background of which was the ancestors' altar niche combined with a general place of worship containing nothing but a set of small elect stones, the *shintai,* which represented the gods of nature. The lady answered all questions about the rites and their meaning through an interpreter who translated the native tongue into Japanese. She then proceeded to show us her most sacred possessions. She donned a ceremonial yellow native robe, put a box upon a wooden stand such as is used in Shinto ceremonies, and seated herself near the altar. Solemnly she unpacked an ancient necklace made of comma-shaped stones, a piece of jewelry handed down from generation to generation and worn only during the yearly festival. The remarkable thing was that the stones (*magatama*) were the same that, since ancient times, have constituted one of the three insignia of the Japanese emperor, which no ordinary mortal is supposed to behold: jewel, mirror, and sword. The same *magatama* are found in ancient Korean graves, and here in Okinawa, far away from the crossroads of trade, the old symbol was still in use and looked upon with awe.

Through our interpreter I asked the *Noro* whether it would be a sacrilege to take her photograph with the *magatama* and in full regalia. After a long discussion we learned that she had no religious scruples but had others. She had a daughter who had been sent to college in Japan and had married a man who now lived in San

Francisco. She took it for granted that, as a foreigner, I must know this man in San Francisco, and she did not want him to see such a photograph. It was rather difficult to explain to her that I should probably never meet her daughter in the United States, for the *Noro* obviously thought of all foreign countries together as of the size of her village. Finally she was persuaded to agree, and afterward she took from a drawer a photograph of her worldly daughter dressed in modish American style with a huge flowery hat. The contrast between this picture and the dear old priestess, tattooed according to old custom and clad in a solemn yellow rag of banana cloth, with the archaic chain around her neck, was overwhelming.

Only too quickly the interesting weeks on Okinawa passed by, and a miserable thousand-ton steamer took us back to Japan. In Tokyo the new breeding season for my experimental work began with all its excitement. There were diseases that endangered the precious animals, there was the constant worry whether enough food for sixty thousand caterpillars could be hauled in and dried if it was wet, and there was the worry whether the results would justify the huge load of work and the expenses. My German preparator and the jolly crew of giggling girls again did their best in spite of the moist heat of the rainy season and the primitive quarters. Finally the day came when I could send home the harvest: the egg batches from which the next generation was to be bred, after my return to Germany, in order to enable me to solve finally the problems that had kept me busy already for fifteen years and were to keep me busy for eight years more, namely the analysis of intersexuality and of geographical variation as related to evolution.

Thus my work was successfully finished, but my contract ran for a few more months, and I decided to use the time for visiting those parts of the eastern region of Japan that I had not yet seen, in order to round out my scientific material by collecting eggs of the moth in those regions and also to supplement my cultural knowledge of these parts. First I had a chance to visit a place that interested me especially—the small Bonin Islands located about midway between Japan and the South Seas, five hundred miles south of Yokohama. I had learned from reading what is probably the only book dealing exclusively with those islands that a small colony of Englishmen had settled there in whaling days, married Polynesian women imported from the south, and established a colony on the formerly uninhabited islands. The colony was rather successful since the seas surrounding the islands abounded in giant turtles, which did their breeding on the shores of the islands. Thousands of the huge animals, four to five feet in length, were captured, and their meat was salted down to be sold to the regularly calling whalers. Only when the Japanese settled the islands to fortify them as a naval base did the good days of the old settlers end and the settlers themselves become a kind of historic relic.

Here was a chance to study a case of human hybridization over a few generations of reliable pedigrees. By chance, one of my former students, Kyoshi Katsuki, intended to visit the islands in the interest of sericulture, and thus I was able to join him on a trip that would otherwise have been scarcely possible, for the Japanese were highly suspicious of foreigners visiting fortified islands.

The trip through the southern seas in midsummer was rather hot but enlivened by the innumerable whales that blew over these old whaling grounds. We might have sung out a hundred times a day, "Thar she blows!" Among the few passengers of the tiny boat was General Count Terauchi, who was going for an inspection of the forts. He was a very jolly and amusing traveling companion, and I should not have suspected that this pleasant boon companion would a few years later as minister of war inaugurate the era of aggressive militarism and play a decisive role in the rape of China. There was a rather amusing scene enacted by both of us after our arrival in the islands. The islanders gave the general a big reception party in the only inn, where we had also put up. When spirits had already risen considerably in proportion to the consumption of sake, Terauchi asked me to join the party, and we made merry with them until midnight. When all the guests had departed, the mild night air and the beautiful moon over the snow-white coral beach induced us to take a midnight stroll. The general remembered sentimentally his younger days as military attaché in Berlin, and, taking my arm, he made me perform with him a regular goose step while singing a martial soldier's song!

I had a very interesting time exploring the pedigree of the settlers, most of whom belonged to the Savory family. They were quite cooperative and took me into their houses where they lived in European style, a little apart from the Japanese colony, in a kind of dignified poverty. The notes I took were later incorporated into a paper that had an unexpected sequel. My paper suggested to an anthropologist working in China the idea of following up the matter with exact anthropological measurements, and he went to the islands for that purpose. All went well for him except in one family, which absolutely refused to cooperate. This was a branch of the Savory family into which a Portuguese Negro had married two or three generations back. The head of the family looked like a pure Negro. I had photographed him as well as the others and had sent him a copy of the picture. It seems that he had never known of his Negroid looks. Since he was a member of the best family in the group, he thought of himself as looking like the others. When he saw my photograph he concluded that I had played a trick on him to spite him, and this he resented immensely.

During this visit I spent many pleasant hours in an outrigger canoe out on the bay that makes a wonderful natural port for the main island. The bottom of the bay was covered with coral reefs, and the water was crystal clear so that with the aid of a glass-bottomed pail I could see every detail down below. Observing the beautiful coral fish, I felt repeatedly the wish to hold specimens of the many different kinds in my hand. To do so, I had only to lower a baited hook and, looking through the pail, bring the bait in front of the fish I wanted. At once it would bite, and I could haul it up, then liberate it again after having looked it over. The trick never failed, and many a fisherman might be envious of such a way of fishing. But in honesty I ought to say that I learned the trick from the village youngsters, who spent their afternoons that way.

After my return to Tokyo I set out at once for a trip to China, Manchuria, and Korea. I wanted to have another look at the great city of Peking and incidentally to fill some gaps in my collection of tomb statuettes, and then to explore Manchuria and Korea for both biological and cultural reasons. Unfortunately the trip started under a bad star. Aboard the Japanese steamer that took me to Dairen, the port of southern Manchuria, I caught a bad intestinal infection. After I recovered I started on my excursions, which were greatly facilitated by introductions received from Viscount Goto, who once in his distinguished career had also been head of the Southern Manchurian Railway. This meant, actually, ruler of the province. The railway, which meant the local government, put at my disposal a beautiful limousine with a chauffeur, and thus I was independent and could go where I pleased. Of course I had to visit schools, hospitals, agricultural experiment stations, and all those cultural establishments in which the colonial government took pride. Such visits were very tedious to an Occidental, for they followed a definite ritual at the basis of which lay the Oriental concept that decent people are never in a hurry. Thus a visit always began with a long session in a reception room over a cup of tea, in solemn silence once introductions had been made. Only when this had lasted for a long time could business begin, and then the conducted tour had to be carried out without hurry. But I visited all the institutions I was expected to see, accumulated mountains of printed matter, exchanged heaps of visiting cards, signed my name over and over again, and at last was free to see what interested me.

The most interesting excursion I made was to the battlefield at Port Arthur where I climbed to the forts that the Japanese had stormed after the bloody siege in the Russo-Japanese War. I think that with today's weapons this formidable fortress could not have stood for twenty-four hours. Needless to say, the ruins of the forts, with a sweeping view over the famous sites of the siege that kept the world breathless fifty years ago, and over the narrow-mouthed harbor of Port Arthur in the background, were very impressive. To my surprise I found in Port Arthur a splendid archeological museum especially rich in works of art of the Chinese Tang period, which the aristocratic and cultured bishop of the Honganji sect of Buddhism, Count Otani, had brought from Chinese Turkestan.

On my way back to Dairen I passed through wooded hills of the type preferred by my moths, and I kept my eyes open. Suddenly I espied an egg batch high upon the trunk of a big tree. I stopped the car, climbed on top, and succeeded in bagging the quarry. The native chauffeur watched my antics with open mouth. When he saw me put the little piece of fluffy stuff most carefully into a paper bag, label it, and seal it, suddenly an idea flashed through his mind. "Is this a secret medicine?" he asked. I answered in the affirmative to save my face. The truth would certainly have qualified me as insane.

By chance I learned of a very interesting kiln in Dairen where a Japanese potter made copies of antique Sung pottery. This artisan owned the most perfect collection of genuine Sung vases I have ever seen, brought together as a study collection so that he could learn the art of producing the unique glazes of that period. All the famous types of white, blue, and green vases were represented in perfect specimens. The man had perfected his technique so that the copies he made were hardly distinguishable from the originals, at least to the amateur collector. The potter sold his products honestly as new ware, but I wonder if, once in circulation, some of the pieces were not promoted by collectors or dealers to the status of genuine antiques.

During the weeks in southern Manchuria I made many observations that convinced me that the next world war would begin right there. In *Neu Japan* I discussed these impressions. The book, which appeared two years later, was reviewed by General Haushofer, the much-discussed originator of "geopolitics," Hitler's mentor. Haushofer recommended it for its geopolitical outlook. It is interesting to remember this now since Haushofer (whom I later met frequently when we were both members of the board of trustees of the purely cultural Japan Institute) is considered by some to have been the actual author of Hitler's plans for world conquest. This is probably untrue. Haushofer's son was to become one of the victims of Hitler's savage revenge after the failure of the historic *attentat*.

The strenuous wandering around in the Manchurian summer heat produced a return of my intestinal condition, and I went for a rest to a pleasant seaside resort, Hoshigaura, which the Southern Manchurian Railway had established near Dairen with a rather comfortable Occidental hotel. But my condition got worse and worse, and, since my experience with one of the railway physicians was not very reassuring, I decided to proceed to Tientsin where many European physicians practiced. The trip on a small coastal steamer was not very pleasant, though. I had for a cabin mate a Chinese businessman who did not move from his bed during the two or three days, never undressed, never washed, and littered the room with melon seeds, which he chewed uninterruptedly. In addition he slept with half-open eyes, looking like a corpse when I entered the cabin at night.

When I arrived in Tientsin I called at once upon a friend to have a good physician recommended to me. He gave me the address of a German doctor whom I consulted. The big ruddy man heard my story and when I had finished declared that I had amebic dysentery and must take the tedious cure for it. Though my medical degree is only an honorary one, I knew that amebas cannot be diagnosed without microscopic examination, and thus I left in disgust the doctor who was willing to treat me without verifying his diagnosis. Then a Russian physician was recommended. This fine-looking old gentleman started at once to make a microscopic search for amebas. After a few minutes over the microscope he exclaimed, "Here they are!" and gave me a description of the characteristics of this famous parasite. Fortunately I had had to lecture on parasitology in my younger days and knew that the features the physician was mentioning were those of a harmless ameba usually present in the human intestine. A look into the microscope confirmed my suspicion, and I paid my fee without telling what I had seen. After these two experiences I decided to leave the ugly town of Tientsin and its largely alcoholic foreign colony and to proceed to Peking where the Germans kept a first-class hospital. In addition there was the Peking Union Medical College of the Rockefeller Foundation staffed with excellent parasitologists. These specialists immediately declared that neither amebas nor dysentery bacilli were present. After a couple of weeks I was dismissed as cured and was able to revisit my favorite places in Peking, enjoying again the timeless charm of that unique city and hunting for tomb figurines to supplement my collection.

I intended to make an extended trip into the interior, especially for a visit to the Lungmen caves and the Gobi Desert. After much delay I received a passport from the ruling war lord—a beautiful document with huge seals. Just then my intestinal trouble broke out afresh, and I began to feel weakened from my exertions in the summer heat without sufficient food. I therefore had to cancel the trip to which I had looked forward with such eagerness. But I decided that I was in need of a proper diagnosis of my ailment, which had not yet been made. Knowing that the Japanese professors had an excellent basic training and were therefore good diagnosticians, I decided to look for the nearest Japanese medical school. This was more than a day's ride away in Mukden, in Manchuria. Armed with some cans of Swiss Tell milk, an excellent safe food, I traveled to Mukden in a terribly hot train filled to the limit with officers and officials of the war lord Chang Tso Lin, who ten years later was blown up by the Japanese in exactly the same train.

The Japanese doctor in charge of the big hospital turned out to be a very good physician who also spoke German fluently. He made the correct diagnosis and prescribed the proper treatment. But the hospital where I had to stay for three weeks was impossible. I have already mentioned the haughty attitude of the Japanese scientist toward technical details. The same excellent physician who acted perfectly correctly from a scientific point of view had no interest whatever, and probably also no influence, in the management of the hospital, which was atrocious. The mattress on the bed in my first-class and rather expensive room was a bag filled with rice straw, which made a surface to lie on like the spiked bed of an Indian fakir. The bed sheet was two feet too short and was not changed once during the three weeks. There was no pillow, and the bed was never touched by the nurses, who took the patients' temperatures, and so on, according to prescription but otherwise did nothing for them. There was no such thing as washing, and I had the greatest difficulty in obtaining water daily for my primitive washstand and still more in having the used water removed. This was not on the nurses' program, and they could not understand why the foreigner wanted such crazy things. Still more impossible was my idea of shaving daily. The Japanese have little beard, if any, and for the nurses a man who shaved every day was an outrageous phenomenon. Thus I had to get up and make the bed myself and wash and shave at the other end of the large room. Also, the diet was left to the head nurses, who sent me the first day as a diet for a kind of dysentery pickled abalone with cucumber salad. After that I ordered water rice and milk as the only diet that the Japanese hospital kitchen could furnish. Fortunately, later the German consul, General Fischer, and his charming Norwegian wife sent me chicken broth and also provided me with books. When I was finally dismissed as cured, I had lost thirty-eight pounds.

My last Eastern trip was to Korea, again both for field work and for personal instruction. Korea, as I knew it then, was a beautiful country with rolling hills and high mountains inhabited by mild-mannered, good-looking people. In their white flowing clothes, modeled after the style of the Chinese Han period of two thousand years ago, they gave a characteristic flavor to the cities as well as to the countryside. The men walking around in a dignified way, wearing the ridiculous little top hat made of horsehair, appeared as symbols of undisturbed conservatism, and one can understand how the friendly, slow-moving people were no match for the aggressive Japanese. The women were frequently very handsome, and among the professional entertainers I found real beauties. I could not help liking these people, and I felt very happy wherever I went in Korea.

In the capital, Seoul, I delivered a lecture at the imperial university, of which my friend Shiga, the famous bacteriologist, was president. Later much time was spent in the two palace museums, which contained beautiful collections of old Korean art, especially the remarkable early pottery and the overslender representations of Kuan Yin in bronze, some of them great masterpieces of sculpture. The hospitality of my Japanese colleagues made my sojourn interesting and successful. The kindness of the governor general, Admiral Saito, opened many a door, and I had the pleasure of a good conversation at the dinner table of this fine statesman who had most successfully administered the annexed country and pacified it after it had been upset badly by the cruel militaristic regime of Count Terauchi, the father of my moonlight-dancing general. Here again the well-known difference between the Japanese army, run by the Choshu clan, and the navy, run by the Satsuma group, became visible. Admiral Saito, who by the way spoke fluent English, was a perfect gentleman of great wisdom and erudition, and it would have been much better for Japan if he and his like had prevailed in the councils of the nation. But ten years after my visit, while he was prime minister, he was murdered by the militarists.

Traveling southward from Seoul I visited the site of the ancient capital of Kaesong. Here was an archeologist's paradise. All around, the country was covered with ancient tumuli, some ornamented with beautiful sculpture of the Tang period. The fields were strewn with decorated tiles of fifteen hundred years ago. On top of a hill was located a gorgeous temple dating back to the Tang period, and nearby, higher up, a cave contained some of the best existing Tang sculpture. I had the unusual opportunity of seeing a two-thousand-year-old tumulus opened. Kaesong was expecting the visit of the crown prince of Sweden, a well-known archeologist and connoisseur of Chinese art. In his honor a tumulus was opened, and I was able to inspect the site, which yielded some beautiful gold bowls.

I had to hurry back to Japan to give my last set of lectures in the imperial university of Kyoto. I was still a little weak from my earlier intestinal trouble and was generally run down. In Kyoto, in fact, I stayed in bed most of the time and got up only for my lectures, which otherwise I could not have carried through, and there was still a considerable strain ahead of me when I returned to Tokyo: final lectures before various learned societies, farewell calls, and innumerable farewell dinners in Occidental and Oriental houses, in clubs, teahouses, homes, mansions, and palaces. Finally the day of my departure came. The station was black with people who had come to wish me Godspeed, and my compartment was filled with flowers and farewell presents. On the platform in front of everyone stood the group of girls who had assisted in my work, clad in gaudy kimonos and crying frantically, "Sayonara," while the train slowly pulled out.

When I look back at my two years in the country of the rising sun, from 1924 to 1926, before the militarists took over, they appear as a beautiful dream. I had set out, aside from my biological research work, to use the unique occasion to study the interesting country as thoroughly as possible. I think I succeeded. I had traveled or hiked over the country from north to south and from east to west, and I had visited all the outlying possessions of Japan except Sakhalin. I had learned much about history and folklore and had learned to cherish and love the greatness of Oriental sculpture, painting, pottery, and all the arts and crafts. I had met with the people of all classes from the highest to the humblest and had seen that they are not different from others—some good, some bad —and I had found that the valuable people in Japan were as easily understood as anywhere and that our differences were no hindrance to sincere friendship. In short, I had observed the whole people in their pleasures and sorrows, in work and play, in their great cultural performance as well as in the shadowy sides of their lives. I think that I not only carried away an inexhaustible treasure of memories but was personally immensely enriched in those two years full of great and lasting impressions.

My trip homeward was made on the Siberian Railway. Once again I traveled all through southwestern Japan, took the ferryboat across Tsushima Strait to Korea, and made the daylight trip through Korea. The Southern Manchurian and later the Northern Chinese Railway took me through the whole length of Manchuria to the Russian border. The train ride through Siberia with its huge prairies and, farther west, its flat country sprinkled with birch groves is anything but exciting except when picturesque Lake Baikal is passed. Conditions on the train itself were still rather poor. There was a well-appointed dining car, but the *tovarischi* who served made it so clear that they did so only as a special favor accorded to the inferior beings called *burschui* (bourgeois) that I did not frequent this institution except for breakfast. At that time the Siberian peasants still had food, and at the larger stations, where the train stopped three times a day for twenty minutes, peasant women sold black bread and butter, roasted partridge, and suckling pig, and in the station restaurant pressed caviar was obtainable. Thus we—an English official of the Chinese customs and I—bought delicious meals and ate them with our fingers in the compartment. None of the major breakdowns usual at that time on the Siberian Railway occurred, and the only excitement was furnished when a German lady sleeping alone in a compartment was robbed of everything, including her warm coat and her passport. The poor destitute children who roamed at that time in gangs over Russia and who boarded the train each night and traveled unmolested on the platforms until daylight—a heartbreaking sight—were blamed for the robbery. But I have reason to believe that it was carried out by the personnel of the dining car.

Finally we reached Poland and then soon the German frontier, and it was a great relief to travel again in clean cars, to see the well-cultivated countryside, the clean farmhouses, and well-dressed people after two weeks of seeing only poverty and misery. In October, 1926, I was back in Berlin.

The difference between the Germany I had left two years before and the country I re-entered in 1926 was amazing. I had left when the country was still suffering the aftereffects of inflation. The houses were run down, and there was no new building; the railway cars were ramshackle, the doors without brass, the windows without leather straps, the seats without upholstery; the shops contained very little and very poor merchandise; clothes were made of shoddy material; there were no imported luxuries like bananas and oranges, not to mention rarer delicacies; there was very little pleasure in life, and there was a terrible class hatred.

Now everything had changed. The streets were again as clean as they had been in old Germany. Houses were being repaired and painted. In the suburbs, large blocks of inexpensive, modern houses were being built. In the afternoons crowds again filled the popular coffeehouses; drank real coffee and forgot the word *Bohnenkaffee* (bean coffee), which had distinguished real coffee from *Kaffee*, which had meant ersatz coffee; and with their coffee munched their beloved fruit tarts with mountains of whipped cream, the product of a cow and not of a chemical factory.

People were well dressed again, and the shop windows in Berlin looked like those of a capital. American factories assembled motorcars in German shops, and normal traffic again appeared in the streets. The theaters were crowded, and stage designers vied with one another in staging large shows either serious or light, but always with highly artistic settings. The great artists of the world appeared again and filled the concert halls, and the diplomatic corps, the state departments, the wealthy bankers and industrialists entertained luxuriously as they had done before the war.

The gloom had disappeared, and people again had a good time without feeling remorse. The levity of the postwar years, which had set in immediately in the victorious nations, now came also to Germany. The dancing craze took hold of the young people, and the old ones traveled when there was a chance. The arts received a new impetus, and there was considerable activity in painting, sculpture, literature, and architecture with the accent on the modern radical styles. Architecture especially made huge strides after the long stagnation, and when building began again some of the great talents erected modern buildings that were milestones in the development of this art. Just at this time American films, which had been excluded by the rate of exchange, came in again, and the great revolution of the talkies occurred. Theaters were crowded with people who came to see the first successful German talkie, *The Blue Angel*, which brought fame to Marlene Dietrich. It was soon followed by an earlier American novelty, Al Jolson in *The Jazz Singer*, much admired for its technical advances though often its cheap sentimentality made it artistically far inferior to *The Blue Angel*.

The general recovery also affected science. The government of the republic did its best to restore German science to its former high level. At the same time everything was done to repair the broken lines of international science. There was no difficulty with the Anglo-Saxon countries, which were anxious to return to intellectual sanity. But official France still insisted upon the boycott of German science and held up the restoration of good will, though individual French scholars came to attend meetings in Germany and to renew old friendships. The Kaiser Wilhelm Society for the Advancement of Science, which had struggled through the hard years to keep its laboratories running, now came to the fore again. The government allotted relatively large funds to make up for the lost endowment, and even in times of the most bitter party strife the Reichstag unanimously voted the funds for the society. With increasing wealth, private funds again became available, and even the disgruntled monarchists, soothed by the fact that the republic did not change the name of the society, collaborated again. Under the spirited and clever mangement of the great scholar and diplomat von Harnack and his aides, particularly Dr. F. Glum, a brilliant and liberal administrator, the laboratories enjoyed an amount of freedom rarely duplicated. We had our funds allotted to us as a whole, and, with no other restraint but ordinary bookkeeping and auditing as required by law, we could use these funds for our work as we saw fit without red tape or bureaucratic interference. It was an ideal condition for work, and I have every reason to be grateful to fate that I had many years of work under such circumstances. My own experimental work could be done on an unusually large scale. A special new unit was built to take care of my needs, permitting me to handle about one hundred thousand animals, and during the breeding season I could augment my standing staff by a dozen extra helpers to carry through the work. Working was really a pleasure with all the conditions necessary for success.

With the improvement of external conditions, foreign scientists began again to flock to Germany, and naturally the Kaiser Wilhelm institutes were especially favored with visitors. I had no teaching duties, I did not accept students, but all available laboratory space was filled with visiting scholars from all over the globe who contributed their share to the intellectual atmosphere of the place. There was also much to do outside the laboratory. The Kaiser Wilhelm Society founded new research centers, took over existing institutes, and considerably widened its scope of interest. In numerous other scientific enterprises it was represented by members of our staffs. I had the pleasure of doing my share in many of these undertakings, either by being delegated to the board of trustees as the society's representative or by being appointed a trustee.

After my return from abroad, I pointed out that the society—with all its international affiliations and the constant stream of visitors—had no social center such as was found in the faculty clubs of American universities. I succeeded in interesting the men at the helm in a project to create such a center, and money was made available to erect the Harnack House, a clubhouse for the institutes, a social center for the society, and a place where foreign visitors could be put up and entertained. I had the pleasure of serving on the board of trustees of this club until the advent of the Nazis (when I voluntarily laid down all my trusteeships), and the house turned out to be a great success.

One unusual extramural activity of mine has some historical interest. The newly created ministry of health had appointed an advisory council on which I served until the Nazis came to power. The problems of this council were mostly of a eugenic nature. We were to prepare legislation on such matters as abortion, help for large families, sterilization of defectives, and so forth. The work was rather interesting. It brought me, who otherwise had always been *Homo apoliticus,* for the first time into contact with the mentality of the politicians. On the board were represented the major political parties, at that time (1926–30) the Catholic Center and the Socialist parties. It was interesting to see that in almost every instance where we recommended some legislation on medical, biological, or ethical grounds, one or the other of the parties objected on grounds based on nothing but cheap party politics. At that time I also learned a lesson about women in politics. I had always been a champion of women's rights, which had been completely won in Germany after the revolution. On this board, the parties were frequently represented by female members of the Reichstag. They had a complete mastery of the techniques of the political speech and talked glibly about all our problems. But it was disappointing to listen to eloquent speeches that did not succeed in hiding the complete ignorance of the speakers, and in this the women considerably outdid the men.

Rather interesting was the last session of this board, which I attended in 1932. After long discussions a well-balanced proposal for eugenic legislation had been worked out, a compromise among the postulates of the eugenicists, the exigencies of legal nature, and the ethical beliefs of the population. It contained the important points demanded by eugenics but surrounded them with caution and moderation in regard to their application. At that time the Nazis had become a large party in the Reichstag, and consequently two Nazi members attended the board meeting. When discussion on the final draft started, the first to speak was one of the Nazis, a young, fiery fanatic who later became the *Führer* of the medical profession. (This great Nordic was, by the way, the son of an Italian fruit dealer.) In a most aggressive and intolerably insolent speech he declared that the Nazis did not give a damn for what we were doing there. Tomorrow, when they were to take over power, they would make their own eugenic legislation, and therefore we might just as well end the meeting. Everybody was disgusted, but not long afterward the fellow's prediction came true. Actually the Nazis took over our entire plan (never mentioning its origin), but substituting the most extreme and most unethical methods of application for our cautious and humane proposals.

Unfortunately during these years, after 1926, the Nazis already had their predecessors in regard to interference with science. But at this time the culprit was the Catholic Center Party, which abused its power as the party at the helm much more than the Socialists had done. No money could be voted by the Reichstag for purposes of teaching and science without the consent of the clever and shrewd but utterly ruthless prelate Schreiber. He was perfectly willing to yield, and he actually did much for the intellectual life of Germany, an uncontestable fact for which he is still today highly honored. But the price for his help had to be paid in the form of professorships for Catholic scholars or duplicate professorships for "Catholic philosophy" or similar presents to the church militant. Of course he also played a considerable role in the councils of the Kaiser Wilhelm Society, where I had to attend many meetings with him and where we had to keep him in good humor. Even there, in the most prominent scientific body of Germany, he succeeded in striking his bargains.

Probably the most disgusting performance I attended had to do with the preparation for a biological expedition to the tropics sponsored by the Kaiser Wilhelm Society and the government. I was a member of a board that was to consider the plans together with such men as Herr von Krupp. At the end of the proceedings the chairman, a very meritorious but political-minded former minister of education, suddenly announced that in addition to the experts chosen to head the expedition another man, a second-rater, was to take part. In my naïveté I objected and gave my reasons. General silence fell, and finally the intimation was given that this appointment could not be changed. Later I found out that Schreiber had agreed to secure government funds on the condition that this second-rater would be a member of the expedition. The prelate had tried before to push the man into a professorship, but the university in question had refused him. The expedition was to be the balm for his wound. I certainly was disgusted and never again gave advice when I suspected political interference behind the scenes. But I must honestly say that, reviewed in the light of events after 1933, even Schreiber turned out to be a poor beginner in the game of political interference with science.

I have mentioned the great interest of the young German republic in the promotion of science. Universities and research laboratories flourished again, and the individual scholar became once more an important member of the commonwealth, both socially and financially. Meetings of scientific bodies were handsomely treated by the government. The yearly general meetings of the Kaiser Wilhelm Society became, with the collaboration of the government, first-class scientific and social events. I remember one occasion at which the Prussian government invited the society to a chamber music concert in the candlelit eighteenth-century theater of a Potsdam palace. Foreign scholars visiting Germany were given every facility and entertained by the government. When in 1927 the first international scientific congress, the Congress of Genetics, was held again in Berlin, the governments of the republic, of Prussia, and of the city of Berlin itself provided such large-scale entertainment with gorgeous banquets, gala operas, and the like that it was almost embarrassing.

My own activities during these years increased more and more, and looking back I can hardly understand how I managed all the different things I had to do in research, lecturing, editorial work, traveling, attending board meetings, writing reports, handling an immense international correspondence, and taking part in social activities in the most diverse circles. A considerable amount of time was devoted to editorial work. I revived the *Journal of Cytology*, which I had founded twenty years earlier but which had become a victim of the war; took over the biological *Centralblatt;* and also joined in the editorship of a few more periodicals, which meant a huge correspondence, conferences with the publishers, and reading manuscripts and proofs in four languages.

What I enjoyed most of this type of work was based upon an old hobby. In my younger days in Munich my old teacher Hertwig had interested me in university extension work, and I had consequently developed a gift for popular writing and lecturing and published a few books of popular science. While in Japan I had been requested to write such a book on heredity for a Japanese popular encyclopedia of science in a series of volumes. This I had done, and my friend Terao had made the Japanese translation. This book I wanted to use as a beginning of the realization of a plan I had cherished for a long time.

I presented to the leading scientific publisher of Germany, my friend Dr. Ferdinand Springer, a plan for a series of popular science books written by eminent scholars. This broad-minded publisher, who never shrank from an undertaking because it meant a financial risk, at once accepted my plan and the proposed title, *Verständliche Wissenschaft (Science Made Understandable)*, and my book, together with one on bees by my friend von Frisch, opened the series and was a great success. The book sold 15,000 copies before the Nazis stopped the sale of this "non-Aryan" work, and it was reprinted after the fall of the Nazi regime. I succeeded in enlisting the interest of many scholars, and most of the thirty or so books published under my (anonymous) editorship fulfilled the expectations. I made a point of checking on every word of every manuscript to be sure that a layman could actually understand it, and I did not issue a book until it came up to the standard I had set. Many scholars who had never written a line of nontechnical prose produced admirable and successful books, and I am proud of this contribution to the culture of republican Germany.

The general and widespread interest in the results of science that went hand in hand with the reawakening of the idealistic spirit under democratic institutions also led to a demand for popular writing. I think it is characteristic of the intellectual situation during these years that the leading daily newspaper of Germany, the democratic Frankfurter *Zeitung,* started publishing weekly reports on the progress of science written by experts, not by newspapermen. I took over the biological department and contributed regular reports for many years. Other papers as well as magazines frequently asked for articles on scientific subjects, and I do not know how many I wrote.

All over Germany clubs, societies, and city governments encouraged and financed lectures on scientific subjects, and I made innumerable short trips in Germany and Austria, as well as the German-speaking parts of Czechoslovakia, to deliver talks to huge and attentive audiences. I enjoyed very much this type of lecturing, for the layman who voluntarily attends such lectures is the most attentive and grateful listener, infinitely superior to even the best student audiences. Another possibility of working in the same direction was offered by radio broadcasts. Radio in Germany was even during the time of the republic a government institution. Each owner of a radio set paid fifty cents monthly, and the radio was completely free of advertising. The government ran two different types of sending stations: one for general broadcasting and entertainment, the other exclusively for educational purposes under the direction of an erudite professional man. I was frequently asked to broadcast lectures over this system, and these broadcasts had the additional feature of being very well paid.

During these years I also made many pleasant trips abroad to neighboring countries, especially to Italy, Switzerland, Austria, and Yugoslavia, for work or pleasure, but only a few deserve special mention. The Czechoslovakian state invited the geneticists of the world to participate in a celebration of the hundreth birthday of Gregor Mendel, the Austrian monk who discovered the laws of heredity named after him. When the young Czechoslovakian state had been established after the war, nationalist zealots had mutilated the statue of the *nemec* (German) erected in Brno in Moravia near the monastery where Mendel had been abbot. Now the marble nose was repaired, and the Czech state claimed Mendel as one of its great men. The celebration, which I attended as a delegate, was a fine demonstration of the international spirit of science. For the first time since the war the Czech and German citizens of Brno were brought together. The municipal theater gave a gala performance in which first a German company performed an act of *Die Meistersinger* and afterward a Czech company an act of Smetana's *The Bartered Bride*. All the participants thought this a good omen for the future of Czechoslovakia and enjoyed the demonstration of good will between the two countries—only ten years before the enslavement of the Czechs by Hitler.

Another pleasant interruption of daily toil was offered by a trip to Geneva. Mrs. Margaret Sanger of birth-control fame had organized a world population conference to be attended by a number of selected delegates from all countries. It was said that her husband paid the costs of the conference, which must have been very high, for the expenses of each invited delegate were paid. I felt that I was not entitled to this honor—I was also asked to preside at one of the meetings—since the field was one in which I considered myself a mere layman. But I could not resist the prospect of a pleasant trip and interesting associations, and thus I spent a beautiful week among the charms of Lake Geneva in the company of some of the finest scholars of the world, many of whom I could call old friends. The organization was perfect, and the hospitality of the organizers and their wealthy friends rather overwhelming.

My most interesting trip abroad during these years took me to Soviet Russia, at that time a mysterious country even to its European neighbors. In January, 1929, an all-Russian genetics congress was to convene, and the Russian scientists invited Erwin Baur, Harry Federley, and me to attend and to deliver lectures. I borrowed a heavy fur coat from a friend who had lived in Russia before the war, and we three went together to Leningrad. The German consul general, Zechlin, a cultured and refined career diplomat with democratic leanings, invited us to stay in the palatial former imperial embassy, which meant not only pleasant company but such rare comforts as a room with bath.

Leningrad was a sad sight. On the famous thoroughfare of the Nevsky Prospect only a single government shop was open, exhibiting the poorest merchandise. All the other stores were closed, and the shop windows were covered with boards. The people looked very poor and miserable. But there were beautiful museums to be seen. We visited the Winter Palace and the Hermitage, with its gorgeous art collections of a hardly believable richness, accessible to everybody and always crowded with the ruling proletariat, eagerly listening to the explanations of official guides, mostly women. In a basement the unique collection of so-called Scythian-Siberian art was exhibited, and it was a real revelation. Another museum contained a glorious collection of icons from their early Byzantine origins on.

Through the courtesy of our colleagues we had occasion to visit many highly interesting creations of the Soviet government, especially schools in which selected men and women of all the manifold nationalities within Russia were trained as political leaders. The famous imperial opera was now the people's theater, to which everybody was admitted. We were invited to a performance of Tchaikovsky's *Swan Lake,* and it was a strange experience to see the former imperial ballet perform their classical dancing before an audience of class-conscious proletarians. In spite of the complete revolution in all the arts, evident in painting, writing, and architecture, in dancing the old-fashioned ballet alone kept the interest of the people. Later on in Moscow I saw a very different performance. Though the dancing was also classical ballet, the work itself, Glière's *Red Poppy,* was a big piece of propaganda, depicting the liberation of Oriental "wage slaves" by the Russian navy. The setting and dancing were so beautiful, however, that one could overlook the crudeness of the political background.

Speaking of shows with a political background, I should mention the amazing film *Salamandra,* which I saw in Leningrad. A couple of years before, a scientific tragedy had occurred which most biologists remember. Professor Kammerer, working in Vienna, had made the sensational claim that he had proved the inheritance of acquired characters. Although he had done much interesting work, it was generally assumed that his data were none too reliable, and it had even been claimed that some of his data had been tampered with. I myself had seen his work in Vienna and was unfavorably impressed with the condition of his experimental setup.

One of his claims was to have produced by external agencies the dark thumb pad that is normally absent in a certain toad in connection with a special mode of propagation. This pad was supposed to be the final proof of Kammerer's contentions. In his collection there was a specimen in alcohol, showing a beautiful pad. This specimen was studied by an American, Professor Noble, who found that the pad had been produced by injection with India ink.

It was never really clear what had happened. Kammerer claimed that a trick had been played on him, but this does not seem probable.

At that time biological science unanimously declined to accept the possibility of the inheritance of acquired characters, but the Soviet government was of a different opinion. Some fanatic had come to the conclusion that the Marxist doctrine required the inheritance of acquired characters. The idea was that the proletarian if given a chance would acquire wonderful traits, and that his offspring would inherit them, thus improving the proletarian state. (It did not occur to these men that the dogma could also be turned around and be used to prove the superiority of the old aristocracy.) When Kammerer, the chief exponent of this so-called "Lamarckian doctrine," had been exposed, the Soviet government offered him a chair in Moscow. He accepted, but before leaving Vienna he ended his own life.

This tragedy had been worked into a propaganda film by the Commissar for Education Lunacharsky, who himself appeared on the screen while his wife played the leading lady. A salamander was substituted for the toad. The hero, modeled after Kammerer, was a great idealist, a great friend of the people, and by implication a Communist. A sinister priest, the villain, induced the hero to accept as an assistant the priests' tool, a German prince disguised as scientist. This man secretly injected color into the professor's specimens. Then a big university meeting was arranged at which the scholar was to present his proofs for Lamarckism, the proletarian doctrine hated by the church and the aristocracy. He made a splendid speech and showed his specimens. When he had finished, his enemy among the professors stepped up, took the specimen, and dipped it into water—and all the dye ran out. The young scientist was chased in dishonor from the university. Living in misery as an organ grinder with his monkey, he finally decided to commit suicide. But Lunacharsky, who had heard of the professor's fate, sent one of his former students to bring him to Russia. The student arrived just in time to save the hero from suicide and brought him triumphantly to the Soviet Union, the country of the free.

At the same meeting there was present an unknown agronomist, Lysenko, who, miraculously soon, succeeded in convincing the political bosses and Stalin himself that the science of genetics, which repudiated the doctrine of inheritance of acquired characters, was a devilish counterrevolutionary invention. He proceeded to replace it by his own brand, a partly mystic, ridiculous doctrine based upon "facts" furnished by his intimidated collaborators. It is well known how Lysenko, under the protection of Stalin, whom he glorified as "our teacher, the transformer of nature," made himself the dictator of genetics and agricultural science; how he liquidated or banished the best geneticists; how he destroyed research and teaching of this great science and made Soviet biology the laughingstock of the world. For twenty years this outrage was accepted sheepishly by all the enslaved nations, and was hailed by the Red press as Soviet biology.

The genetics congress in Leningrad was extremely interesting. I had never before witnessed such genuine enthusiasm. The huge halls were crowded with listeners, and the papers, lectures, and discussions were on a very high level. I greatly enjoyed meeting many of my old scientific friends and making the acquaintance of the fiery young generation of enthusiastic Bolsheviks. My colleagues of the older generation, of whom few if any had been converted to communism, still held their positions but had to be very cautious. Their private lives in very small apartments were not cheerful, and most of them worked day and night in their laboratories, for outside life was too drab to be enjoyed. The government had given these scholars special funds for entertaining foreign guests, and thus my friends were able to provide some of the old-fashioned Russian hospitality. The dinner parties in the small, overcrowded, and shabby apartments, usually only a bedroom, were the most elaborate culinary performances. Mountains of the rarest and richest food, perfectly prepared, were washed down with streams of vodka and Crimean wines. The happiness of the hosts and guests, all of whom had seen better days and still had the grace, charm, and erudition that used to characterize the Russian intellectuals, made us glad to be the cause of a sunny day in their not too pleasant lives.

Among the interesting excursions in which we could take part one was especially pleasant, a visit to Czarskoe Szelö as guests of the Red Army. At the station we were met by sleighs driven by Cossacks. In the harness were the famous Orlov trotting horses, a breed used in former days in the imperial stables, huge nervous creatures that trotted at an unbelievable pace over the frozen snow while the Cossack drivers raced one another. We were shown through the Summer Palace, a very beautiful example of Italian baroque architecture filled with exceedingly beautiful old furniture, hangings, and fixtures, then a national museum but destroyed in the second World War. The last czar had disliked this sumptuous palace and had erected nearby a modest villa, the interior of which was a showplace of the degeneration of a great family of rulers. Whole walls were plastered with unbelievable numbers of cheap icons, and the drawing rooms were filled with knickknacks of the worst kind, including pictures cut out from newspapers and pasted to the walls. After having seen this place one understands the tragic correspondence between Nicholas and his empress and the fantastic dependence of both upon Rasputin.

From Leningrad we proceeded for a week's visit to Moscow. I lived in the room that my friend the great biologist N. K. Koltzoff occupied in his laboratory. He himself was out of town, and I suspect that he had left on purpose in order to avoid suspicion, for he was being closely watched by the secret police.

I had first met this fine scholar and charming and cultured personality as a young student working at the Russian marine biological laboratory in Villefranche, and we had become friends for life. Like all intellectual Russians, Koltzoff had been a liberal under the old regime. Being a man of independent means he spent a good deal of his time abroad and could often be met with in the laboratories of western Europe—in Naples, Heidelberg, Munich, and Roscoff—an always welcome visitor. He eventually became a professor in Moscow and made his reputation by excellent research work.

At the beginning of the Soviet regime he got into a bad situation that was not his fault. When the White Russian general Denikin marched on Moscow he made up a list of prominent men whom he intended to put in charge of the state, and Koltzoff was one of them. Denikin was beaten, the list was found, and Koltzoff was imprisoned with the others and condemned to death. Finally he was pardoned because, it was said, too many had already been executed. While in prison he contrived to make daily exact measurements of his metabolism, following carefully the changes produced by prison food and by such mental shocks as the death sentence and the pardon. He afterward made his peace with the Bolsheviks and kept completely away from politics. To me he spoke only once of the dangerous subject, when he was my guest in Berlin. He said that he and his wife, who had been very wealthy before, felt much happier now that they were poor.

Koltzoff succeeded in building up the first and finest Russian laboratory for experimental biology and the center of genetic research in his country. But in spite of his official position he was always closely watched and frequently got into trouble, for example, when he worked on the pedigrees of great Russians like Pushkin and honestly said that they were not of proletarian origin. Many times rumors went abroad that he was in serious trouble, but somehow he managed to keep his place. When, in 1927 or 1928, a group of the leading Russian scholars was sent to Berlin for a Russian scientific week, he was the leader and charmed everybody. It was the last time I saw him. Only a few years before his death the clouds gathered again. I have mentioned the intrigue against the science of genetics started by the plant breeder Lysenko. When this fanatic ignoramus won out, Koltzoff was forced to close his famous genetics laboratory. Things must have become very unpleasant for him, for he stopped answering my letters, and this meant that correspondence with men abroad exposed him to suspicion. It is a miracle that in the age of purges and liquidations he died a natural death. I am proud to have had such a noble man as a lifelong friend.

Koltzoff's room was a nice large one, which was remarkable since housing conditions were still abominable. Old Professor Nawashin, for example, one of the classic botanists, had his bed behind a curtain in his laboratory, and this was all he had at the end of a distinguished life. Another well-known scientist occupied half a room with his family, and behind a curtain another family lived in the other half. New building had only started in 1929, and what is now a modern metropolis was then not much changed from imperial days. The houses were in bad repair, and the town looked rather gloomy. There were hardly any automobiles, and the streetcars were overcrowded.

But food seemed to be plentiful. A market already famous in Czarist Russia as a source of delicacies was open for business and was stocked with huge barrels of caviar and piles of sturgeon. When I wanted to buy some caviar to take home and hesitated between the different brands, I was given a spoonful of each to taste, an amount that would be worth many dollars in America. There were not many public eating places, and we had dinner only once outside our friends' homes, in the large hotel kept for foreign visitors. As soon as we sat down a man took a seat at the next table and started reading a paper. He was, of course, an agent of the secret police, but I wonder if he understood the German conversation.

We were fortunate to receive a special permit to visit the Kremlin, which at that time was otherwise closed to the public. In front of one of the numerous buildings an old lady sat on the stairs in the warm midday sun. It was Clara Zetkin, once a violent and rabid leader of the German Communist party, who had come to end her days in the Bolshevist paradise. With her stood the state president Rykov in a heavy fur coat and cap, quietly chatting.

In 1928, I had occasion to realize that I was not any longer as young as I wanted to be. I celebrated my fiftieth birthday. My wife had invited as a surprise a big party of my friends. Before dinner a quartet of old instruments performed seventeenth-century music, and my friend, the conductor Dr. Ernst Kunwald, played for me the "Appassionata." I had every reason to be happy, and I felt as strong and active as could be. The word fatigue was unknown to me in work, play, and exercise, and I could not imagine that this was not to last forever. But soon afterward I caught a severe flu, which ended with an unpleasant heart condition, a first warning. At that time I did not heed it. When I had recovered I went for a few weeks' work and rest to the Naples zoological station, an ideal refuge for the biologist, and soon I was again climbing the hills and playing a good game of tennis with a coach.

My experimental work with the material I had brought from Japan proceeded well, but when I was ready finally to finish with the problem that had occupied me for the past eighteen years I realized there were still a few gaps in my material that should be filled before I could drop the subject as finished. In order to have a complete picture of the geographic variation of my moth in connection with evolution, I had to find material from missing or critical localities in a series of stations all over the Eastern region. Thus I had to consider another short collecting trip to Japan. This time it was not difficult to finance the expedition. I laid plans to arrive in Japan at the time in late summer when I could expect to find the newly laid eggs of the gypsy moth and could return with them in time for normal hibernation until hatching time in spring. Very few preparations were needed, and in August, 1929, after a short visit in England, I sailed for Canada in order to reach Japan by the shortest sea route.

12: THE ORIENT ONCE MORE

The crowded steamer on which I enjoyed the jolly company of Hans Zinsser of Harvard took me to Quebec, whence I proceeded to Toronto. I knew that the Ontario museum contained the finest collection in the world of the old Chinese tomb statuettes of which I was a collector and student, and I was most anxious to study the material. The collection had been gathered by a businessman, Mr. Crofts, who had traveled a great deal in the interior of China and had actually been present at the secret openings of some of the tombs. It was therefore a most authentic and complete collection, though unfortunately Mr. Crofts left no notes. My visit was certainly no disappointment, and I was able to go carefully over the immense material and learn quite a few new facts and interpretations.

From Toronto the excellent Canadian Pacific took me across the continent and over the glorious route through the mountains to the beautifully located city of Vancouver. Then on one of the fine Empress boats of the Canadian Pacific, actually a former German boat, I embarked on the foggy, cold northern route to Japan via the Aleutians.

The company on this trip was rather interesting. There was the late Professor Hobson of the British Museum, the greatest authority on Chinese pottery, who was on his way to China in company of the poet Binyon; the anthropologist Seligman; and a few other China collectors like Sir Percival David. Hobson impressed me especially by the fast game of deck tennis he was able to play at his advanced age. I met him once later, when I called on him in London in the interest of one of the victims of Nazi persecution and he showed me through his famous collection. Two men aboard were treated as the most honored guests by the Canadians: one was a newly appointed minister to Japan, a politician whose head seemed to have been turned by this honor and who paraded himself like a peacock. The other was a modest and insignificant-looking wiry young man who was on his way to a position as a forester in Malaya. But he had been for years the champion sculler of Canada,

The author and his wife with the Hassan family, Hyderabad,
1926

The Maharana of Udaipur, 1926

Corner of the Goldschmidt home in Berlin

and this made him such a big man that even the ambassador talked to him.

When I arrived in Japan I was received by my friends and started at once to prepare my collecting trips to the regions I had mapped out. I remained only a few days in Tokyo, where I delivered a lecture to twelve hundred students in the new auditorium of the rebuilt university. Then I started north to collect in the Nikko and Karuizawa mountains to fill a gap in my knowledge. In both regions German friends residing in Japan had summerhouses, which I could make my headquarters.

In Karuizawa I had a piece of bad luck. One hot day after lunch when everybody in the house was having the customary siesta I went off to climb a nearby wooded hill where I expected to find some material. While I was looking up the tree trunks in my search, I stepped into a hidden hole and sprained my ankle terribly. With the greatest difficulty and pain, I succeeded in making my way home on the steep mountain path and lay down on a couch in the garden to wait for my hosts to appear. When they finally came, my foot looked like an elephant's foot, and a doctor had to be called. Fortunately nothing was fractured. But I had to keep on my back and could move only by hopping on one foot. The following night about midnight I was awakened by a terrific explosion, which I could not understand. Only when I heard people rushing out of the houses did I realize what had happened. The neighboring eleven-thousand-foot volcano Asama, which I had climbed fifteen years before, had erupted. Soon hot pumice stone began to rain onto our roof. Fortunately none came through, and no other explosion followed. But I did not feel very happy with the thought that I would not be able to walk if evacuation should become necessary.

When the swelling of my ankle had gone down sufficiently to allow me to hobble around in one shoe and one slipper I had to move on. My plans had to be carried out according to schedule, and the time approached for a trip covering the narrowest part of the main island from the port of Tsuruga on the Japan Sea to Ise Bay on the Pacific and certain surrounding territories, especially the shores of Shikoku. My oldest Japanese student, Kyoshi Katsuki, had offered to be my traveling companion, and I gladly accepted, for his presence eased many problems of transportation and police supervision, the plague of foreign travelers in parts of Japan not often visited. I later learned that in his devotion to his teacher Katsuki had spent all his savings upon this rather expensive trip.

This devotion to the teacher is one of the finest traits of the Japanese, and I had many occasions to be grateful for it. On this trip, wherever I went my former students came from hundreds of miles away to meet me and usually traveled with me for a few days so that our evenings could be passed in pleasant company. During the day they assisted me in collecting. Usually the government entomologists of the region helped me also, so that my egg hunting was often done in company with six or eight men, some of them acquainted with local conditions.

The way this field work was carried out is worth reporting. In the beginning I worked under the usually correct assumption that the gypsy moth lays its egg batches on tree trunks, occasionally on telegraph poles but preferably on isolated trees. Therefore, we went usually on foot, sometimes by bus or car, to the region selected for working and hiked all day long over the hills looking at each isolated kaki or *kiri* or hinoki tree. Sometimes we were successful, and sometimes a whole day's work was in vain. Then I made a surprising discovery. In Japan, where all homes were built of wood, the moth had assumed the custom of flying for egg-laying to the nearest house, when one was available, and laying its egg batches in the shade of the overhanging roof. After this discovery, work became very simple. Instead of roaming the woods and mountainsides in strenuous search, we just proceeded to the nearest temple ground, which was always covered with trees, or to a public park. Very soon the spongelike egg batches would be spied under the roof of a temple or of a teahouse in the park. A friendly priest would not object to bringing a ladder when we explained the situation to him. Thus we could move swiftly from place to place and cover considerable ground in a single day. When, somewhat later, I came to southern Japan I called on my colleague Professor Y. Tanaka, the best silkworm geneticist in the world, in Fukuoka. He had tried to collect material for me in his neighborhood before and had always failed. Thus he was convinced that the moth did not occur there and smiled ironically when I told him that I had come to look for myself. When I returned after an hour from the famous and beautiful park of that city with a whole box full of egg batches the laugh was certainly on my side.

These trips carried me to many regions of the country where a foreigner was hardly ever seen, and I had a fine chance to renew my acquaintance with the still untouched old Japanese customs. Hospitality and helpfulness were met with everywhere. How often did we enter at noontime a schoolhouse where the teachers welcomed us at once into their reception room and brought tea to go with our light lunch of *zushi* (rice sandwiches boiled in vinegar) or *soba* (buckwheat noodles). In the small provincial towns there was always some society or a wealthy and prominent citizen to give us elaborate parties featuring the delicacies of the region, special vintages of rice wine, and the local geishas.

One such party in a small town on the shore of the Japan Sea impressed me especially, for unexpected reasons. At the time I was a passionate cigar smoker, and, since no cigars could be purchased outside of the big towns, for only a very few Westernized Japanese smoked them, I always carried my own carefully counted supply on such trips. After a delicious meal in a large beautiful room, served by pretty geishas, I happily lighted a good Manila cigar. The effect was revolutionary. None of those present, except my traveling companions, had ever seen a cigar smoked, and my antics in lighting the "big brown stick" produced a sensation. The host asked me for a try, so I gave him one. He lighted it, took a few puffs with every sign of horror, and passed it on to the next guest squatting beside him. Thus the cigar went the rounds like an Indian peace pipe but, judging from the grimaces and the coughing, was not a great success. This amused the geisha who squatted in front of me to serve me with sake and to make conversation, and she begged for a cigar as a souvenir. What could I do but give her one? She carefully wrapped it in tissue paper and it disappeared into the great depository of her kimono sleeve. Thereupon each geisha and guest asked for the same souvenir, and my whole box of irreplaceable cigars disappeared into the kimono sleeves—to dry up unsmoked in some souvenir box. I smiled but certainly did not mean it. The evening ended in a very characteristic way. When I took my leave to go upstairs, all the geishas came with me, put me to bed, and tucked me in like a baby, with continuous chatter and giggling. In this small provincial town the bed, spread on the floor, was the most gorgeous one I ever slept in, made up of comforters of heavy silk stuffed with fluffy silk wadding.

Thus, after the day's work, many a pleasant evening was spent in good company. Occasionally the work was interrupted for a day or two to visit some famous landscape like the bizarre tonguelike peninsula of Amanohashidate or some ancient temple or to be shown the private art collections of some of the former ruling houses in their old-fashioned noble mansions. For a lover of great art it was certainly a memorable experience to hold in my hand masterpieces of the great painter Sesshu, otherwise hidden in the fireproof *kura* of the mansion. Sometimes a day of rest was spent at one of the *onsen* (hot spring resorts), where usually an old-fashioned hotel with beautiful rooms opening into small and delightful Japanese gardens offered quarters full of the quaintest charm. Thus this field trip ended with complete success and satisfaction.

A short interval in either Tokyo or Kobe, where I stayed with old friends, was used for sorting, packing, and shipping my material, sleeping in a real bed, eating Western food, and delivering an occasional lecture or address. While resting for a few days in Kobe before starting again on a strenuous field trip, I had one of those small experiences, those fleeting episodes, that add color and beauty to a life filled with work. My friends had asked me to attend with them a concert given by a Spanish guitarist. I went along with a kind of snobbish condescension, for the guitar was known to me only as an instrument for accompanying the German equivalent of hillbilly music, or as associated with the repulsive *Wandervögel* of the early youth movement. I had never heard of the Spanish revival of the old instrument as a vehicle of serious music, though I was an inveterate and rather sophisticated concert-goer. When Andrés Segovia started playing I stared at him open-mouthed, just as I had done decades before when I first had heard his countryman Pablo Casals play the cello with the lightness and sweetness of a violin. Such musicianship on a guitar seemed unbelievable. Afterward I met the great artist many times and had a chance to be useful to him as interpreter in a difficult purchase of valuable corals. A few weeks later I saw him again in Tokyo. Once when I was sitting alone with him in his room discussing some musical subject he spontaneously took out his famous old instrument and played for me what amounted to a private concert. Only kings used to be able to have such an experience.

One of my trips took me to the beautiful region of the inland sea and the out-of-the-way island of Shikoku. This excursion was made in company of my old friend Ishikawa, whose inexhaustible knowledge of the country and its lore as well as his charming and jolly personality made him an ideal traveling companion. Again I found what I was looking for and saw in addition some new and interesting parts. Traveling to and from Shikoku I was surprised at the number of young professors aboard the small steamer. The reason was an unexpected one. The island of Shikoku is the home of the great Kompira shrine, and it was customary for Japanese going on a long trip abroad to worship first at the shrine, and then to come back to say their thanks after a happy return. I had not expected that the matter-of-fact young scientists would follow this ancient religious rite, and none of my friends and students had mentioned it. I must say that I liked them for their faithfulness to the ancient spirit of their country.

A last extended trip was made to cover the extreme southwest and the island of Kyushu, where transitional features between Japanese and Korean moths were expected to occur in my moth. Again former students joined me and traveled part of the time with me. The collecting went on as usual, the hospitality of old and new friends was charming, and many interesting spots could be visited incidentally.

In Nagasaki, which I revisited remembering the first glimpses of Japan I had received there fifteen years ago, I decided to spend a couple of days at the spa of Unsan. This resort, at that time popular in summer with the foreign residents of the hot cities of China, is located inside an extinct crater, the bottom of which is covered with hot springs, boiling mudholes, and *solfataras*. The place catered especially to foreigners, with foreign-style inns erected on flimsy scaffolding and looking anything but stable. We climbed the mountain on a rather hot and close afternoon. Soon after we arrived, the expected typhoon set in. Cloudbursts poured down, and the storm howled, shaking the flimsily built house to its foundations. The low atmospheric pressure made us feel nervous and miserable. Soon after I went to bed the house was shaken by a terrific earthquake. I jumped out of bed, and I must honestly say that I was frightened: the combination of earthquake, typhoon, and a shaky house built inside a volcano was too much for ordinary nerves. I listened and heard that my friend next door was up also, but since he did not leave his room I did not want to appear less courageous—we were the only guests in the house—and I stayed inside, too. I pushed an armchair near the door and slept there fully dressed, ready to leave at once if necessary. Two more smaller shocks came during the night and frightened me (and also my Japanese friend as he confessed next day), but nothing happened.

Back at Nagasaki, whence my student was to return to his university, we had an amusing experience before parting. At night we went for a stroll from our suburban hotel to the city. Returning in the pitch-dark night, we lost our way. After passing a dark canal we found ourselves near a large house, and fortunately there stood one of the new one-price taxis that would take you anywhere for two yen. We hailed it and gave the address of the hotel. The fellow drove his car around the corner, and there we were. We had entered the taxi at the side entrance of our hotel. Of course we had to pay two yen, which I found rather amusing, but it made my friend angry. The poor young scholar had to look at life from the viewpoint of an instructor earning forty yen a month.

My last stop on this trip was the charming town of Beppu, a popular spa. There hot springs were found under the sands of the beach, and the hot sand baths were considered a good cure for rheumatism. All around the city columns of vapor were seen on the lovely hillside. In the smaller spas near the town, the large pools were still used by both sexes simultaneously, and the bathers could be seen walking home from the bath with hardly any clothing on. But in Beppu itself the police rules, which forbade the old style of bathing, were observed.

The last day in Beppu brought me an agreeable surprise. Strolling through the streets I passed a residence at the gate of which hung large posters with Japanese inscriptions. My poor knowledge of Chinese characters did not suffice to read the announcement, but I gathered that an art sale was going on. I entered the house and found an auction sale of paintings. While I was looking over the exhibition of not very remarkable pictures I suddenly saw a beautiful old painting, which I was sure, on closer scrutiny, was a genuine work of one of the early Kano masters of the sixteenth or seventeenth century. I hardly believed my eyes, for the Japanese are great collectors and connoisseurs, and what we call "picking up" very rarely occurs in Japan. But there was no doubt about the quality of my find. Cautiously I inquired and was given a quotation extremely low but still too high for my purse. When I expressed my regret the auctioneer offered to call up the owner of the picture and submit the price I was willing to pay. To my great surprise the owner agreed, provided that he could get immediate cash. Fortunately I had the sum with me and could carry away triumphantly my picture, which experts pronounced to be exactly what I had taken it for. The painting has since been shown in many exhibitions and still adorns my home.

My work had been done successfully, the collected material had been safely sent to Berlin for hibernation, and I could say good-bye for the third and, as I know now, last time to the country of the rising sun. A Dollar liner was to take me to Manila. A couple of years before this journey, the president of the University of Manila had been my guest in Berlin, and when he left he entreated me to let him know whenever I came to the Orient. This I had done, and arrangements had been made for a course of lectures.

I arrived in Manila, which I had not visited before, with three weeks to spend in the islands. Since I had to give ten lectures and some addresses, I was not able to see more than any casual visitor would. I should have liked so much to visit the natives in the interior and on the islands of the Moros. But this was not possible, and I had to be content with seeing a few Igorot in the open market of the fashionable hill station of Baguio.

Since I was the guest of the Philippine university, which at that time had almost exclusively native professors, I mostly associated with the highest class of Filipinos, and this was in itself an interesting experience. The university was run after the model of American colleges, and many of the professors had taken their degrees in the United States. The teaching was excellent, and research showed promising beginnings. It was a novel experience to lecture to a class of small, white-clad, brown-faced men and girls at a temperature more than trying. The students did not seem different from any other student audience, and they apparently understood the lectures, which were given in English. Professors, students, and the hospitable president did their best to show me their institutions and customs. Gatherings were arranged in which native music and dances were performed by young people dressed in national garb. There was obviously a strong national movement among the intellectual classes, which expressed itself not only in the cry for independence but also in a renewed interest in the folklore and traditions of the islands—certainly a commendable aspect of nationalism.

Thus I had an interesting visit although I had to stay mainly in the hot city of Manila. Aside from the walled city, destroyed by the Japanese in World War II, and the water front where one took the air toward evening, Manila was just another tropical town in which the white men and some rich natives lived their separate lives in comfortable houses, cool clubs, and hotels, with much rather shallow social intercourse. Only a few were interested in the lives and problems of the natives, but I had the good luck to become acquainted with some exceptionally erudite men from whom I learned many things and who gave me reliable literature to read during the hot hours of the day when it was preferable to keep quietly indoors.

Through old friends residing in Manila, I also came in touch with the German colony, which was rather strong in some lines of business. Most of the big tobacco manufacturers were Germans, who showed me their interesting factories and provided me with a goodly stock of excellent cigars. Needless to say, I had to lecture at the German club, as everywhere, and to attend the unavoidable official functions. The cultural department of the Foreign Office had, without my knowledge, announced my arrival to all the consuls and embassies on my way, and in Manila as everywhere the German diplomats were most agreeable hosts and did everything to assist me. They were all career diplomats of the old school who served the German republic faithfully, though probably many of them were monarchists in their hearts.

During my stay in Manila another traveling German was entertained, the Olympic long-distance running champion Peltzer. I had met him in Japan where he was a member of a visiting team of athletes who had just succeeded in beating the Japanese by a small margin. Peltzer had been very unpopular on account of his grandiose prima donna manners. He had now come to Manila to run an exhibition match against the army and navy. He was received like visiting royalty, and even the American governor general gave a reception in his honor. It was probably the last glory of the swift-footed schoolteacher. When three years later the Nazis came into power he was put into a concentration camp because of his well-known homosexuality. This type of perversion was reserved for party leaders.

A charming feature of the Philippines was the retention of the old dress by the women. Men had adopted the tropical suit of the white conqueror, and the native suit was worn only for dance performances. But the women still wore the becoming dress derived from an old Spanish court style, with long skirts showing

250

at the bottom a rich lace petticoat, and a strange high stiff collar of medieval shape that emphasized the neckline, the main beauty, I think, of the native women.

This note on fashions reminds me of a perplexing feature of colonialism in those years. A man over twenty usually does not know anything of fashions and leaves it to his tailor to clothe him properly. Not so in the tropical colonies, where the fashion in dress prescribed strictly what a white man could wear without losing caste. When I first came to Java I brought twelve tropical suits—one uses two a day—cut after the fashion of the German African colonies. I found out immediately that this had become in the Dutch colonies the style for half-castes and westernized natives, and in order not to lose caste I had to order new suits with a military jacket closed in front, a high collar, and silver buttons. For dinner one donned a fresh suit of the same cut and added a shirt with cuffs. Black shoes had to be worn with the white suit and a black derby hat at night!

When I later came to the British colonies I had to discard my twelve new Dutch suits. Only half-caste clerks wore this garb, and the white man had to wear Palm Beach suits of duck or fine cotton. For dinner full dress with a boiled shirt was *de rigueur* whatever the temperature. When I returned a few years later to the same places, the duck suits had become the style for half-castes and only pongee or a similar material would do for me. Now, in the Philippines in 1929, my wardrobe had again become low-brow and had to be discarded, for a self-respecting white man had to wear white trousers with a cream pongee jacket and at dinner time a white monkey jacket. Since I never liked to look like the professor in the funnies, I simply had to follow suit and get new clothes each time as I changed from Dutch to English to American colonies. Thus even a learned man may be made to suffer from the inexorable tyrant, fashion.

For New Year's Day, 1930, I had a date with my wife in Ceylon. I left Manila on one of the worst passenger ships I have ever traveled on—one of the old group of Dollar liners. The discipline aboard was so poor that members of the crew fought on the promenade deck, food and service were abominable, and the purser, the officer with whom the passengers had most contact, was a roughneck who answered questions with insults. I understood why an American friend who had traveled to Siam on a boat like this wrote to me, "Never travel on such a bum boat!" But the "bum boat" did one good thing for me, or even two. Since the staterooms were exceedingly large, and I occupied one alone, I decided to take all my big baggage into it. While we were in Singapore a fire broke out in the baggage hold, and all the other passengers had their belongings damaged either by fire or by sea water. The second good thing was that it was decided that the ship would stay in Singapore over Christmas. This gave me a chance to make a trip through the beautiful and interesting Malay states and go aboard again in Penang a week later.

A Czech government official returning from the world power conference in Japan joined me, and we took the train to the capital, Kuala Lumpur, which we made our headquarters. From there we made beautiful excursions into the nearby mountains covered with gorgeous virgin forest, now the stronghold of Communist guerrillas, and saw also some of the local agriculture, especially the huge rubber plantations. One night, returning from such an excursion, we had an experience so typical of the tropics that it ought to be narrated. At sunset we arrived at a little station from which a train was to take us back to Kuala Lumpur. As we had to wait for two hours, I proposed to try to find some dinner. My Murray guidebook mentioned a dak bungalow (travelers' resthouse) somewhere in the neighborhood, and we engaged two Chinese ricksha pullers to take us there. The men ran off at full speed into the pitch-dark night through groves and paddy fields. My companion, who was visiting the tropics for the first time and probably had seen horror films of opium dens and murdered foreigners, was terrified and wanted to return. He did not believe me when I told him that a Chinese ricksha man in those parts either understood where you wanted to go and delivered you there safely, day or night, or did not understand and then took you to the nearest brothel. In this case, after some more racing through the night we saw a light on top of a hill and soon landed safely at the door of the dak bungalow, where a surprised native keeper hastened to prepare the usual meal of chicken and rice, moistened by a whiskey soda.

Kuala Lumpur, a pleasant tropical city located in a beautiful valley, boasted a museum with a fine collection of Malay arts and crafts and also a zoological collection. Entering the museum hall I noticed a stone slab with the names of benefactors and former officers, and my eyes were arrested by the name "E. Duncker." It brought back to my mind a strange adventure this man had told me when he was for some time a guest in the Munich laboratory.

More than twenty years before, a millionaire in Hamburg had organized a "scientific" expedition to the South Seas for his playboy son in order to get him away from night clubs and race tracks. Duncker was hired as a zoologist, and the yacht started on its way. But soon Duncker discovered that the playboy had taken his boon companions along and that a considerable part of the "scientific" outfit of the boat consisted of champagne and liquor. Life aboard turned out to be a continuous orgy. When the yacht arrived in Singapore, Duncker jumped ship and found himself in the Orient with hardly any money. By some chance he learned that a zoological curator was needed in Kuala Lumpur. He spent the last of his money to get there and was given the job. For years he did good work there until he returned to Hamburg.

Meanwhile the playboy's expedition proceeded to the South Seas. On one of the coral islands the members went ashore and in their intoxication cut down coco palms and made a bonfire. Sitting round the fire and carousing, they started taking their guns apart to grease them. But the natives, incensed by the wanton destruction of their trees, pounced upon them at this moment and killed all of them. When Duncker told this story, he added that after all it seemed it was sometimes wise to jump ship. Now, after more than twenty years during which I had not seen the man again, I found his name engraved on a stone tablet in the heart of the Malay peninsula.

When we reached Penang we learned that our steamer would be five days late because of the fire. So we enjoyed some charming though hot days roaming around this beautiful tropical island in the daytime and walking the streets of the picturesque Chinese district at night. Finally the boat arrived and took me to Colombo in Ceylon, where I found my wife in the hotel at which we had arranged to meet. She had arrived from Germany the very same morning.

The following weeks in Ceylon were one of the happiest vacations I ever had. Too much has already been written of the tropical beauty of this island, and the pen of a poet is needed to do it justice. Nowhere have I found such a combination of manifold charms. There was the most beautiful landscape—the shore with the surf rolling into quiet coves overshadowed by coco palms, the great mountain scenery, the gorgeous virgin forests enlivened by herds of monkeys, and the quiet lake of Kandy amidst forest-covered hills. Fitting in with the scenery was the beauty of the mild Singhalese men and women going quietly about their work in the villages hidden among fruit trees and palms. There were the great ruins of the ancient city of Anuradhapura, dotted with huge stupas, and the rock fortress of Siliguri with its gorgeous view. There was the most sacred temple of Kandy, with its off-shoot from the Bo tree in the shade of which Buddha had meditated and the holiest of all relics, Buddha's tooth, exhibited in a small tower watched over by yellow-robed priests. (As a zoologist I feel rather miserable that I have to say that it was certainly not a human tooth but seemed to me to be a crocodile's tooth. But such details of natural history are irrelevant when millions believe that they have set eyes upon Buddha's tooth. What, after all, does the body of the Buddha mean to those who have listened to his teachings?)

We spent a quiet week at Kandy visiting the bazaars and walking around the holy lake after the daily thunderstorm had subsided. A series of more or less extended excursions then took us in a leisurely way to many of the beauty points on the island, with pleasant rides through jungle and forest inhabited by monkeys and wild elephants and with stopovers at the simple, beautifully located resthouses. There was not the smallest thing to disturb the harmonious beauty of those days. When and where will the present generation find a chance to pass such weeks of carefree enchantment at peace with all mankind?

We had to get ready for our planned trip to India, which involved one chief preparation, namely, engaging a valet, without whom no white man could travel. Indian railways did not provide sleeping accommodations, and each traveler had to carry his own bedding. A native valet took care of the bedmaking, the baggage, and all intercourse with lower castes, and even in the hotels he provided the room service. Railway cars included a small compartment for the servant with a little window opening into the master's first-class compartment.

The fellow we engaged had been highly recommended, but he made a very bad impression. A mean-looking, elderly, black southern Indian by the name of Joseph, a Christian convert, presented himself. Since his credentials were good and no other man was available we had to take him. He certainly contributed to our entertainment. There was no day without some trick being played on us. He cheated far beyond what one would reasonably expect from such a man. He stayed away whole afternoons and returned intoxicated. He shunned any work and did not move a finger if he could help it. He cheated his own countrymen even more. When we took a train he engaged three to six carriers for our little baggage—he never burdened himself with anything more than a small parasol my wife had bought—and he did not pay the carriers in spite of all remonstrances until the train moved. Only then he threw a few miserable coppers onto the platform and left the men howling with rage. On our bill we found afterward at least ten times the sum he had spent. We finally called him "Joseph *der Hund*" (the cur) because his meanness was subhuman. I could fill pages with all the tricks he played on us. When we stayed at Darjeeling in the Himalayas we froze terribly at night in our thin blankets. We were sure we had carried extra blankets for this trip, but Joseph *der Hund* denied it. When we returned to hot regions I found the extra blankets in our bedroll: Joseph had used them for himself. The only time he grew meek was when I dismissed him at the end of the trip without the customary tip. My first and last experience with a valet was certainly no success!

We crossed on the ferryboat over the so-called Adam's Bridge from Ceylon into the southern tip of the mainland, and at once everything changed. The luscious beauty of Ceylon gave way to mud, desert, and flat ugliness. The beautiful, gracious, and happy-looking Ceylonese were replaced by dark southern Indian peoples, still handsome, and the slender women frequently even beautiful, but looking poor, miserable, and sad. We knew that we had come to a country of poverty and unhappiness for the masses. One of the sources of their abject condition we could recognize at once: the oppressive religion of Brahmanism.

Our first stop was Madura for a visit to the famous Hindu temple. Here we had our first chance to live in the accommodations offered to the foreign traveler by the Southern India Railway. The less said the better, especially regarding the sanitary arrangements. Our visit to the temple, one of the few great Hindu temples that the foreigner was permitted to enter, was arranged for the night, with an old dignified Brahman as guide. Among the many sights I have beheld in my life I do not remember any that could compare in outlandish, almost terrifying weirdness with this one.

255

The temple was a huge walled enclosure, the high walls adorned with a series of towers, gopuras, covered over with stone masonry in that wild style so characteristic of southern Indian Hindu architecture. Inside this quadrangle was an intricate arrangement of halls, courtyards, and pools. The interior was illuminated with thousands of small oil lamps, which produced a mysterious dim light. The halls and courtyards were filled with innumerable worshipers, all quiet and in apparent religious ecstasy. The large pool was filled with bathers who also drank from the holy water—what a source of cholera and typhoid! One long gallery flanked by columns with especially savage masonry was filled with sadhus (holy men), most of them naked, terribly besmeared with ashes and paint, their hair and long beards unkempt. Some of them squatted and seemed to wait for alms; others prostrated themselves with their faces against the stone floor. It looked, in the flickering light, like a scene from Dante's *Inferno*.

As we turned a corner an immense old elephant with painted ears approached us, begging with his trunk. At the end of another gallery a door led into a dark passage at the extreme end of which an arrangement of lights could be seen. This was the holiest part and not accessible to us. Breathless and in actual awe we walked around; it all seemed to be a dream and a horrible one, too. Finally we returned toward the entrance, which we never would have found again without our stately old guide. In the last hall one of the highest priests saluted us and hung *leis* of highly scented flowers around our necks. The guide whispered that the priest expected a present. (Imagine a bishop or dean waiting for a tip!) I handed him two dollars, which was then a huge sum for an Indian. Expostulating wildly in his own language he returned the money and asked bluntly for five dollars, which he could say in English. Now I got disgusted and returned his flowers to him.

This was only the first experience. Our entire trip through India, especially in and near temples, was to be a constant fight with beggars of unbelievable insolence, lepers who begged stretching their rotten limbs right into our faces, priests of the highest caste shouting angrily for tips, even babies at their mothers' breasts putting out a hand. Some beggars, especially some with ugly sores, followed us around for hours, clamoring and whining. I never had seen before such misery and depravity.

The same temple revisited in the daytime, when only a few worshipers were around, did not exert the weird fascination it did at

256

night, and we were able to study more closely the architecture
and sculpture. Afterward we visited many comparable temples
and especially the old temple ruins in the neighborhood of Tanjore,
Madras, and Puri. They were extremely interesting as a strange
architectural development, and some of them were adorned with
fine sculpture in the classic Indian styles. But these statues never
impressed us as works of timeless greatness as did the sculptural
masterworks of old China and Japan. Even the highly interesting
works of the Greco-Buddhist era from western India exhibited
in India's museums seemed to be monuments of great historical
importance but not great works of art that could make the be-
holder feel a better man.

Thus we traveled from Madura to Tanjore and Madras, looking
at the remains of a great past and seeing incidentally, on our excursions, the primitive villages and the general poverty of the
natives, the mud huts plastered on the outside with cow manure
drying for fuel, the naked or half-naked children playing in the
hot sun, and the only creatures who have benefited from the
Brahman nightmare, the half-wild sacred cows and bullocks who
are the real masters of the road. In Madras, a relatively comfortable
big city boasting even an aquarium and a kind of biological station, we left the coast and went inland through arid country inhabited by huge herds of gazelles. The dust blew into the train
through the closed windows, and the heat became formidable. Our
goal was Hyderabad, then capital of the largest state ruled by
the immensely rich Nizam. Traveling through the state we wondered how these princes succeeded in squeezing their riches from
the terribly poor population. Hyderabad was a rather attractive
city with pleasant Mohammedan—that is, originally Persian—
architecture. In the surrounding area we visited old forts and
templelike mausoleums of princes and scholars on high rocky hills
overlooking the gray, sterile countryside. It was frightfully hot,
and the primitive inn did not furnish much comfort. But by a
strange chance we had a most interesting experience.

One of my students in Berlin was a native of this town and in
good standing with the ruling class. He had provided me with introductions to a series of maharajas, and I was to announce my
arrival in order to be put up as guest of the state. But I did not
feel like making use of this and went as an ordinary traveler to the
simple inn, nor did I intend to call on the great to whom I carried
introductions. One day as we strolled through the hot streets we

passed a bookshop that sold English books and entered to look for a local guidebook. While we were waiting I spoke to my wife in German. A young good-looking Indian dressed in the typical homespun garb of the Gandhi followers, obviously the owner of the store, overheard us and addressed us in perfect German. He had lived for four years in Leipzig to learn the trade of publisher and bookseller. He told us that his younger brother was just ready to go to Germany to study as an engineer and that another brother had already been there for some years, sent by his government. I asked where he worked. "At the Kaiser Wilhelm Institute in Berlin," he answered. Thus it turned out that the bookseller was the brother of my student.

When I later, after our return, asked my student why he had given me letters for all those maharajas but none to his family, he answered, "They are too humble people for you." Actually, when the young Gandhi follower took us to see his family we met some very charming people and had the interesting experience of entering a strictly Mohammedan house. The old father was a theologian who was writing a book on the sectarian differences between Shiism and Sunnism. He greeted us and then quickly disappeared into his study. The mother, of Persian birth, was one of the finest women I have ever met: intelligent, witty, energetic, a great linguist, and in addition a fine-looking lady. She and her daughters and sons made us feel at home. They were outwardly strict Mohammedans, and the ladies kept the rules of purdah. The daughters went to school not only heavily veiled but in addition in a cab with closed, blackened windows. But it seemed that foreigners were considered to be outside the strict rules, so I could sit with the unveiled ladies and even take their photographs in the garden enclosed by high walls. This entire family contributed greatly to our pleasure, and we were grateful for their hospitality.

Advised by young Hassan, the publisher, I afterward made use of two of my introductions and did not have cause to regret it. One was to Sir Hydari, then minister of finance and education, considered to be the most prominent Indian statesman under British rule. He turned out to be a man of great distinction and erudition who was especially proud of the things he had done for education and art. He kindly offered me a special guided trip to the famous Ajanta caves with their ancient murals. Unfortunately I later had to cancel the arrangements because we cut our stay by two weeks. While we were in his mansion for tea the sunset approached and the host bade us excuse him, as he had to say his prayers. Meanwhile he left us in two rooms that contained a gorgeous collection of Mogul miniature paintings more than equaling the famous ones in London, and we had leisure to enjoy them quietly.

Another maharaja, Sir Salah Jang, with whom we arranged a visit, was of a different kind. He was obviously only a very rich snob who owned a number of huge palaces where we were received. In the first one he showed us his collection of old armor and old Persian books illustrated with miniatures, rare and beautiful treasures. Afterward he offered to show us his major collections in another palace. After what we had seen we were prepared for a great surprise, and surprised we were, though in a somewhat unexpected way. The nobleman—or maybe his father—had apparently traveled a great deal and brought home about everything in bad taste that the tourist and souvenir traffic produces. Of these horrors he had not one piece each, but rows of them, and a large number of rooms and halls were filled with them. From France he had brought a whole army of plaster of Paris nudes; from Italy cheap marble and alabaster busts of nude women; from Egypt furniture in a mixture of Pharaonic and *nouveau riche* style, tables and chairs with elephant tusks for legs. England had contributed hundreds of canes; Germany a huge array of horrors in all materials, such as a statue of Bismarck clad as a blacksmith and forging the German empire with a hammer. Thus it went on through halls and rooms, and it was certainly difficult to express polite admiration. But in the midst of all this we came to a room with numerous pieces of the most beautiful old Chinese celadon porcelain. We certainly were glad finally to leave these chambers of horrors, although we were told that we had seen only a part of the "collection." We could not help thinking of the miserable peasants who had to toil in abject poverty on the estates of this and similar noblemen to furnish the money for the purchase of such abominations. I hope that our host, who was personally charming, could not read our thoughts.

A frightfully hot and dusty long trip with an additional night of sitting up in the waiting room of an isolated junction brought us from Madras to Puri on the shore of the Bay of Bengal. Famous for the mysterious Juggernaut temple, Puri also has a perfect beach stretching for miles with gorgeous breakers rolling in hour by hour. A small but clean inn offered us a chance to rest from the heat of southern India and to walk in the refreshing ocean breeze. Far away we could see the smoke of the funeral pyres, as the corpses of pious people were brought here for cremation at the open shore near the great temple.

The temple itself was closed to non-Hindus, but we were permitted to climb to the flat roof of a nearby house from which we could see at least the architecture and general arrangement, not very different from those of other large Hindu temples. Near the temple an open shed contained the god's cart, standing on huge wheels and forming a kind of richly carved miniature tower. This was the cart that was dragged triumphantly in procession at the temple festival when, it was said, religious fanatics used to throw themselves under the immense wheels to be crushed by the god. The unusually broad boulevard where this procession took place was empty when we visited except for the sacred bulls who were the masters of the sidewalks. In the surrounding area of Puri some of the most beautiful and richly sculptured temple ruins were found and could be visited in pleasant rides throughout the countryside. But they were infested with swarms of beggars, from priest to leper, worse than in any other place we had visited.

Rested, we continued our trip to Calcutta. The town was a strange mixture of huge greens and boulevards and horrid slums, where we visited some of the ghastly temples of Kali dripping with the blood of sacrificed goats. In one of them we ran right into a cremation, the details of which it is better not to remember.

While in Calcutta I remembered that Sir J. C. Bose lived there. I had met him before and was anxious to see the working place of this much advertised scientist. We informed him of our arrival and received an invitation to tea and a visit to his institution. Bose was originally an engineer but later turned to botany. He used his engineering talent to build refined instruments, which were attached to plants. The instruments produced graphs, which Bose explained as recording the heartbeat of the plant, and he wrote some books on his experiments in which he claimed to have discovered the soul of plants. Though the books revealed a complete ignorance of plant physiology they were much advertised. Bose became a famous man, was knighted, and considered himself the great Indian scientist. As he was very wealthy he traveled often to Europe, lectured in a half-scientific, half-mystical style, and of course made a great success of it, though the profession did not think very highly of his work.

In his home town Bose founded and endowed a laboratory where the most marvelous things were to be done, a kind of unification of the spirit of all living creatures. The place turned out to be what I had expected. A number of halls and galleries surrounded a large courtyard; the halls were the laboratories, and they clearly showed that no work was going on. But in some of the rooms and galleries an instrument was installed, and an assistant stood by to make a demonstration. We were to see the heartbeat and soul of plants. In each instrument hung a withered bit of some plant in touch with a lever, and from the instrument one could read oscillations. The oscillations were there all right, but nobody could say where they came from. One could think that Bose was honest, but too ignorant to know or to find out what his instruments were taking down. I have an idea what it was—but it certainly was not the heartbeat of the plants. The whole thing was just a joke, and I wonder how he could get away with it and be feted all over Europe as a great man.

Afterward he showed us his lecture hall ornamented with symbolic murals; he explained them as meaning that a kind of scientific Messiah would come, of course from India, to solve all the problems of the universe. Behind the desk stood a thronelike armchair, and this, Bose said, was reserved for the Messiah. No man as yet was great enough to sit in it, though there was a hint that he thought that he himself was nearest to that honor. Tea in his house was served by an English lady, in Indian garb, who lived in the house as a kind of adoring disciple. This made me believe that after all Bose was a fake.

We were glad to leave the uninteresting town of Calcutta to go up to Darjeeling in the Himalayas. It was winter, and this summer resort was supposed to be deserted. Indeed we actually had the mountain village, situated about seven thousand feet high and right in front of the highest Himalayas, almost to ourselves. The first pleasant surprise was the people, who are closely akin to the Tibetans. One of the most oppressive features of India was the eternally sad expression of the people. Thus it was a real relief to be again among smiling and laughing people. When we entered an Indian village we were soon surrounded by begging children with sad, unsmiling faces. In the villages around Darjeeling the youths also tried to get some pennies out of a foreigner, but they did it with laughter and riots of fun. We had another surprise here. With our baggage there was a rather heavy steamer trunk, and Joseph, our valet, always had trouble getting it lifted by a crew of Indian porters. At the station in Darjeeling a little, very old woman took the trunk, fastened it with straps to her forehead, and, putting her shoulder under it, singlehanded or rather singleheaded carried the huge and heavy thing on her back up the steep path to our hotel on top of a hill.

After a cold night, freezing miserably under our thin blankets, we got up at sunrise for our first glimpse of the Himalayas, which had been completely hidden in clouds the day of our arrival. The morning sun fell upon a long, high, snow-covered ridge, which soon disappeared again in the clouds and remained so the whole day. But when we got up the next morning we saw that the snowy ridge was a miserable group of foothills, maybe eighteen thousand feet high, and behind it towered the unbelievable height (actually over twenty-eight thousand feet) of the gorgeous massif of the Kinchinjunga. During the whole week we gazed at this mountain range whenever it was visible. We gaped in awe and admiration.

In the brisk cold mountain air of wintry Darjeeling we took many pleasant walks to the nearby villages of the natives and spent hours in the picturesque market, where the native women, carrying all their earthly fortunes in gold or silver around their necks, sold their goods. We were lucky to find a few really good pieces of Tibetan metal work and jewelry, and bargaining for them was great fun. Occasionally we met on our way our precious valet Joseph, who had nothing to do these days but make our room and sleep in our blankets. Because he spent for drink the money we had given him for warm clothes, he froze miserably. He had wrapped his head in a shawl like a man with a toothache, and he certainly was a great sight.

Our next goal was Allahabad. Here at the confluence of the two sacred rivers, Ganges and Jumna, is one of the holiest places of Hinduism, and every four years a great religious fair takes place to which over a million believers flock. They camp in the triangle between the two rivers and spend their days bathing in the holy floods, praying, and making great processions. This was the year of the fair, and though it was nearing its end we were in time to see some of it. The great masses were already gone, and the big procession in which hundreds of elephants and thousands of sadhus had participated was over. Unfortunately also one sadhu who had stolen the show had departed. He had swung over a burning fire suspended by his feet, for days on end. But there were still thousands of sadhus present, encamped in an area by themselves. They were either naked or clothed with a rope around their loins, and they looked ferocious and ugly. They had, we were told, repeatedly rioted, and people were afraid of them since nobody could possibly lay hands on a holy man. I suppose that most of them were more or less insane, which enabled them to stand unbelievable pain or, more correctly, not to feel it.

The rest of the still large crowd consisted of peasant families who waded in prayer in the shallow river or sat around on the ground doing their miserable cooking with a handful of flour and a little grease made into a paste. I wondered if a more cheerful and less exacting religion would not help raise the standards of those poor people. Whatever the sins of the British rulers may have been, they could not do very much in the face of exploitation by priest and landlord, and the barriers of caste and superstition.

A strange background to this fanatic fair was furnished by the University of Allahabad, one of the colleges then under British jurisdiction and run like an English university. I had not intended to visit learned institutions and colleagues in India, as I considered myself on a vacation. But, as I had known my colleague in Allahabad before, I informed him of my presence and was received most hospitably. Needless to say, I had to improvise a lecture, look over the laboratories, and meet the professors, some of whom, like the physicist Saha, were men of international reputation. I was especially impressed by the prominent role the ladies played here. Hinduism is in this respect very different from the usual Oriental notions. The town of Allahabad, located at the main highway to Calcutta, is rather pleasantly built, with stone houses painted in gaudy colors. But the best accommodation available was atrocious, and sanitation did not seem to have progressed very far in this university town.

From Allahabad we went to the centers of the old Mogul culture, Agra and Delhi, visited by all tourists and equipped with modern accommodations for the Westerner. On our way, like all tourists, we spent a day in Benares, that quaintest and queerest of all the holy cities of Hinduism, stretching along the banks of the Ganges. The river front with its palaces, temples, towers, and burial and bathing places has been described and pictured innumerable times, and it is just as strange a sight as one expects. I think it is, taken purely as a sky line, superior even to the New York water front or Michigan Boulevard in Chicago.

The sight of the innumerable funeral pyres upon which the dead were cremated in public next to the bathing places, and the whole religious life centering around the holy floods of the Ganges, was as weird and disheartening as anything we saw in India. Visiting the palace of one of the native rulers nearby, we had a chance to pass a large square where a popular fiesta was taking place, or what would have been a fiesta in Italy, Spain, or wherever people like to have a good time. Here a silent, sad crowd walked around; there were no stalls where anything could be purchased for grown-ups or children, no shows, no merrymaking. Only a very cheap and unappetizing confection was sold to the children. Again we were impressed with the poverty and the absence of laughter and happiness.

Agra, the city of the Taj Mahal, and Delhi, then the capital, have been too much described to call for another description here, as have the great Mogul monuments in the surrounding area. New Delhi was still abuilding. Away from the unbelievably filthy native town, in which the sidewalks were mostly occupied by the sacred cows and bulls and their excrements, Britain was building a modern capital laid out on an unbelievable scale with marble walks and huge and pompous government palaces and monuments. When finished it was to look like a dream of one of the old emperors come true, but I preferred the strict architecture of the Moguls to the Oriental-Occidental mixture of the viceroy's seat of government.

In Delhi we witnessed something that could be compared to the "Big Game" at an American university: the finals of the National Polo Game. The town was filled with maharajas who drove around in huge made-to-order Mercedes or Rolls Royces, clothed in the most fashionable English style, but with a diamond-studded turban on top. The game itself, in which the Maharaja of Jodhpur led his nobles against the team of an English lancers regiment, was the greatest sport I have ever witnessed, truly breathtaking. The tempo of the game was unbelievable. The Jodhpurs won in their national game, and they deserved the victory.

While we were in Delhi we made a decision typical of the Goldschmidt family. We fell in love with some Persian and Mogul miniature paintings, but the price was so high that we could not afford them if all our traveling plans were to be carried out. Faced with this situation we finally chose the pictures. We were already heartsick from the filth, misery, and poverty of India in spite of Mogul architecture, fascinating temples, and the strange life of the cities and countryside. Since some of the planned tours were only repetitions of similar sights elsewhere, and would mean many days of hot and dusty travel, we could easily renounce them. The interesting northwest and Kashmir were inaccessible at this season, at least for the traveler without unlimited time. Thus the only serious loss was a contemplated trip southwest to see the paintings in the Ajanta caves, and we decided to renounce even those in favor of the pictures for our own walls. We exchanged our passage for accommodations on an earlier steamer, which had the advantage of being a gay Italian ship instead of one of an English line with a reputation for dullness and poor food.

What was left of the more extensive original program was a trip to the independent states of Jaipur and Udaipur, in the country of the proud warrior race of the Rajputs. This last excursion turned out to be especially charming. Jaipur was a lovely town with big, beautifully ornamented, gaudily painted houses. The ruler, who inhabited a huge palace within the city, seemed to be especially fond of elephants. Nowhere else had we seen so many beautiful elephants being ridden through the street. I remember specially one young animal trotting with an elastic and elegant gait like a nervous thoroughbred horse. For a Westerner an elephant used as an ordinary riding animal is always a sight, and wherever we met with these intelligent giants—bathing and rolling over like happy children in a stream in Ceylon, begging like everybody else in south Indian temples, or trotting beautifully caparisoned through the streets of Jaipur—we enjoyed seeing them. Only once, in one of the courtyards of a south Indian temple, an immense old bull with long tusks gave us a scare. When we approached he suddenly charged my wife with a terrific trumpeting. Fortunately his hind leg was chained to the wall, and he could not get at us, but he certainly succeeded in scaring us.

Still more charming than Jaipur was Udaipur. The city with its quaint narrow streets made its way up a hill on top of which the immense and picturesque palace of the maharana stood overlooking a lake. In the little government resthouse where we spent the night an old English general told us that on the following day the birthday of the crown prince would be celebrated by an elephant fight. He volunteered to get us an invitation.

The next day the whole town had changed. Everywhere we saw nobles in elaborate old-fashioned dress covered with gold, silver, and jewels, wearing ceremonial swords and riding on beautiful ponies. The men looked exceedingly fine as so many Rajputs do. Most of them wore whiskers parted on the chin and standing out like quills, which produced a martial expression. We went up to the palace. At one end of the entrance courtyard the roof of a low building was divided into two sections, one for the foreign guests and one for the maharana and his court. Sitting in our section we watched the medieval picture of nobles galloping into the courtyard, jumping from their mounts, and taking their seats.

After some time the eighty-year-old maharana appeared, a most beautiful man with his white hair and beard dressed in the Rajput style. He was clothed in gorgeous jeweled brocade, and at his side was a heavy jeweled sword. When he was seated, the crown prince and, in the background, his ladies appeared on a balcony high up in the main palace. The poor prince was paralyzed by syphilis and could only watch his birthday celebration from the balcony. He looked fat and sad, very different from his picturesque father, who was said to have personally strangled a former wife of the crown prince. The elephant fight, in which the contenders were separated by a heavy barrier to prevent them from harming each other seriously, was not very interesting. But the whole setting was like a tale from the *Arabian Nights*. After the fight we were presented to the maharana and his court and were able to admire the costumes and jewelry, which the men were glad to show. And Elsa, impressed with the beauty and austerity of the old maharana, made her first and probably last deep curtsy.

At that time I wrote down: "This interesting day was a proper conclusion of the Indian holiday, showing the India which is usually the only one noticed by writers and movies, and which is an unimportant remainder of days that are bound to end, whatever the political future of India. After all, the native princes with their diamond-studded robes; stables of elephants; coaches of solid silver; Rolls Royces; cellars filled with coined gold, emeralds, and diamonds; concubines, tiger hunting, and trips to Paris, are parasites, belonging to ages long past and kept alive only artificially

266

for political expediency. This stands though there are some exceptions—princes who try to do something for their states, among them some very efficient women. Once in Berlin I was visited by the Sakwar of Baroda, one of the richest of all Indian princes, and his wife. He was rather uninteresting and supposed to be interested only in Parisian females. But his fine-looking wife, who wore an emerald set into her forehead, was as lovely as could be, interested in all problems, highly cultured and informed, and she probably made up for her husband's deficiencies. I suppose it was she who ran the state, which is said to be well administered."

From Bombay, where we had our last glimpse of the terrific social and population problems of India, we sailed for home on an Italian ship of the Triestine Lloyd line. This formerly Austrian line had kept up the good traditions of friendliness, good service, and good food, and thus we had a real pleasure trip through the Indian Ocean. The steamer was filled with English officers and officials and their wives bound for the long-looked-for home leave. They were in the greatest of spirits, making merry from morning to night and enjoying the pleasures of material civilization after dreary years in a cantonment somewhere in India. One of the happiest passengers started his breakfast with beer and continued with what would have been a holiday dinner for ordinary mortals. He had a face completely distorted by scars, which hid the visible expression of his jolliness. He was famous as a great tiger hunter, but once a tiger had got him and mauled him terribly.

We arrived in Venice after two weeks of uneventful traveling. As our ship turned toward the pier, past the Doges' Palace and into the mouth of the Grand Canal, past the church of Santa Maria della Salute, we espied our two grown-up children, Ruth and Hans, waiting on shore to welcome us home to Europe.

13: THE END OF THE GERMAN REPUBLIC

The following two years in Germany were very happy ones. I devoted my energy to finishing, on the basis of my new material, two major pieces of work—one on intersexuality and one on geographic variation—which had occupied me for over twenty years. In very large-scale experiments made possible by the excellence of my facilities and my technical helpers, I settled the last questions, published the last of a long series of papers on these subjects, and finally stopped working with the gypsy moth in favor of other studies that I had meanwhile begun. At the same time I was busy with all my other activities, gave numerous technical and popular lectures in different places, and enjoyed social intercourse with many groups of people.

The only unpleasantness came from the political unrest in the country. In spite of an excellent government and outwardly flourishing conditions, unemployment increased and with it the hosts of malcontents who adopted the Communist or Nazi creed. The two radical groups fought each other with fists and with words, and class hatred grew. The rising tide of Nazism openly defied the government, and uniformed Nazi guards marched around insulting or beating up citizens. The democratic government did not believe in force and did not act energetically. The *Junker* and the big industrialists paid Hitler in the hope of using him to destroy the hated republic, and Nazi fanaticism was reflected even in public life. Citizens who went to the beaches of the Baltic for a summer's rest found them converted into battling camps. Everybody built a sand castle upon which he planted his flag—rarely the black, red, and gold of the republic, more frequently the colors of the old empire or the swastika. This led to fights and unpleasantness, and people spent their vacations hating one another. Already anti-Semitic signboards appeared with slogans like "Here Germans want to be among themselves," and in smaller towns with large Nazi groups, Jews were beaten up.

We preferred under such circumstances to take our vacations abroad, especially in the form of spring trips to Italy. But we certainly did not foresee what was to come, for in 1931 we bought the house in Schlachtensee that we had rented for a long time and put in some improvements. The Kaiser Wilhelm Society was flourishing, its institutes were highly respected, and this reflected upon the standing as well as the material situation of the scientist. I led a most active life intellectually and socially and was able to make use of whatever talents I had inside and outside the laboratory.

Of course, the political rumblings had not appeared suddenly. There had been the free corps and the murder of Rathenau soon after the vengeful and stupid Treaty of Versailles. There was the childish Kapp *Putsch* and the famous tragicomic Beer-hall *Putsch* of Hitler and Ludendorff. If one had access to information on the underground doings of the Reichswehr, one knew that they, together with the big captains of industry, were preparing the overthrow of the hated republic. I had once watched such a group in action. During my second stay in Japan a kind of half-official mission arrived, led by Admiral Behncke, a good-looking and pleasant retired navy man who, however, served only as a front dressing. The real spirit of the group was a small navy captain—Captain, later Admiral Salwächter—a bombshell of energy and fanaticism. The German ambassador, Solf, was unhappy and embarrassed, for he had been warned that the group, which had been sent by the undercover militarists, not the government, was going to try to make secret arrangements with the Japanese militarists behind his back. I had many occasions to listen to the rabid conversations of the little captain, and I realized that he was indeed the spokesman of a military group bound to overthrow the Weimar government.

Besides the Nazis, the Communists, the moderate nationalists of the Stahlhelm group, the rabid militarists, and the different groups of reactionaries, there was another powerful influence at work to undermine the state. This was composed of the followers of the former great strategist of World War I, General von Ludendorff, after his separation from Hitler. Though they were not organized as a party, their intensive propaganda in speech and writing reached a large number of people, especially malcontents.

The soul of this movement was actually not the general but his wife Mathilde. Before the first World War, this remarkable woman, then Frau von Kemnitz, had been one of our friends, and we knew her extreme intelligence and devouring ambition. Her husband, one of my regular skiing companions, was killed by an avalanche, and after his death Mathilde had developed an interesting program of political participation for women, not as partisans of political parties but as exponents of the special gifts of women. I heard of this only after my return from the United States in 1919. One day while visiting in my home town I saw a poster advertising a lecture by Mathilde von Kemnitz and went to hear her. When she saw me in the crowd she gave me a signal, and after the lecture I spent some hours with her during which she told me the story of her second, unsuccessful marriage and discussed her political ideas, which were intelligent and clear.

Soon afterward she made General von Ludendorff divorce his wife and married him. Now a completely different woman emerged. Supported by the general, she began a career of wild political agitation focusing around savage anti-Semitism and anti-Freemasonry. She edited a magazine that was read by all the cranks in Germany and flooded the country with pamphlets and books on these themes. I myself read one book in which she "proved" that Mozart had been murdered by the Freemasons because he gave away their secrets in *The Magic Flute*. Schiller had also been murdered by the Freemasons with the connivance of Goethe! This stuff was read and of course used to undermine the republic because democracy was represented as being the hellish invention of Jews and Freemasons. (She disregarded the fact that German lodges were closed to Jews, who had to organize their own lodges.) We have often wondered what had happened to Mathilde. Had she gone crazy? I do not believe it. I think her burning ambition got the better of her intelligence. She thought she would succeed in making the general the dictator of Germany, with her as the first lady and the power behind the throne. For such a goal she was ready to prostitute her mind. She failed because Hitler was a much better rabble-rouser.

Among the trips abroad in those years, three were especially pleasant. The Kaiser Wilhelm Society entertained plans for a tropical biological station. I suggested a location in the Netherlands East Indies that could combine marine and inland work, and I proposed enlisting the help of the Dutch government. As it happened that my old friend and host in Java, Dr. Koningsberger, was Holland's minister of colonies, I was sent to the Hague to confer with him. I had a very interesting time, and the plan would probably have succeeded except that only two years later Adolf Hitler took over Germany.

Another trip took me again, after quite a number of years, to Paris. The University of Paris, the Sorbonne, had received an endowment for lectures by foreigners, and I was honored with an invitation as first incumbent for a group of lectures to be given in French. Before the first lecture I waited with my host Professor Caullery, still the dean of French biologists, in a small anteroom adjoining the huge lecture hall. From the hall came an ever increasing noise of shoutings and finally the sounds of a terrible hullabaloo. Professor Caullery became more and more nervous and finally told me that he was afraid there would be an anti-German demonstration staged against me by nationalistic students. He was quite pale when we entered the hall, which was filled to the brim with students and professors. But immediately the crowd was silent. The students had only been having some fun while waiting for the lecture, and now they listened in perfect order. I spent a very pleasant fortnight in Paris, visiting old sights and especially the museums of Oriental art. It was on this trip also that I finally paid a visit to Mr. Kahn at his estate in St. Cloud and delivered my belated thanks for the fellowship I had enjoyed seventeen years before.

Last but not least there was our silver-wedding trip. I had received, just in time for this occasion, a handsome honorarium for a new edition of my textbook on genetics, and Elsa and I were therefore able to take our children in grand style to Sicily. We went both ways on two of the luxurious steamers of the Italian-Egyptian line (both of which have since been sunk). It was a great pleasure to see again some of the beautiful sights of Sicily and add a few new ones, especially in southern Sicily.

For the summer of 1932 the American geneticists had invited the scholars of the world for an international congress, held every fifth year, and the German geneticists prepared for participation. At a meeting of the German Genetics Society, of which I was president, it was proposed to re-elect me for a third term with the assignment to represent the society at the congress. I was elected with one dissenting vote, that of Professor Plate, a second-grade zoologist known for his violent aggressiveness, the prototype of what is called Prussianism. He was, of course, a rabid anti-Semite and certainly did not hide it.

This pleasant person did not give up when he was outvoted. At that time the German trade balance was very bad and no one could take money out of Germany. This made it impossible for many German geneticists to travel to the United States. Our American colleagues, realizing this situation in Germany and other European countries, magnanimously collected a fund so that they could invite as guests a number of scholars and in addition arranged for paid lecture trips to enable these visitors to pay their expenses. I was so fortunate as to receive such an invitation. Plate, and such of his friends who had openly voted for me but were ready for an intrigue behind my back, now circularized the members of the society urging that it should not be represented at all since only very few members could attend the congress. Unfortunately one leading geneticist, Erwin Baur, whom I had considered my friend, took this movement in hand and invited me to resign my commission and attend the congress as a private person. I answered that I had been duly elected and would represent the society no matter what the men behind the scheme did.

Here is a strange twist of fate: the man just mentioned turned a Nazi when Hitler came to power. But he was a character and not ready to do everything the 150 per cent Nazis wanted him to do. Thus he had to fight for his and his famous laboratory's existence, and he ruined his health with the constant excitement and even danger. He died suddenly in his best years, a Nazi killed by super-Nazism.

The question of my representing the society was settled, but soon Hitler's paper, the *Volkische Beobachter,* brought notice to the congress of the importance of genetics for the Nazi racial creed. Unfortunately, they wrote, no real German could afford to attend the meeting; only two Jews had the necessary foreign exchange to do so. These are, of course, nowadays small, unimportant anecdotes, and I certainly only despised these people at the time, but I know now how completely I underrated their strength.

In the summer of 1932 I sailed to New York on a small, one-class, German boat. After fifteen years I revisited Woods Hole for a lecture and found that biological summer colony still a charming and congenial spot. Then I attended the meeting, which took place at Cornell University in the August heat—rather trying for those accustomed to more temperate climates.

Some of the delegates were made even more unhappy by prohibition, but I must say that I was more troubled by the necessity of drinking hard liquor than by prohibition itself. Whenever I went for a ride, somebody soon got out a bottle, and people who ordinarily never would have thought of drinking in the daytime or on the road did so. The home-brew I had to swallow under the name of beer was certainly hard on a former inhabitant of Munich, and the general interest in drinking, even among the learned profession, was amazing. I have never had so many unnecessary and uncalled-for drinks in my life as in the Eastern states during prohibition. The congress, though, was scientifically and humanly a great success and is pleasantly remembered by all participants from everywhere.

As my lecture trip was not to begin until September, I decided to carry out an old wish and spend some time in Bermuda, where a biological station at that time run jointly by Americans and British offered a fine chance to look at the fauna of the coral reefs. I spent a charming month in the lovely islands, working at a leisurely pace, watching Dr. Beebe preparing for his bathysphere dives into the abysses of the ocean, and playing a wild game of deck tennis in between. I made my first descent in a diver's helmet and generally had an instructive and pleasant semivacation.

This rest was badly needed, for the following lecture trip to the Middle West, Far West, South, East, and even to Canada was a rather strenuous affair. Innumerable lectures, speeches, and talks, and still more numerous parties and receptions offered by my hospitable colleagues, required considerable strength and endurance. For the first time in eighteen years I revisited California and Berkeley, honored as a visiting German scholar and completely innocent of any idea that this was soon to be my home and my country.

How innocent I was, in spite of all I knew, is best illustrated by the following episode. While I was staying in Woods Hole I was asked to speak on German political conditions in an open forum held on the lawn of Dr. Warbasse's mansion. The main thesis of my full review of the situation—in August, 1932—was that the danger of a Nazi government had definitely passed and the quiet elements in Germany had the situation well in hand. Since that time I have given up the business of prophesying. (It must be said, however, that at that time Hitler and his movement were at the end of their rope and would have disappeared but for the stupidity of big industry, which saved him in order to use him against communism. They actually believed they could handle him for their own purposes and later drop him. What fateful ignorance!)

My trip around twenty or so universities, renewing old acquaintances and making new ones, went on. When I came to New Orleans there was a flu epidemic, which I dreaded since I had once had unpleasant aftereffects from a case of flu. In New York I was attending a seminar given by J. B. S. Haldane, who was making a tour similar to mine, when I suddenly felt very miserable and went down with the flu. But since I had to give some lectures in Dartmouth three days later which were rather important for my budget, I stayed in bed only two days and continued my trip.

After Dartmouth I went up to Montreal to deliver the Sommerville Lecture at McGill, and I felt perfectly well again. After an elaborate French lunch with quite a bit of brandy I took a walk over snow-covered Mount Royal with my friend, the late Professor Huskins. There was a formal dinner, and then I started my lecture in a large, crowded hall. When I was about three-quarters through, I suddenly felt miserable, cold sweat broke out, and a ring seemed to be tightening around my chest. I sat down and, using all my energy, finished my lecture without anybody's noticing how I felt.

I assumed that this was again the effect of the not completely cured flu. The next morning I consulted a professor of medicine who did not make much of the case. Since I felt horrible, with disagreeable heart symptoms, I went to bed in the club where I had been put up. I was the only guest, and the old butler had to play nurse. I felt so miserable that I sent word to the professor to come and see me. His answer was that he would come only if I paid him. This I had, of course, taken for granted. But after his statement I felt that it would be just as good to have no physician. Thus I stayed in bed doing nothing special and feeling very low.

Events happening six years later prove that I had actually had a rather mild coronary attack, which should have required hospitalization. But my constitution must have been a pretty strong one, for I got up after three days, canceled my other engagements, and went to New York to sail home. I remember how I walked the streets of New York with a friend for hours before sailing time, an activity that ought to have killed a man in my condition. I had fortunately booked first class on the luxury liner *Bremen,* and I was able to rest on deck wrapped in blankets during the whole trip, except at mealtime, reading Axel Munthe's *Story of San Michele,* which was much talked about at that time, and which I thoroughly disliked. I felt rather poor for some months more though the physician could not find much wrong with me. Only after a spring vacation in Naples did I become fit again.

Meanwhile the world had changed tragically: Adolf Hitler had come to power. It will be good to remember, and to remind the Germans, too, that this criminal did not seize power but was elected in an honest democratic election that gave him a majority. President Hindenburg, already senile, was persuaded by the intriguing fox

The author's reception room in Berlin-Dahlem, 1932

Departure from Berlin, 1936

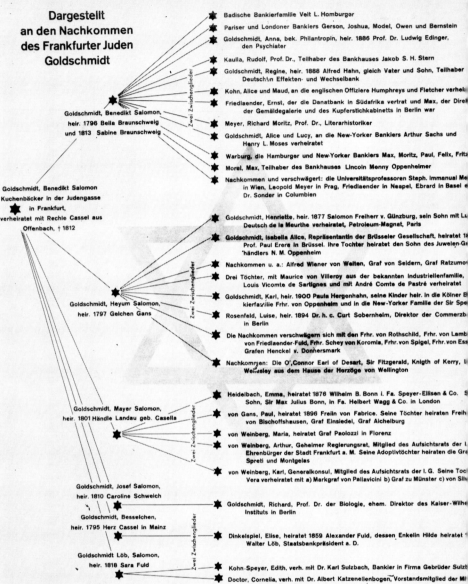

A Nazi propaganda poster tracing the Goldschmidt family tree

von Papen to offer Hitler the chancellorship. Hitler had arrived legally, and in the beginning showed—or played at showing—great deference to Hindenburg. Though he proceeded slowly in the beginning, I realized at once what was to come and decided to prepare for emigrating, though I was not yet molested personally. Many people did not take the new rulers seriously in the beginning, and even those who did thought that the Nazis, once in power, would become less extremist and fanatical. There were large groups among the industrialists, *Junker,* and even moderate conservatives who believed that they could use Hitler for their own purposes. Their leader, the stupid politician Hugenberg, remained for this purpose in Hitler's cabinet, and so did the leader of the Stahlhelm, a kind of American Legion but politically monarchist. They all had to learn their lesson.

What was in store they ought to have realized when the Nazis began to work. Hitler asked and received from the weak Reichstag the power to rule by decree, ignoring the constitution. As soon as this was done he began to organize the totalitarian state according to plan. One thing after the other was changed until soon the moment came when he openly defied whatever was left of law and right and took over the whole nation. All constitutional rights were suspended, and the Reichstag was dismissed and replaced by a body of S.A. men appointed by the *Führer.* One after the other the individual states were deprived of their rights, and the government of the whole Reich by Hitler's gauleiter was instituted.

Nazis were put in all decisive positions, though the actual work was still done by the old bureaucracy, which functioned like robots without asking who pulled the wires. Hitler's choice of the subleaders should have opened everybody's eyes. I do not think that ever in the history of mankind has a successful dictator surrounded himself with such a group of the lowest specimens of humanity: the vain, ridiculous, brutal, and efficient Goering; Goebbels, perhaps the greatest scoundrel who ever held an important position, but very intelligent and a great organizer; Röhm, the homosexual soldier of fortune, who later was murdered by his friend Adolf; Himmler, a sadistic schoolteacher, who first kept in the background but later, as head of the Gestapo, became an executioner and torturer who made Torquemada appear angelic; Hess, the homosexual melancholiac, slow-witted, but honest in his fanaticism; Frick, a narrow-minded, second-rate bureaucrat, but one of the most dangerous of the group because of his savage fanaticism; Rust, an unintelligent, morose schoolteacher who had been dismissed because of his inability and to whom German education and science were entrusted; Rosenberg, a half-Lett and former Russian, a clownish Wotan cultist and hyperracist, whose ideas were so totally mad that they appealed to Hitler beyond anything; Streicher, another sadistic schoolteacher, dismissed for cruelty from his teaching job, made ruler of Franconia and entrusted with the organization of pogroms and the publication of the filthiest sheet ever printed; and the gauleiter, less generally known, all of them completely uncultured, brutal, many of them drunkards or morally tainted. And what happened in key positions was going on all over the country. In every workshop, factory, business, laboratory, school, a Nazi took charge; in most cases he was the one who was known to everybody as a low type, a frustrated or unsuccessful person or somebody with a grudge, but always a man of fanatical devotion and energy.

The field I watched most eagerly was, of course, science. When the Nazis came to power it was expected that their first victims—aside from the Jews—would be the wealthy men, for the mass of the followers of Hitler were not much different from the Communists in their economic views. Actually the working classes, with the exception of the fanatical Communists, did not make much opposition and quietly accepted the dissolution of their Socialist party and strong labor unions. Maybe they were tired out from long unemployment, which Hitler at once successfully combated with an immense armament program. Maybe they thought that the Nazis, since they called themselves Socialists, would turn against capitalism. But in fact capitalism was largely left alone, and the first onslaught was against science and all fields of culture. I think that Hitler himself was mostly responsible for this. As a typical autodidact he hated exact science, and as an astute politician he knew that totalitarian rule requires first the control of the minds. His henchman Goering expressed this clearly when he stated in a speech that the only role for science in the Third Reich was to provide substitutes for missing raw materials and to prove the correctness of the Nazi *Weltanschauung*. Thus Hitler's bloodhounds were set on the trail of science, which had contributed more to Germany's standing in the world than any other performance of the German nation except, perhaps, music.

Rust, the failure as a schoolteacher, was made minister of education, which meant dictator over all universities, schools, and religious institutions. He at once dismissed or immobilized the old experienced councilors and put young fanatics, mostly unsuccessful university teachers, in charge of the departments of his ministry. Soon he employed five times the number of officials needed under the republic, and they began their work in Nazification. Non-Aryan professors were dismissed, non-Aryan students turned out of the universities. Slowly but unrelentingly, the freedom of the universities, academic freedom, the pride of German culture, was abolished. The rector was at first still elected by the faculty, but under pressure, and soon was simply appointed by Rust. Of course a reliable Nazi was chosen, a man who was willing to execute orders. Again, with rare exceptions, it turned out that the Nazi choice was an individual of bad reputation, frequently a man known to be more or less insane. But he followed orders. New chairs were established for deserving Nazis, chairs of military science first of all, even before chairs of race doctrine. Another important point for the Nazis was to see to it that in case of a vacancy the proper man was put into the university. The faculty still had the right to nominate the candidates, but the ministry simply appointed its favorites. If there was no vacancy and a non-Nazi professor was in a chair, a new job was created for the Nazi. Thus there was a heyday for all the unsuccessful second-raters who had joined the Nazis out of resentment. They got chairs galore, and the great and famous German universities sank down step by step, some, like Göttingen, beyond recognition.

There were, of course, neutral subjects that were not interfered with except for the purge of non-Aryans and the appointment of second-raters. Chemistry, engineering, and Sanskrit did not have much contact with the fanatic nonsense that the Nazis called their *Weltanschauung*. But there were other fields dear to their hearts, and these were at once tampered with. The pet sciences of the Nazis were anthropology and eugenics, which had to prove the Nordic race doctrine. Chairs were at once created for these fields, and the teaching of the most perverted type of race history was started. All schools had to follow in line, and race offices were started in all the special Nazi organizations like the S.S. and the S.A. to disseminate the official doctrine.

All over the country magazines for race study sprang up and published such perfectly insane nonsense that even good Nazis were sometimes shocked. A central race office watched over the teaching of the pure doctrine. The professors of anthropology, instead of objecting to the perversion and falsification of established facts, either kept quiet or went over with full sails to the Nazi camp. The anthropological research institute of the Kaiser Wilhelm Gesellschaft, founded more or less by the church, purged the Jesuit Muckermann, who had been the founder. The director, E. Fischer, formerly a Catholic politician, started to conform with the official idea and made speeches clad in the storm trooper's brown uniform, saying the opposite of what he had said a few weeks before.

Soon the institute took over the organization of teaching courses in racism and became the pseudoscientific center for the falsification of the results of racial anthropology. Fischer, a very active though not very intelligent man, was even found ready to prepare for the government an *expertise* deciding whether in a dubious case (lack of documents) a man was a pure Aryan or not—a thing that is of course impossible. It was rather a joke that for the teaching of genetics, which had to furnish the basis of racism, two of my books were considered the best and were in general use, though frequently only clandestinely. About three years later, however, their sale was forbidden, and they could not even be mentioned in publishers' catalogues.

If anthropology presented a sad sight, prehistory was still worse. Everybody knows that in Roman times the Teutons were still savages. But now it had to be proved that for ten thousand years and more the Germans had possessed the greatest of all cultures. To express doubt would have meant a prison sentence for slighting the German nation. The amount of falsification and dishonesty displayed in this field—some of it on the basis of crankishness and paranoia—surpasses the wildest imagination. Thus it was one of the official tenets that civilization had started in Nordic Germany, migrated south and east to inspire the cultures of Egypt, Babylon, and even China, and only later returned from these places under a foreign disguise. The extravagances of Nazified prehistory could easily be made into a hilarious (though utterly sad) vaudeville show.

Of course economics, history, and philosophy had to be on their guard. Socialism and Marxism were not to be mentioned except with horror; history had to be falsified so that everything great was done by Germans and everything that went wrong was due to the wickedness of non-Germans. Consistency was not needed: if the political situation required it, Slavs, Gauls, Anglo-Saxons, Latins, and even Japanese were declared great Nordics and Aryans, while Jews were ranged with Negroes. But the next week Slavs or Latins might be Jewish mongrels if the political situation had changed. Certainly the school children had a hard time following all this nonsense, and many parents found it difficult when the children brought home the new teaching from school.

Not even such a field as medicine, one of the great prides of German science, was left alone, for Hitler and his gang had decided that everything must be changed. Of course the excellent and popular Jewish physicians were coerced step by step until finally their practice was completely forbidden to them. But even "Aryan" medical science was at once regimented. An ignorant, slow-witted, brutal soldier of fortune, Wagner, who had been a kind of physician, was appointed *Führer* of the medical profession. He had not only to "Aryanize" it, which was after all easy if one had only to make pronouncements and call them law, but he had to do more. Like so many self-educated or otherwise unbalanced people, many of the Nazi leaders, like Hitler, Hess, and Streicher, hated scientific medicine and clung to quacks. One of the tasks of the medical *Führer* was to introduce the quacks into the profession. Chairs were erected for different sorts of quackery, and the annual conventions of the medical associations were forced to feature quacks prominently on their programs. Streicher even organized special bodies of cranks and quacks as exponents of "German medicine."

One would have thought that the leaders of the profession would protest violently, as the church leaders did when their turn came. Nothing of the kind. The conventions listened in silence and awe to the half-witted nonsense that *Führer* Wagner pronounced at the openings. At the first such convention after 1933 the president, a well-known clinician, said that, although one could not deny that some Jewish scholars like Ehrlich and Wassermann had done something for medicine, one must assume that their success was due only to their Aryan surroundings!

One would have thought, also, that physics had nothing to do with Nazism. Not so to the Nazis! It happened that among the great theoretical physicists of our time (and also among the experimentalists) there were a very large number of Jews or part Jews, including those who had laid the mathematical foundations of modern physics, for example, Einstein, Minckowsky, Bohr, Franck, Hertz, Born, Michelson, Warburg, and many others. There existed even before the Nazis an anti-Semitic group of physicists who had obstructed especially the theory of relativity and had even started mass meetings of laymen to protest against what they called "Jewish physics." This movement was led by two notorious cranks.

Stark had been an excellent experimental physicist but had to quit his professorship and other jobs because of his crankish unbalance. Lenard, one of the really distinguished experimental physicists of our time, a Hungarian who considered himself a great Nordic, had always been an anti-Semite of the most violent kind who had gone so far as to refuse to examine Jewish students. Neither had ever been taken seriously outside of his professional work, but with the advent of the Nazis their day came.

Stark was given a series of important jobs, and Lenard was made a national hero. Both provoked the laughter of the scientific world, one by publishing in an English periodical a letter denouncing all theoretical physics as "Jewish" or developed by Jewish-influenced scholars, the other by writing a book on "German" physics. They succeeded in hampering German physics considerably. Not only did the great non-Aryan scholars emigrate, but a number of so-called Aryans followed, so that actually only one great theoretical physicist was left, and he, I am sure, had a hard time. Needless to say, Einstein's name could not be mentioned in scientific literature, nor could the names of other non-Aryan scholars. I saw papers published in Nazi Germany in which my own work was pilfered without quoting the source. Into what an abyss of contemptibility German science sank under the Nazis!

A typical incident of that time was connected with the death of the great physicochemist Haber. Haber, Nobel laureate in chemistry, was not only a great scholar but also a great organizer whose Kaiser Wilhelm Institute for Physicochemistry was a Mecca for the whole profession. He was in addition an active German patriot, who by his work on the fixation of nitrogen and gas warfare had done a great service to the German army in the first World War. When the Nazis came to power all his Jewish collaborators were dismissed, and Haber, himself a Jew, resigned and went to England. Soon afterward he died in loneliness. The Kaiser Wilhelm Society and its president, one of the greatest physicists of all time, Max Planck of quantum theory fame, decided to hold a meeting in commemoration of the man who had done great things for the society. When the ministry of education heard of it, the meeting was forbidden. Planck decided not to back down and to hold the meeting, but tried to make the ministry change its mind. Finally, the very last day, he succeeded in persuading Rust to agree.

Rust promised to send a telegram to the speaker, Professor Bonhöffer, one of the fine men who kept their shields clean during the

Nazi regime. Practically all his family was later wiped out. Bonhöffer had been forbidden to deliver his address. Now Rust promised Max Planck to cancel the stricture and also the order forbidding all professors to attend. Nothing was done, and later it was found out that the fanatical young councilors of the ministry had disobeyed their chief and not sent the telegrams. They knew that the party would back them even in insubordination if it was in the cause of anti-Semitism.

The next day the meeting took place. Planck opened it with the Hitler salute, and I knew that he did this to demonstrate that the meeting was not meant as a political demonstration against the Nazi state. But it was heartbreaking to see this great man perform the salute of slaves and dupes. The hall was filled with an audience of old men who listened to the dignified services. Otto Hahn, another shining light in the dark times (and later discoverer of nuclear fission), volunteered to deliver the oration. The active university professors and Haber's other colleagues had followed the instructions by the Nazi rector, the same ill-famed Eugen Fischer, not to appear. The only men in active service who declared that they were backing Planck and attended were three men from our institute, of whom I was one. Nothing happened to them.

As a matter of fact, the only bright spots in the Nazi campaign against science were the research institutes of the Kaiser Wilhelm Society. Only Haber's institute was reorganized with nothing but second-raters in charge and later disappeared from the list of famous institutions of learning (but has now been resurrected as Haber Institute). All the other institutes were left alone, and vacancies caused by the dismissal or voluntary departure of Jewish scholars were filled with the best men available. New and good institutes were founded, and the funds available for research were unlimited. During the remainder of the Nazi era, when the rest of German science had struck a very low mark, these institutes were still flourishing. Fortunately they were resurrected after the fall of the Nazis under the new name of Max Planck Institutes and are again on their way to former glory.

One of the worst features, probably encountered in all revolutions, was the heyday of the denouncers. Disgruntled people began to denounce the real or assumed sources of their worry, and the jails were filled with their victims. It was an ordinary occurrence for the maid of a Jewish family, at the instigation of her Nazi boy friend, to charge her employer with a fictitious assault. The man would go to jail and have a hard and long time proving his innocence.

But in this respect the gentiles were not much better off than the Jews. We had an old friend, Professor Rhoda Erdmann, an elderly lady in rather precarious health who was a professor in the medical faculty of the University of Berlin. One day she disappeared, and we soon found out that she had been arrested by the Gestapo. One of her technicians had denounced her as a Jew and a Communist. The rector of the university, a very contemptible Nazi convert, and the dean of the medical faculty, both of whom could have verified the innocence of the lady, refused to interfere out of sheer moral cowardice. When Dr. Erdmann proved that she had no drop of Jewish blood and had belonged to the Democratic party she was accused of having had Jewish students in her laboratory and Jewish friends outside—a crime of which every German professor was guilty. They kept her in jail over a month and would have kept her longer if an American professor of the highest international standing, Ross G. Harrison, a friend of hers and mine, had not hurried to Berlin from a vacation in Switzerland, walked straight up to the Gestapo, and secured her release.

The end of the sad story is also typical of Nazi rule. After her release the energetic lady fought vigorously for her rehabilitation. Finally she succeeded in getting a clean bill from the ministry of education. But neither her professorship nor her laboratory, which she had built up mostly with funds from the Rockefeller Foundation, was restored to her. The Nazi government could never err, and what was once done could not be corrected. But the ministry gave her a good salary and a completely new laboratory outside the university with ample funds, an act utterly typical of the low-bred vanity of the Nazi officialdom. In this case it was too late; the jail had broken Dr. Erdmann's strength, and she died soon afterward. Nobody knows how many thousands of such cases occurred, but they must have been legion.

Science was not the only victim of Hitler and his executioners. The heroic fight of the German church is known everywhere. It is general knowledge that the only group in Germany who behaved like upright men were the churchmen, both Lutherans and Catholics. I must confess that before that time I had not been very favorably disposed toward the clergy. Since 1933, I have been willing to lift my hat to them. Pastor Niemöller's church was not far distant from our laboratory, and it was refreshing to see that people all around who had not been inside a church for decades now flocked to Niemöller's courageous services. The effect of this one speck of resistance against totalitarianism was observed in many ways. Among my friends was a member of the diplomatic service, a man whose charming wife turned out to be Jewish when the Nazi inquiries began. The man had to quit, and he at once went to a divinity school to become a preacher in Niemöller's footsteps.

To art-loving people like ourselves the Nazi attack upon art and literature was especially hateful. The Nazis at once proposed to free art from Bolshevism and non-Aryanism and to make it purely Nordic and sound. Here Hitler was personally at work. He seemed to believe that he would have become a great artist if his enemies (invariably called Jews) had not prevented him. Now he wanted to show what art really was.

Goebbels was entrusted with the organization, and when it was perfected nobody could teach or create art who was not permitted to do so. First, of course, Jews and non-Aryans (people with one-fourth or more Jewish blood) were forbidden to have anything to do with art and literature. Afterward it was the turn of gentiles who either did not like Nazism or had an artistic taste different from that of the omniscient *Führer*. The result was catastrophic.

Music, dear to the heart of every German, was almost wiped out. It happened that a great many of the best conductors, composers, violinists, cellists, and pianists were either Jews or gentiles with character. The first were expelled, like the composer Schönberg; the conductors Walter, Klemperer, and Blech; the pianists Schnabel and Serkin; the violinist Flesch; the cellists Piatigorsky and Feuermann. The rest left in disgust, like Adolf and Fritz Busch, Hindemith, Edwin Fischer, and many others. When the Nazis were through with their work the only composers left were Richard Strauss and Hans Pfitzner, the only great conductor Wilhelm Furtwängler, no violinist, no cellist, no pianist of fame. All the great quartets were gone, and only the opera remained under the special patronage of Goering. And of course modern music—any music after Wagner and his followers—was completely taboo. The insolence and meanness with which this purge was carried out were staggering. I remember that Goebbels announced publicly that a man like Hindemith would have to undergo years of probation, and that only after thorough atonement might he be permitted to compose again.

Painting and sculpture followed music. There were not very

many non-Aryans to purge, though. Max Liebermann, the president of the academy of arts, was a very old man who used his short remaining span of life to pronounce witty bon mots against the Nazis. He died in time to save himself from a concentration camp. I do not remember any non-Aryan sculptor produced by Germany in the nineteenth or twentieth century. Adolf Hildebrand had been half-Jewish, but he was dead, and his works were not purged. But all painters and sculptors had to renounce modernism if they wanted to exhibit their work. This meant not only abstract art or the much discussed works of men like Klee, Schmidt-Rottluff, Hofer, and Kokoschka, but practically anything that was original, daring, or looking for new forms of artistic expression. Exhibitions were now filled with insipid, smooth repetitions of old themes dear to Hitler's megalomaniacal dilettantism. Whatever was cheap or boisterous, and especially whatever was based on motives that Nazi creed called German, was also good. The muses hid their faces.

The great art galleries were also purged. Their finest possessions of modern art, back to the French impressionists, were stored in their basements, and directors who did not quickly decide to fall in line with official bad taste had to quit. Only once did the Nazis score an artistic success. They divided the great annual art show in Munich into two sections, one containing what they called sane art and another called Bolshevist art, which was of course meant to be a slight. But the public filled the halls of tabooed art, and the exhibits of the officially approved Nordic painters remained empty.

It would have been a miracle if Hitler had not focused his attention upon architecture. Modern building had made great strides in Germany after its start in Holland and Finland. A number of architects did really great work. In addition to the Dessau Bauhaus, whose leaders all emigrated to the United States and were received with open arms, there were many less extremist architects who cultivated the modern line, like Poelzig or Fahrenholz. I do not hesitate to call Poelzig's office building of the dye trust in Frankfurt one of the greatest pieces of architecture of this time.

It is true that some of these artists were rather Pink, but the radicalism of artists is of a different kind from political radicalism and must not be taken too seriously. As a matter of fact, Fascist Italy outdid the Russians (before Stalin imposed his own bad taste) in architectural modernism. A Fascist anniversary exhibition that I saw in Rome could just as well have stood in the Moscow of the twenties.

Hitler, who was utterly devoid of humor, had not only decided to change everything that had developed during the republic, but in addition he considered architecture a field in which he was thoroughly competent and where his taste should be the beacon for future developments. Like all tyrants of all times he wanted to leave a memorial in stone and marble, and he therefore set out at once to embellish German cities. Needless to say almost all the great architects were expelled, and many of them, like the scientists, musicians, and painters, are now contributing their share to making American cultural performance lead in the world. It was at once decreed what type of building was German and what was Bolshevist or non-Aryan. Flat roofs, which had come to the fore in some schools of modern architecture, were declared to be non-Aryan; only high gabled roofs could appeal to the real Nordic.

Then the building of palatial structures began. Nobody knew where the money came from, but, since there was no public budget and no control of the expenditures in the Nazi state, it could be assumed that Hitler did not much care where it came from. He ordered something to be built, and it was built under the supervision of his favorite architect, Speer (later jailed as a war criminal). The start was made with gigantic structures in Nuremberg to house the yearly big parades. I did not see these since I did not care to visit Streicher's realm. But what was done to the most beautiful town of Germany, Munich, I saw at least in part.

One of the beauty sites of Munich was the Königsplatz, built by the art-loving King Ludwig I after the style of the Acropolis. A square covered with grass was flanked on two sides by noble Greek temples housing art galleries, and on the third side by a copy of the Propylaea. The fourth opened into a beautiful street flanked by old mansions and trees. This was embellished by Hitler. Since no beauty was imaginable without parading troopers, the square was laid out with large flagstones. Since the ground was low, on rainy days these were covered with water, and the people called it the *Plattensee* (a lake in Hungary; flagstones may be called *Platten*). Thus the proper setting was removed from the temples. This did not suffice. Next a kind of memorial tabernacle was erected in the *Plattensee* for the Nazis who had been killed in the beerhall *Putsch* and were considered something like saints. The unbelievably ugly structure was called by the people the filling station in the *Plattensee*. Next came the open front of the quadrangle. Here an immense palace was erected, the *Führerhaus*, headquarters of the Nazi party. I understand that later, after I had left, the embellishment of Berlin began according to plans made by Speer, with Hitler's personal collaboration. Speer lived near our home and had built himself a residence that was architecturally simply ridiculous. I am glad that I was not there to see the great things he did for Berlin.

The less said about literature the better. Goebbels, who had once studied literature in Heidelberg under a famous Jewish esthete, Gundolf, took it into his own hands to Nazify literature. Again all non-Aryans and liberals were either expelled or left voluntarily in disgust and shame: Thomas and Heinrich Mann, Franz Werfel, Carl Neumann, Arnold and Stefan Zweig, and countless others. Needless to say, no non-Aryans or liberals could write any longer for papers or magazines. Publishers had to stop publishing their works and in many cases even to destroy their stocks. Just as in music Mendelssohn and Offenbach could not be played any more, literature was correspondingly purged. Heine could not even be mentioned, and his *Die Lorelei* could not be sung any more. Room was made for what Goebbels considered real German literature, and all the second-raters, especially those who had written shallow books of the Pan-German type, now became the heroes of German literature. Whoever wanted to be in with the powers-that-be started a novel with an ancient Teuton wrapped in a bearskin as the hero, or he discovered a great German whose fame had been maliciously suppressed by foreigners and made him the center of a book. The bombastic language of the Nazi press with its orgies of nastiness set the pace for real German literature.

Bad as was the destruction of science and art, worst of all, I think, was the systematic destruction of all the foundations of law. The Nazis began at once with the preparation of a new code of law. In the interim they showed what this was to be. The basic principle was: what is good for the state is right. Since the state was identified with the Nazi party and the *Führer,* this meant: what the *Führer* and the party do is right. I still cannot understand how it was possible that decent Germans quietly accepted this doctrine.

This first became clear when Hitler's atrocious purge was made. We lived only a few miles from the officers' school in Lichterfelde where most of the victims in Berlin were murdered. Friends living in the neighborhood heard the firing squads all night, and we, like everybody else, had known directly or indirectly some of the victims. Everybody knew that at least a thousand men had been murdered, among them all those against whom Hitler had an old personal grudge, like von Kahr in Munich. The next day Hitler stood before the nation and said that sixteen or eighteen conspirators had been legally shot. All Germany was horrified, and I have never seen more depressed faces around town. But nobody moved. The attorney general declared that Hitler had acted lawfully. A famous professor of law gave a decision that what the *Führer* did was implicitly right. Herr von Papen, whose secretaries—the men who had written his speeches—had both been murdered, and who himself had barely escaped, remained in office and served Hitler to the end. A lady in our neighborhood, whose husband was murdered, as it turned out, by mistake, was given an audience with the *Führer* a few weeks later. In the anteroom, aides said to her, "Do not be too hard on the *Führer*." She went in, gave the Hitler salute, and had her audience with the murderer of her husband without even thinking of revenging his death. What can be expected of such a people?

With the organization of the Gestapo the last shreds of protection by law disappeared. There was no appeal against the Gestapo's secret acts, and torture and murder became official tools of the government. There was no German, at least in my area, who did not know this. But nobody—again except a part of the clergy—dared to speak.

Thus equal law, the basis of all culture and decent living, passed out of German life. And what was worse: the youth was taught that this was a proper condition, and a generation of young people grew up with the idea that the will of the *Führer* was law and right, no matter what this might mean. The complete breakdown of law and moral values was further fostered by the Nazi attitude toward the ruffians and hooligans whom they considered their great men. The storm troopers who were sometimes killed in the nightly fights with Communists or police under the republican government were later made great national heroes, and their memory was worshiped. At one of the busiest points in Munich a monument to them was erected. A Nazi storm trooper stood guard, and passers-by had to give the Hitler salute. How many times did I and thousands of others make a detour to avoid this salute!

Streets that had been named after great men of the past were renamed for these martyr ruffians. In our neighborhood, a fine residential quarter, a monument was erected to a low-class writer who had edited a miserable anti-Semitic sheet, the *Hammer*, back in imperial Germany. The statue showed the great man killing with a hammer a serpent with the head of a Jew as pictured in anti-Semitic cartoons. The moral influence of such exhibits as these can be imagined.

Many decent Germans, even those with mild Nazi leanings, especially resented the creation of a new national anthem to glorify one of the Nazi martyrs. The young man Horst Wessel, who had been forbidden his parents' home because of the lewd life he led, was one of the professional rowdies who fought the Communists at night in the suburbs of Berlin. The Communists had shot him before he could kill them. Like so many youngsters he had rhymed occasionally, and one of his products, atrocious in rhythm and language, was forced upon the German people as a national anthem. All non-Nazis were thoroughly ashamed of the text, the morose melody, and the almost deified author of the *Horst Wessel Lied.*

It is well known that the Nazi regime immediately began to build up the German army. The signs of this were visible everywhere. There had always been a class of Germans whose sons made up the majority of army officers. During the republic these families had missed the possibility of placing their sons in a respectable, quick, and safe career. Now the young men flocked into the army. A great many went into the air service, which at the beginning was built up secretly and in such a hurry that one heard constantly of fatal accidents that were never officially reported. Friends of ours who were high up in the manufacturing industries did not hide the fact that their factories were being transformed into arsenals. As a rule the German people liked this. Not only were they at heart militaristic, but they had suffered so much from military impotence after World War I that they wanted the backing of a powerful army for future politics.

There is no doubt that the masses of the people did not want war, though Hitler and the generals obviously had this in mind from the beginning. The people certainly believed that the army was being built up for the defense of Germany's claim to a place in the sun. They might have wondered when they saw Goering building his air ministry occupying a whole city block though no air force was yet visible. They might have wondered when they saw architects specializing in air-raid cellars and when, in 1935, training of civilians in blackouts and air-raid precautions began. People I knew who could look behind the scenes did not doubt for a moment that ultimately the preparations would lead to war, though they believed it would be only for the restoration of Germany's prewar status.

I do not think that anybody outside the inner party and military group thought of war for the conquest and rule of Europe. There were actually many people opposed to Nazism who looked forward to war as the only chance to get rid of Nazism. But even they would certainly have been horrified if they had known what was actually to come. Yet the system of controlling the press and radio and of using organized lies on a large scale, together with the complete secrecy of all governmental doings, kept the people totally ignorant of what was being cooked up in Hitler's mind.

14: FAREWELL TO GERMANY

During these early years of Nazism I continued my research quietly, keeping more to myself and staying away from gatherings where I might have to meet with Nazis. Everybody in the laboratory behaved perfectly, including the Nazis themselves. Actually there were not many genuine ones except among the mechanics, gardeners, and young assistants. I must honestly say that these found themselves in a difficult situation. I was still the boss, and the Nazis were taught the *Führerprincip*. But they were also taught to hate the Jews, and if they had wanted they could have got me into trouble. I absolutely refused to give the Hitler salute and to pronounce the hateful words "Heil Hitler." I also refused to attend the meetings that were ordered whenever Hitler made one of his speeches filled with lies, distortions, falsehood, and hate. The whole crew had to assemble in the library, listen to a loudspeaker, and stand at attention with raised arms when the ridiculous new national anthem was played. But I never was denounced for not attending, and everybody said "Good morning" to me instead of heiling. I had the impression that the men respected me for not throwing up my arms. This condition did not change in the laboratory up to the last day of my stay, and I am glad to say that all my employees, academic or not, remained true to me to the last.

But outside of my immediate surroundings the picture was less pleasant. In the beginning the Nazis moved slowly with their anti-Semitic measures, which were mostly directed against the intellectuals. Hitler himself, who knew exactly what he was going to do later, did not yet tell frankly. One day I met an Australian professor who was spending a vacation in Berlin and with whom I used to have a good game of tennis. He was in a condition of extreme excitement. He took me aside and said: "I just had one of the most terrible experiences of my life. Do you know where I come from? From Hitler!" By some chance he had been granted an interview with Hitler. He had finally broached the subject of the Jews to Hitler, who answered that he had nothing whatsoever against the Jews except those who were Bolsheviks. But then he talked himself into a rage and raved so much that the professor was still trembling an hour afterward.

It took about two years for legislation against Jews to be perfected, and three more years before the Jews became completely enslaved, and three more before they were murdered in gas chambers, a fate that overtook all my relatives and friends who could not leave in time. Though many Germans had always been anti-Semites and loved to call the Jews names and to oppress them in a small way, the majority of them did not want bloody persecution, pogroms, burning of temples, ghettos, and yellow insignia. They would not have minded the distribution of Jewish money among genuine Nordics or the replacement of all Jews in their jobs with Germans. But they did not want real cruelty, and I have learned that even to the last the gentile neighbors secretly helped the maltreated Jews.

Thus the German people had to be slowly prepared for the real thing, and this was done systematically. The best barometer was the foreign embassies. For a year or so Jews were still invited to their functions. But suddenly this stopped, and the Japanese, whom the Nazis among themselves called "tree monkeys," were the first to stop. Obviously a hint had been given that Nazis did not want to meet Jews. In private life I did not have such an experience. But some of my friends had the pleasure of seeing people who had called themselves friends, and who had flattered them, turn against them in the ugliest way.

All over the towns and especially near schoolhouses the S.A. erected show boxes in which the latest edition of Streicher's sheet *Der Stürmer* was exhibited. The front page usually showed a cartoon of a Jewish banker raping his Nordic secretary or a similarly pleasant subject, accompanied by the appropriate story. The youth clustered around these boxes and certainly drew from them much inspiration. In smaller towns and villages, streamers were hung across the highways with inscriptions like "One-way road to Jerusalem" and other less harmless ones. Thus the S.A. slowly prepared people for more to come.

It came usually at the yearly party meeting in Nuremberg, where new decrees against the Jewish citizens were always promulgated. First, typical of the beastly meanness of the Nazi gang, a decree came forbidding Jews to have maids under the age of fifty. The meaning was obvious. There is no doubt that the Nazis knew that maids liked to work in Jewish households where they were treated humanely. In my own family maids used to stay from thirty to fifty years, practically their whole lives. I am sure that no German outside of the most rabid Nazis believed in the implications of this decree. But it had to be followed, and we had to submit to the ignominy. The following year the Nuremberg laws took citizenship away from the Jews and made them helpless slaves and chattels. Three years later pogrom and robbery were officially sanctioned, and afterward the extermination by assembly-line methods began.

I have mentioned that I had decided to quit immediately after Hitler came to power, but I wanted to act without haste and to wait for a chance to build a new life and to continue my work. When the scores of so-called non-Aryan professors were dismissed, rumors spread abroad that I was one of them, and I received at once an invitation from the University of London. A few months later I had a chance to thank my English colleagues personally for their kindness. I suggested that whatever means were available for the support of displaced scholars ought to be used to take care of those who had been driven away and that men like me who were not yet molested ought to hold out and wait for developments and look out meanwhile for regular appointments abroad. I am glad to say that I succeeded in finding jobs for all my former students who had been dismissed, and all of them have shown themselves worthy of the confidence placed in them by their foreign hosts.

Another offer that I received soon afterward tempted me more. A progressive Turkish government, advised by a prominent Swiss educator, Malche, decided to take advantage of the unusual situation to build up a modern university in Istanbul. Similar situations had occurred in Europe before. When the Inquisition drove all the Jews out of Spain, they took many of their capacities in trade and manufacturing to host countries, which profited immensely—as the diamond-cutting and lens-grinding industries of Holland demonstrate. The Turkish government now called fifty or more of the dismissed German scholars, some of them leaders of their profession, to Istanbul and set funds aside for the erection of laboratories, hospitals, and the like. The organizers of this ambitious project got in touch with me and wanted me to join. I went to Switzerland in 1933 to talk things over and then decided to accept if my conditions could be met—mainly the guarantee of facilities for research work and the necessary funds for a successful building up of my university work. After some time I was informed that the Turkish ministry had accepted all my conditions, and I received a beautifully sealed and signed official invitation. Thus I went to Geneva to talk things over with Mr. Malche.

We arranged that my final acceptance would be dependent upon a personal visit to Istanbul, where I wanted to convince myself that the prerequisites for successful work were actually available and also that proper housing and living conditions could be had. For a long time nothing happened. Finally I learned that a new minister of education had come to power who was less enthusiastic and more careful of the available funds, and who thought me a too expensive acquisition. But I had a hunch that some double-crossing was also involved, since first a friend and country fellow of one of the advisers—not a displaced German scholar—was appointed, and after his premature death a German who was not displaced, though a very good scientist, took the chair.

While these things were going on I had received an invitation to deliver a couple of lectures in connection with the Chicago International Fair of 1933. The fee was unusually large and offered me a chance to make it possible to send my daughter Ruth to the United States to finish her medical education, for no money could be taken out of Germany. The governmental permission without which no German scholar could now lecture abroad was granted by Mr. Rust, who treated me personally perfectly decently while I remained in Germany. I do not know what secured me this privilege, since I never made any concession to the new order, but I was able to go to Chicago to lecture in the terrific heat of July, have a look at the not very beautiful fair, and succeed in finding an unpaid internship for my daughter, though I did not succeed in finding a job for my son. After only a week I left again and, before returning, paid a visit to my friends in London to inform them of conditions in German science and to enlist their help for a number of victims of Nazi oppression.

The winter of 1933–34 passed quietly. I kept to my work, did not attend any more scientific meetings or lectures, and kept away from all places or gatherings where I might have to perform the Hitler salute. In Berlin, general conditions for the non-Aryans were still rather good. Obviously the Nazi government did not want the many foreigners to see too much. In small towns Jews could hardly appear in public, could not eat in restaurants or visit shows, and their stores were boycotted. In Berlin only occasionally signs appeared in shop windows, "This is a German store," and the Jewish stores did as much business as ever, though sometimes groups of storm troopers tried to prevent the public from entering. People with very Semitic-looking faces were sometimes beaten up in the streets by storm troopers, but just as often as not the victims were South American or Egyptian or Italian, for to the hooligans black hair and a prominent nose meant Jew. It was not pleasant to return from a concert at night and to ride in the suburban train with a gang of storm troopers who were singing the beautiful song, "If the Jew's blood drips from our knives, we feel so happy, oh so happy." But these things still were mere pinpricks compared with what was to come later after we had left.

In spring we went again to Naples to breathe for a few weeks the clean air of Italy, which at that time had not yet been Nazified. Actually the people hated the Nazis, and anti-Semitism was completely unknown to them. The few young Nazi scientists who were working at the marine laboratory behaved themselves, and we enjoyed the sunshine, the noisy street life, and the beautiful surroundings. For a few weeks Nazidom could be completely forgotten, and once more I was able to celebrate my birthday with my former student Paul Buchner, whose birthday was the same day, at his beautiful villa on the island of Ischia. (He later exiled himself voluntarily from the Third Reich.)

For the summer of 1934 I had received a very pleasant invitation. The Spanish Republican government, anxious to promote science, had organized a summer university in the seaside resort of Santander in the Basque country. A former royal palace and park were given to the university to house all students and professors. The best advanced students of the country, boys and girls, were sent there in the summer for a two- or three-month course. The political science professor Fernando de los Ríos, later minister of education and ambassador to Washington, was the president. (We were to meet again six years later in California, both refugees.) The best scholars of Spain did the teaching, and in addition a small group of foreign scholars was invited as honored guests. For the second session in 1934 I received an invitation. The Nazi ministry gave me permission to accept, and I left in August.

At that time one was permitted to take fifty marks (twelve dollars) out of Germany, and in addition two hundred marks (forty-eight dollars) could be accredited abroad if the authorities gave permission for the trip. I went first to Paris for a couple of days where I met an old friend, at that time a refugee in Paris and almost destitute. I could do nothing for him but invite him to a good meal, which cut deep into my twelve dollars.

When I arrived at the Spanish border and wanted to board the Spanish train it turned out that the French conductor on the night express had kept my Spanish ticket by mistake. The express was gone, and I had to use the major part of my remaining funds to buy a third-class ticket to Santander. But to get there I had to stop over one night at the Basque capital of Bilbao, later to become famous in the civil war. I had to make it clear to a taxi driver, who preferred to speak Basque, that I wanted a very cheap hotel. Finally I found one, not very respectable looking, but where the room with two meals cost exactly what was left in my purse. I spent the rest of the day sightseeing. It was a very hot day, and people sat in the sidewalk cafes sipping cool drinks. I could only look at them with a dry tongue, as I had not a cent left, and Bilbao was one of the few places in Europe where I knew nobody. Thus the day passed rather unpleasantly.

The next morning I took my train. The hard, narrow coach seat was softened somewhat by my fellow travelers, a group of dancers, among them one of the greatest beauties I have ever laid eyes on. I arrived in Santander at noon, took a taxi to the bank to which I was accredited with forty-eight dollars, and let the taxi wait. When I produced my letter of credit the young clerk turned it all around and finally said, "No good." With not a cent in my pocket and the taxi waiting outside, I got angry. In a horrible mixture of bad Spanish and better French I asked for the bank president and made such a noise that he finally came to see what was going on. He took the letter, which was all right. The young clerk had been unable to read German or French and simply did not want to be bothered with it. I heaved a sigh of deliverance when I received my money.

The days in Santander were extremely pleasant. To be an honored guest in a hospitable country is always agreeable. In addition the place was charming. One could bathe in the ocean right from the house, walk in the park, or sit on the cliffs. The company was excellent. I met some old acquaintances among the Spanish professors and made new ones. (I am afraid that most of them are now refugees, since most scholars were Republicans at heart. Some of them, very fine men, I met many years later in Mexico.) The students were eager, and all had complete mastery of French, in which I delivered my lectures. My friends took me for many pleasant trips, for example, to the quaint old town of Santillana, home of the famed Gil Blas. I was especially grateful for a chance to visit the caves of Altamira and to see with my own eyes the remarkably life-like and artistic paintings of bison and wild horses that prehistoric men had produced innumerable thousands of years ago, showing that the sense for artistic expression of form and movement is an old possession of mankind.

The winter of 1934–35 brought increased Nazi attacks against Jews, liberals, Protestants, and Catholics, and everybody lived in a constant state of excitement. More frequently than ever one had to hear the harsh bellowing of Hitler's voice and his crude lies and falsehoods shouted out of loudspeakers attached to lampposts all over town. Every second day the swastika flag had to be flown in honor of somebody or something, and the whole life of the nation became hectic and maniacal. Nobody was really happy except the hundred-percenters and the youth, who no longer had to study in school but were marched around playing at soldiers. Parents were unhappy because their children were systematically alienated from them, had to be out at night to attend a thousand and one Nazi affairs, and did not stay home on Sundays, which were devoted to crazy military marches. Parades and parades filled the time in be-tween. Educators were unhappy because the quality of the students deteriorated, and interest in scholarship disappeared. Preachers were unhappy because they found themselves maligned and in constant danger of jail and concentration camp. Wives were unhappy because their husbands were away nights and Sundays performing marches in military outfit or attending Nazi schools. Trained and intellect-ual women were unhappy because they were being removed from their jobs and told to bear children for cannon fodder. Working-men were unhappy because they had to pay a considerable part of their scanty wages to the party. Manufacturers were unhappy because the government interfered with everything, and business-men were unhappy because so many rules were promulgated, all carrying the threat of imprisonment for noncompliance, and it was impossible to know and follow them all. But nevertheless all of them raised their arms and yelled, "Heil Hitler." When the day of reckoning finally came all of them deserved their misery because of moral cowardice, all except the clergy and a small group of intellectuals, aristocrats, and Socialist workingmen.

My decision to quit was soon taken, and I began to get in touch with other countries and received a number of offers that I was following up. Although I had not yet made up my mind when I intended to leave, I privately informed the president of the Kaiser Wilhelm Society, the great physicist Max Planck, of my decision. Planck's reaction shows how little decent Germans foresaw where things were going. Actually in tears, he entreated me to stay and to sacrifice my private feelings and continue my work for the sake of science. But I knew that it would not take long for the Nazis to throw overboard what little decency was still left, and I wanted to leave on my own before they forced me to go.

The spring of 1935 was spent for the last time in beautiful Naples, out of reach of the Nazi atmosphere. We rented a room in an old palace with gorgeous settings and lived the pleasant half-Bohemian life that suits so well the atmosphere of Naples. Many beautiful excursions were made to our favorite places on the Sorrentine Peninsula and the island of Ischia, where I again celebrated my birthday with my friend in his villa. But the most beautiful part of the trip, made with friends in their old Ford car, was the visit to the hill towns of Perugia, San Gimignano, Siena, and Orvieto, and the overwhelming experience of a first visit to Assisi. I am glad that we could add to our store of fine recollections one more perfect trip before Europe went completely downhill.

For the summer of 1935 I again had an interesting invitation. There was to be an International Entomological Congress in Madrid and an International Zoological Congress in Lisbon, and at both of them I was asked to deliver one of the main addresses. In addition, the University of Madrid wanted to give me a degree and offered to pay my expenses. This meant a chance to go abroad without the unpleasantness of securing governmental permission to take a small sum of money out of the country and the still more hateful necessity of traveling as a member of a delegation under a Nazi leader and with some stool pigeon around all the time. According to Nazi law, however, I had to secure permission to go abroad on a scientific mission. This was granted me, strangely enough, by the ministry of education in a written statement. They did not even take away my official passport, which I still had from pre-Nazi days. It turned out that once in my life at least I was to profit from a Nazi act. Because of all the difficulties with foreign exchange I decided to fly to Spain in a German plane and had asked my Spanish friends to have a little money sent up to Barcelona, where I would land penniless. In Stuttgart I had to change from a smaller to a larger transcontinental plane. When I passed through the customs' barrier to board my plane an officer said, "Is your name not Goldschmidt?"

"Yes, it is."

"Come up to my office. You cannot leave."

It then turned out that the Gestapo was looking for a man of the same name, perhaps suspected of fleeing the country with his money. Though there were thousands of people of that name in Germany, the officer had only orders to arrest a Mr. Goldschmidt. I tried to explain to him who I was and what my intentions were and showed my correct passport. But he did not waver. Suddenly he asked, "What is your denomination?" This was the danger point. If I had answered, "Jewish," this would have meant my certain arrest. But I continued talking vehemently without answering the question, and suddenly I remembered my traveling permission signed by the Nazi minister. This I showed him, assuming the commanding voice to which a German officer is accustomed, and finally, with a suspicious look, the man, who of course was thinking only of his own job, let me go. When the plane rose I suddenly felt rather shaky thinking over my escape from the tender mercies of the Gestapo. I shuddered, but soon the plane was roaring over the well-known summits of the Schwarzwald mountains, across Switzerland to Geneva, and, after a short stop, down the beautiful valley of the Rhone and straight across the Mediterranean, visible through a glacierlike bank of clouds, toward the Spanish coast. It was a glorious flight.

In Madrid I had a most interesting time, aside from the scientific congress. I gorged myself with Spanish painting in the Prado. Beautiful trips took me to the Sierra de Guadarrama, El Escorial, and to Segovia and Toledo, all of them soon to be drenched with the blood of the civil war. The greatest impression was made by Toledo with its glorious cathedral and the unforgettable El Grecos, which I think rank with the greatest masterpieces of painting of all times. Charming friends made these days exceedingly pleasant. Some of these friends have been dispersed since as refugees over the world; others embraced the Fascist doctrine and may still visit all those places, now so full of meaning to all liberty-loving Spaniards. How horrid and unbelievably mean the happenings of our time have been!

In Madrid I saw also my first and last bullfight. With all admiration for the courage and dexterity of the *torero,* I think it is a very ugly sight, and the public around me, in its brutal excitement, was just as ugly as the show. After this experience, and after having seen nightly the misery of swarms of beggars while I sat at the sidewalk cafes before the late dinner hour, and the general expression of dissatisfaction and hatred in the faces of the men in the street, I understand better the ferocity of the already brewing civil war. The suave and soft-spoken president of the republic and his collection of bourgeois gentlemen, whom I met at a reception in the pompous palace of the former king, did not look like men who could stem the surging tide.

Lisbon, and Portugal as a whole, was a great surprise to me. I was accustomed to consider southern countries picturesque but untidy, a combination that makes Naples and Sicily so fascinating. But Portugal turned out to be spick and span and one of the pleasantest countries I have ever visited. The area around Lisbon with its hills, castles, parks, and beaches was delightful, and I spent many pleasant hours there with hospitable old and new friends. Also the countryside in northern Portugal was most charming, and the old university town of Coimbra was a southern equivalent of old Heidelberg.

One of the surprises was meeting a style of medievel architecture, native in Portugal and very little known to the nonprofessional outside world, that is beautifully exemplified in the cathedral at Belém. Another pleasant surprise for me was a visit to the old port of Setubal, which in the days of sailing vessels was the main port of call for ships sailing from Charleston to Europe. Many years ago I had picked up an old painting, obviously from the late seventeenth century, depicting a harbor surrounded by pleasant hills covered with strong fortifications. I had never been able to locate the unusual landscape, and here I suddenly beheld my old picture in the original. Even parts of the old fortifications were still there.

The Portuguese scientists had done their best to make the international congress a success. The hospitality offered was overwhelming. I do not think that in all my life I had imbibed as much delicious port and sherry as I did in one week in Lisbon, and this at the most unusual times of the day. The scientific meetings had one novel feature. The first formal meeting started at ten at night. When Professor Caullery of Paris and I were through with our addresses it was midnight, and there were still two more papers to be read. The last unfortunate speaker was a Portuguese. When he finally started at one in the morning everybody disappeared, and only Caullery and I, who were in the chair, had to hold out while the man unperturbedly read his paper from beginning to end.

One morning when I left my hotel I saw in a shop window the morning paper with big headlines containing the word "Nuremberg." I stopped and deciphered the Portuguese story. It reported on the Nazi congress at Nuremberg and the promulgation of the so-called Nuremberg laws depriving German Jews of their citizenship. The Austrian paperhanger whose ancestors beyond one generation were shrouded in illegitimacy had deprived me of my citizenship, me whose ancestors had lived in the same section of Germany for about eighteen hundred years and in the same town for over four hundred years, whose family had given to Germany scores of prominent citizens in all walks of life. Now there was no more time to look for a proper place for emigration. I made up my mind that I wanted to go where liberty still was cherished, and I wrote to my American friends to secure for me at once an invitation for lectures, to enable me to visit the States and look for a job. I made it clear that I had no ambitions and would accept any position if only it was in America. The last days of the meeting and the following trip through northern Portugal took place under the depressing influence of the news, which all Europeans had read. I certainly did not show outwardly what was going on inside. But it was an ordeal to make the trip back on a German–South American steamer together with the German delegation. Though the delegation contained only a couple of genuine Nazis and everybody made believe that nothing had happened, I had to use much self-control to appear indifferent and even gay. No word was spoken of what was in everybody's mind.

Soon after my return to Germany the American invitations sponsored by my magnanimous friends arrived, and we prepared to sail as soon as possible. I still hoped to beat the Nazis by quitting before I was dismissed. But I did not succeed. A short time before the sailing date the administrative director of the Kaiser Wilhelm Gesellschaft (who soon afterward was himself dismissed for not being a Nazi) came to see me with an expression of sadness on his face as if he were calling on a young widow. I told him at once that I knew why he had come and that he should not worry, for I was perfectly well able to take care of myself. Only when I was already in the United States did I receive the official document,

which read: "You are pensioned beginning January 1, 1936."
No "Dear Sir" or "Yours truly" or "I regret to inform you."
Just a small, untidy slip of paper. I had been on the job for thirty-five years, starting as an assistant and attaining the highest possible position, but whatever the Nazis did always had to be done with the maximum of meanness. However, they did one good thing for me. They permitted me to sail.

We booked passage on the palatial S.S. *Europa* and boarded it in Bremen. We disappeared at once into our stateroom as I had learned to do on repeated occasions since 1933. The reason was that aboard leaving and arriving steamers the band, which formerly had played folk songs, now was ordered to intone the hateful Horst Wessel anthem. Everybody had to stand at attention and give the Hitler salute. From this performance we hid ourselves.

We arrived safely in the United States, but the following three months belong to the most unpleasant ones of my entire life. Everything depended upon my finding a job. I had some invitations in my pocket that would have opened interesting prospects but would have taken me away from the center of science and were considered therefore only as a last refuge. The enervating thing was that I could do nothing myself. I knew that my friends were looking out for me, but the passive waiting was hard on already high-strung nerves.

Elsa and I stayed with our daughter in Chicago until Christmas. Then I attended the St. Louis meeting of the American Association for the Advancement of Science in order to meet friends and inform them of my situation. The results were not always gratifying. The very powerful president of a large foundation, whom I had known for a long time, answered with a sanctimonious expression when I mentioned the uncertainty of my position, "Yes, there are many uncertainties in this world." Fortunately his ugliness stood almost alone, and my old friend E. B. Babcock, from California, told me confidentially that something was going on in my behalf. After the beginning of the new year I started on my lecture tour, encountering everywhere the usual hospitality and friendship. But still no definite hope became visible. The time was quickly approaching when we had to return to Germany, and I had already made up my mind to accept one of the invitations outside the States. Then one day as I sat, rather despondent, in the tiny room of a cheap uptown hotel in New York, the telephone rang. The gentlemen of the Rockefeller Foundation, who had acted wonderfully in my behalf, called to say they had received a telegram from President Sproul in Berkeley offering me a professorship. Happiness made me speechless.

Soon afterward we sailed for the last time in our lives on a German steamer back to Germany. Once more we landed in Bremen and hid ourselves for the last time until the heiling was over.

In Berlin, we got busy at once settling our affairs. This meant first selling our house. We had the good luck that when it was opened for inspection the early spring sun shone brightly upon the many-colored crocuses in the garden, and the house was sold the first day. Of course we did not care about the price since we could not take any money with us anyway. Then all the complicated formalities for emigration had to be gone through. The permission from any number of authorities had to be obtained. One quarter of our property had to be handed over as a so-called flight tax. I spent another quarter of our assets lavishly on the packing and shipping of our belongings and on fitting our son Hans for staying for some time behind us to settle his own affairs. The remaining half I gave away to relatives who enjoyed the income for two more years until they were finally robbed of everything. Fortunately, we were still allowed to take all our movable belongings after inspection by an official. Packing my library and collections took quite a long time, but finally everything was finished, packed into two large crates and fifty small boxes, and shipped to California.

In the laboratory I was the only cheerful one during those months. I knew that I was to escape into liberty, and the beauty of California in addition. My colleagues and employees, down to the simple charwoman, felt rather miserable and ashamed, and the behavior of the few genuine Nazis showed that they did not feel too happy to see a man whom they had always respected forced from the place he had built up, from his work, and from his country. When I finally took leave of my colleagues and my staff, presenting each member with a keepsake, I saw more men in tears than I had ever beheld in all my life.

Finally the day of departure came. The big crates in front of our house with the destination painted in large letters certainly filled with envy many onlookers who were sick of their slavery but could not get away from it. A wealthy friend who hated the Nazis, though he had to work with them, sent his huge luxury limousine and chauffeur, and we left, not as miserable emigrants, but in state. Our neighbors, many of them Nazis but also shocked by the fact of our departure, bade us Godspeed, the ladies in tears.

We went first to Munich to say good-bye to my dear old teacher, Richard Hertwig. On the train we realized once more how glad we were to be leaving. The train was filled with Nazi big shots, all of them of that brutal, roundheaded, close-cropped, thick-necked type so characteristic of the bad type of German. As a biologist I think them to be the result of an incongruous mixture of Teuton and Slav, for the type is at home in the regions where this mixture has largely taken place, which were also the regions of the greatest Nazi strength. We were happy in the knowledge that we should never have to see them again.

The last hours with Professor Hertwig, then eighty-five years old but still strong, were sad. Both of us knew that it was a parting for life, almost forty years after I had first entered his laboratory as a young student. He died, a German scholar and patriot of the old school, a year later.

We had three last minutes of excitement at the Dutch frontier. Would we pass the frontier without trouble? Nothing happened; the train pulled into Holland; we were free people again. As we rode into freedom with nothing but the eight dollars allowed between us, it was good to know that our friends in Holland and England had provided for lecture engagements. Thus I made some pocket money and had a last couple of weeks among the pleasant hospitality of still happy Holland and merry old England. The *Normandie* took us in state from Southampton to Le Havre, where a strike and belated sailing procured us an unexpected holiday in beautiful Normandy. Finally a poor and untidy steamer of the French Line, which made up for discomfort with delicious food, brought us through the Panama Canal to California.

The twenty-sixth of July, 1936, we landed in San Pedro. At the pier stood our daughter Ruth and the friendly colleagues of the University of California. Less than a year later our son Hans arrived with his bride. The pursuit of happiness and the blessings of liberty were again ours.

15: VITA NUOVA

More than twenty years have passed since we arrived in California, years pregnant with the most important events for mankind. I had thought that the rest of my life would consist of quiet scholarship, inside the ivory tower as it were, without any events worth recording, though I realized that the end of Hitler could never be brought about without a major upheaval. The idea that the Nazis could stay on never entered my mind since this would have meant the negation of all moral principles in the world. That much was already clear, although at the time the most horrible fact of the world's history, the extermination of ten million harmless people by assembly-line methods, could not have been considered within the realm of possibility. But in 1936 in California it was still possible to think of Hitler and his gang of hand-picked criminals and the heiling and arm-raising Germans, including a shamefully large contingent of university people, as a faraway nuisance.

Nevertheless, soon after our arrival we realized that even California was within reach of Nazi meanness. While we were living peacefully in the house of Professor Kofoid, who was traveling in Europe, a couple of German-Americans called on us and then came again, though we were rather cold toward the man, who claimed to have lived the last years in Germany for business reasons. We soon found out what this business was. Professor Kofoid's nephew, also named Kofoid, had left his uncle to make a little trip into Germany by himself. When he gave his name at the frontier he was brought to the office of the Gestapo and quizzed. He was told that I was living in Kofoid's house in Berkeley and was asked to confess that I had sent him into Germany with some secret order. The young boy, who did not speak German and who hardly knew of my existence, had great difficulty in convincing the Gestapo and certainly suffered the shock of his life. It was more than obvious that our German-American visitor was an agent of the Gestapo who, in order to justify his pay, had concocted some story about me and sent it to them with the information that the Kofoids might be going into Germany. It was of course typical of such bodies as the Gestapo to waste their money and energy on perfectly silly pursuits in order to demonstrate their efficiency and omniscience.

Since we were well acquainted with America and came at once to live among friends, we had no trouble in adapting ourselves to the American way of life. Especially some time later, when we were able to "buy" a lovely, heavily mortgaged home and furnish it with the nice things we had brought with us, we felt completely settled. Soon our daughter joined us, and our son with his bride, and California really became our home.

It was a little more difficult to adapt myself to my new work as professor at the University of California. I had been terribly spoiled in Berlin, where I had had the best laboratory in the world with unlimited space, technical help, assistants, multilingual secretaries, the best instruments and equipment, and complete freedom to use all this without bureaucratic interference, without requisition slips or purchasing departments. My time had been completely my own, and I was even free to move anywhere and take my funds and salary with me if I thought my research required it. And of course I had no teaching, but only advanced, fully trained collaborators from all over the world.

Now I suddenly became a professor like all the others, in a state university that professors and students alike called "school," as if it were a grammar school, not a university. I was given a tiny room in which I could never do experimental work or install my scientific books. Now I had to start teaching again, after twenty-three years of pure research as my own boss, and in the beginning this was not easy. I was assigned a freshman course in general biology for about six hundred students who had to take such a course for credit. This meant that about one hundred had some little interest in the subject, while the rest had to pass the course in order to remain in college whether they liked it or not. In Germany universities were professional schools, and the students were the equivalent of graduate students who wanted to learn the subject and had done their elementary work in the middle schools. I had had considerable experience in teaching laymen and liked it, since I was endowed by nature with the ability of making even difficult things clear. But I had always lectured to laymen and students who attended the course because they were interested in the subject. Though I was told that I did a creditable job I found the work most hateful and felt rather déclassé. I called it my kindergarten class and felt miserable each day when it was over and I had looked at so many blank faces of students who could not understand why the professor tried to explain a thing they did not want to understand anyhow, instead of assigning some textbook page for memorizing.

Fortunately the next year I was relieved of this unpleasant job and assigned to advanced classes where I could teach a group of good students on a real university level, and I flatter myself that the thousands of students I taught in the following twelve years took home not only knowledge but also respect for learning and independent thinking. I never followed texts, and I tried to emancipate my students from memorizing, substituting instead clear analytic thinking. I tried to foster the same thing in postgraduate seminars, which I started in our department as a systematic way of teaching advanced students and especially of awakening them to courageous independent thinking in animated discussions. In time, as I acquired also a number of fine students working at a doctor's thesis that I had suggested, my status as a part-time teacher instead of a pure research scholar became rather pleasant, much more than a sheer necessity. The signs of gratitude that I received from the young men and women and am still receiving after my retirement show me that I did my duty and probably more.

Finally, after a year I was also able to leave my impossible quarters and receive a good large laboratory with the necessary equipment and assistance. Thus, after a loss of two years, I could again start my research work, and this meant happiness.

Private life went on pleasantly. Everybody had received us with hospitality and friendliness, and it was not difficult to feel at home in one of the beauty spots of the world and in a community of fine people. During the summer of 1938 we went to southern California to attend a conference. On the way back we stopped in Santa Cruz, where we stayed in the cabin of a friend. One morning we went down to the beach for a swim in the rather cold water. While we were returning home in wet swimming suits one of the children insisted on leaning out of the open window of the car, so that we were exposed to a cold draft, a treatment unsuited to a man of sixty. The result was that I returned to Berkeley with a high fever and tonsillitis of streptococcal origin. When it was over there were signs of heart strain. Later it turned out that the streptococci had moved into the kidneys. I became sicker and sicker in spite of a rather heroic treatment that turned out to have damaged the heart. I went to bed, got worse and worse, and one day suffered

Exhibit of the author's collection of Chinese tomb figurines, M. H. de Young Museum, San Francisco

The author's last lecture, Berkeley, 1948 (*photograph by Nathan Cohen*)

a frightful heart attack that almost knocked me out. But it seems that I had good reserves, and after anxious weeks in the hospital and many more at home I could finally start work again.

A short time before my illness I had received the genuine honor of being invited to deliver the famous Silliman Lectures of Yale University. While convalescing in our lovely garden I wrote these lectures, which were later published as a book, *The Material Basis of Evolution,* that put a finger on some major errors in present-day evolutionary theory. Though it is still violently attacked today by the partisans of one very fashionable way of looking at evolution, I am certain that in the end I shall turn out to have been right.

In December we went to New Haven for these lectures. As I was still rather weak, and in addition was suffering from clam poisoning, while my wife had flu, these weeks at Yale among many friends were unfortunately not what they could have been otherwise. But a restful stay at Pass Christian in Mississippi and later in the clear air of Arizona restored my strength. Nevertheless, it took altogether two years until I felt that I had finally licked the illness.

This might have meant that now the enjoyment of life and liberty was to begin again. But fate did not will it, and once more we had to become Hitler's victims in a small but unpleasant way. The years from 1938 on are history: occupation of the Rhineland, the rape of Austria, the revolt of the Sudeten Germans and Munich, the attack on Czechoslovakia, the treaty with Soviet Russia for the dismemberment of Poland, the attack on Russia, the World War. We were not yet American citizens, as only three of the necessary five years had passed. But, needless to say, our hearts were where they belonged, with America and her allies, and we were violently opposed to the Nazi criminals. Thus, it was a bad shock when the ice-cold bureaucrats of the Department of Justice declared us—together with thousands in the same position—to be enemy aliens. We, united with others, tried to enlist the help of prominent friends and sent lawyers to Washington to make it clear that we had severed all ties with Germany and hated its regime more than any American possibly could. It was all in vain, and we were never able to find out why the Department of Justice insisted on this injustice.

Not only did we have to endure the sting of being called enemy aliens in the country where we had found a haven from persecution, but there were some actual inconveniences. The general entrusted with defenses in California decided to save the West Coast from dangerous enemy aliens by establishing for them a seven-o'clock curfew, prohibited zones, and a series of *verboten* activities, such as moving more than five miles away from one's residence. The curfew was the easiest part, for we are homebodies who do not care to go out much at night, but the forbidden zones were more serious. One limit was laid right through our street in the middle of a residential area with nothing but residences far and wide. Fortunately we lived on the east side of the street; otherwise we should have had to move, as did some of our friends. But we had friends and neighbors on the west side with whom we could not visit. They came, of course, to our house, which made the whole thing look still more idiotic. The five-mile rule cut us off from the major shopping centers in Oakland and San Francisco, as well as from various recreational areas. Thus private life was rather unpleasant for years until we finally became citizens—for, though we were dangerous enemy aliens, we nevertheless remained candidates for citizenship.

In retrospect these unpleasant things may look more important than they were at the time. Actually most of the day was occupied with teaching and research, which did not leave much time to think of anything else. And the university itself was a friendly haven where everybody treated me as a friend and prospective American citizen. There was not the slightest bit of hysteria of the type we had known during the first World War, and the scientific world behaved in a way worthy of its traditions. My son, an engineer, could do his duty in an advanced position in the Kaiser shipyard, while my daughter had already acquired citizenship, and her husband was serving at the front.

Thus the war years passed, and the wonderful day came when the thousand years of the Third Reich came to an end. Only then the stunned world learned the details of the ghastly deeds of history's most beastly criminals.

Though I had anticipated a rather quiet life for the end of my days, it turned out to be full of interesting things both within and outside of my profession. I could still accomplish what I consider to be some major pieces of my work and develop a number of rather daring ideas that have now come into their own after a long struggle. My intellectual fertility has fortunately remained intact, and I have never ceased to enjoy experimental work as well as analytic and synthetic thinking and the chance to present my ideas in special lectures and lectureships. Fortunately I have never run dry, even long after my retirement, and I can be content with the use I have made of my inborn gifts, practically to the last day.

Even my hobby of traveling still had some chances of development. Soon after the war we were able to spend some interesting months in the remarkable cultural surroundings of Mexico. And in 1947 a long lecture trip took us to New Zealand, with a few months also in Australia. Nowadays so many people visit these once remote regions that a detailed report is hardly needed. This trip got off to a bad start. There were no passenger ships running to Australia and New Zealand from the American west coast, but the Matson Line had taken over a military transport, the *Marine Phoenix,* on which one could travel for a first-class fare in conditions resembling old-time steerage. There was no covered deck to protect the passengers from the tropical sun, and the only luxuries were a number of juke boxes, which rattled day and night. The low-ceilinged dining room in the bottom of the hull was a nightmare in the tropics. The passengers were anything but cheerful. Many of them were young Australian war brides, who, disappointed that American life had turned out so different from what they had been led to expect, had either run away from their G.I. husbands or were taking them back to Australia. Innumerable babies for whom no provision had been made in the frightfully hot cabins were a pitiful sight. I had acquired sinusitis, for which the doctor knew no remedy, and for many days enjoyed the pleasure of a high fever in the tropics without a chance to get away from the draft. It certainly was the most uncomfortable sea voyage of my life, and the return voyage on the same ship was made even worse by one of the most disagreeable captains I have ever traveled with.

In New Zealand I lectured in all the universities and agricultural colleges, and thus we went all over the two islands. As always, on such occasions, we met innumerable fine people and experienced rich hospitality. We saw a good deal of the bush, remarkable virgin forests, and the snow-covered mountains where glaciers border on forest land. We also saw something of the Maori, the aboriginal inhabitants of New Zealand, and found out as much as we could about the remarkable and much described social security system.

The greatest surprise was Australia. We had expected a rather uninteresting and not very beautiful country and found a most interesting and most beautiful one. The big cities Sydney and Melbourne bristled with life. We found good modern architecture, comfort, good food and delicious native wine, and much cheer. Sydney's location around a deep bay is glorious, and its near surroundings, with water, forests, and mountains, are charming and interesting. I could, of course, not escape from delivering some lectures and had the pleasure of meeting charming old friends and making new ones, in both Sydney and Melbourne. The amazing capital of Canberra, laid out for a million and inhabited by fewer than one hundred thousand people, was another worth-while sight. But the high point was a month's sojourn in one of the Capricorn Islands of the Great Barrier Reef, in the almost tropical north. Living in the most primitive conditions, surrounded by coral reefs on which one could walk at low tides, awakened in the morning by the chatter of the cockatoos, making excursions to the other islands and the main barrier reef, we had a wonderful and memorable vacation. Needless to say, the naturalist could study the strange creatures of land and sea all day long and have a real holiday from laboratory work in the great outdoors.

Two European trips were still to come. In 1948 I attended two international congresses in Stockholm and Paris that gave me, among other pleasant experiences, the new thrill of flying the Atlantic. In 1953 we made the last voyage of an inveterate traveler. We spent two glorious months among the beauties of Switzerland and met once more many old friends, actually some of our oldest ones, a number of whom came from Germany to see us on Swiss soil. It was a fitting end to my scientific career and to my long fight for progressive ideas, shocking to the *"ewig Gestrige"* but now understood by the more independent minds, that I was elected president of the Ninth International Congress of Genetics in Bellaggio and could deliver an appropriate address to the more than eight hundred members.

It is probably also a proper consequence of my nature that I overstrained myself during this trip by walking uphill too much in Switzerland and undertaking too many things—sightseeing, visiting art galleries, meetings and discussions, and what not. The result was a bad case of angina pectoris, recognized first, after many small attacks, in Florence after a morning among the treasures of the Uffizi Gallery. This, then, means sooner or later the end of an unusually rich and wonderful life of work and play, hard thinking and the pleasures of the world, fighting for what I believed to be right, intellectual and esthetic delights, and unending search for deeper understanding of nature. I have been blessed with all the forms of happiness of mind and body; with deep ethical convictions not dependent upon organized religion; with passionate understanding of and respect for all ideals, for everything beautiful in man's soul, in nature, and in art. I have accumulated a wealth of knowledge in innumerable spheres and enjoyed it as an always ready instrument for exercising the mind and penetrating further and further. Best of all, mine has been a life of loving and being loved. What a tragedy that all this will disappear with the used-up body!

APPENDIX: MY WORK

The foregoing account touches on my work as a research scholar only here and there. Autobiographies of scientists are usually loaded with details of university life, stories of the laboratories, reports on every pie in which they have had a finger, and pointedly modest descriptions of honors received. It is obvious that I have had my share of all these things, that I enjoyed those that were signs of successful work, and that, in some instances at least, I was proud of them. But they have never meant as much to me as, for example, a good concert. Yet my work has been my life, and what I have accomplished and what I have done wrong is of deep concern to me. Since I am by nature critical I feel that I may be my own best critic and that I may be able to discern where my abilities have appeared at their best and where my weaknesses have showed up.

The mainspring and basic feature of my scientific mind is, first, a natural ability to see at once what is new and to be able to make quick factual discoveries based upon observation. My life work is filled with innumerable newly observed facts, many of which were hidden in other work and only occasionally recognized by the specialist. I have been able to exercise this faculty in many different fields, each of which is usually considered to be the entire occupation of any single worker, such as cytology, descriptive and experimental embryology, histology, neurology, microscopic anatomy, physiology, taxonomy, entomology, parasitology, genetics, and evolution.

The second major feature of my mental construction is the absolute need of placing any new fact in its proper place within the whole realm of our science. Whether I wanted to be one or not, this has made me a theoretician who has had to propose and just as often modify or abandon far-reaching theoretical constructions meant to serve as a frame of reference for a huge body of facts, whose mastery the happy gift of a good memory permitted. Thus I have constantly built and rebuilt my vision of the deep connections within our science.

In addition to this synthetic ability, a third basic aspect of my mind is an analytic tendency that makes me strike at the roots of things and, in addition, makes me skeptical of the scientific fashions of the day, with their warmed-over arguments. Many times—though frequently only in my mind—I have put my finger upon weaknesses of enthusiastically received wrong ideas and have turned out in the end to be right. Thus my ideas have often been far ahead of their time and understood only much later, when their origin was long forgotten—quite a satisfaction, but mixed with a sting!

These basic properties of my mind also have their reverse ideas. I have been happy when I found the ideas fitting the facts and vice versa, and sometimes my enthusiasm has run away with me. Thus it has happened that I reported on a case before the facts were sufficiently established and later had to swallow my words. These occasions were holidays for those of my colleagues who never had an idea and therefore never had an erroneous one, and I am glad to have contributed to the pleasure of these gentlemen. Only once did I feel that I had reason to be ashamed of myself. I thought I made a major discovery in a field in which I was not at home, but it turned out to be based upon an error in observation. My excuse is that at the time I was so overworked that, had I been wise, I should not have written anything.

For about ten years after my first paper on the parasite echinococcus (1900), I worked in the field of morphology, in which I believe I have made a sufficient number of lasting contributions to establish my position as a zoologist of merit even if I had never done anything else. The first major contribution was the establishment of the nematodes (roundworms) as cell-constant animals by clearing up the amazing cellular structure of their heads. The same principle was extended to other organ systems. There was, for example, the important finding that the so-called body cavity is a pleroma consisting of a very few liquid-filled giant cells. The most extended work was done on the nervous system, which is completely cell-constant so that every single ganglion cell could be described. The amazing factor concerning the interconnections between these cells, anticipating the recent emphasis on nerve diameter, has never come to the attention of the neurologists. This is partly because two Russian vertebrate neurologists, completely ignorant of the aberrant histology of the nematodes, stained all kinds of cells and syncytia with methylene blue, considered everything blue to be nerve, and thus described what would be the craziest nervous system under the sun. The insolence of their ignorant criticism may have frightened away the neurologists, most of whom disregard the lower animals anyway. Perhaps some day this work, which cost a huge amount of tedious effort, will come into its own if some broad-minded neurologist hits upon it.

The second major group of papers of this time deals with the morphology of the Acrania, the primitive fishlike ancestors of the vertebrates. These little lancelets were known to be epithelial animals, not yet possessing a connective tissue system. I figured out that, if they had such a system, it would probably look different from that of other animals. When I went to work at the marine biological station in Banyuls, with the first Askenasy award of Heidelberg University, I decided to look for a connective tissue in *Amphioxus* and especially to try to see it in vivo in the transparent lancelets. I succeeded very quickly, probably because I was prepared to find something of an unexpected type. Later I was also able to stain the few small cells located at unexpected points and thus to establish this organ system also for the lancelets. This was later confirmed by Krüger.

At this time I took over the task of preparing a monograph on the strange late-metamorphosing larvae of tropical Acrania. I believed that they were neotenic Acrania of a different family, but later I and others gave the correct explanation. (I returned to this subject once much later, in 1932, when my sojourn at the Bermuda biological laboratory and acquaintance with Beebe, who had fished some specimens, awakened this interest of my youth.) In the monograph I published a number of major discoveries. One was the finding of the hitherto unknown, remarkable visceral musculature of these animals. More important still was the difficult finding of solenocytes in the so-called Hatschek's nephridium, establishing an oral nephridium of the type found in annelids. This was later confirmed and extended by Goodrich. Another discovery was the intricate system of lymph canals of unknown function.

A third major piece of work of this time (1904) dealt with the so-called chromidial apparatus of *Ascaris*. As this complicated functional structure is difficult to fix and stain, some quick and superficial repeaters of this work (Dobell, Vejdowsky) declared the structure to be an artifact. But many others since have shown its existence. It is known to cytologists that the idea of chromidia has undergone many changes, and some of the sweeping generalizations I made turned out to be wrong. But it is worth while to reread this old paper today because later work on nuclear-cytoplasmic relations has led to results that in a general way and with different terminology largely revive my long-forgotten ideas.

It should be added that at this time I had a great many students who did their doctor's theses under my constant supervision on many topics of cytology and protozoology, and many of their discoveries were actually mine. But, since I was the younger man in Hertwig's laboratory, credit for this work was frequently given to Hertwig, who had nothing whatsoever to do with it. Even today I still read that someone who has published a book or celebrated an anniversary was a student of Hertwig, although actually his work was done exclusively with me. I mention this because I spent an immense amount of time and energy upon my students' work, and, since I am proud of their accomplishments, I do not like to be replaced as scientific godfather. A few names are: Buchner, Seiler, Schaxel, Katsuki, Koehler, Erdmann, Ehrlich, Blankertz, von Kemnitz, Schellenberg, Lindner, Jörgensen, Nachtsheim. Most of their work is published in the *Archiv für Zellforschung*, which I founded in 1906 and edited as long as it ran. There also are found many of my minor papers of this period.

In the next twenty-five years my work with the gypsy moth *Lymantria* stood in the foreground, though in between many other things were accomplished. Actually my first piece of genetic work was done with the nun moth (*Lymantria monacha*), with which I attacked an important problem of microevolution, the so-called industrial melanism, where a kind of microevolution had taken place under the observer's eye, the replacement of a light variety by a dark one. The genetic analysis was made between 1909 and 1914 but could be published only after the war. On the basis of the genetic results I tried to calculate with my own crude methods—the modern ones were not yet available—the mutation pressure needed to replace one form by the other, and came to the conclusion that it is too high, and that therefore the melanic mutants must have a selective advantage. Very few geneticists know that this old work made me one of the pioneers of population genetics, a science whose exaggerated claims I was later forced to criticize.

The first great problem of my *Lymantria* work was the problem of the genetics of sex determination. I am proud to say that its solution starts with this work, published from 1911 to 1920, which resulted in a number of decisive discoveries:

1. The phenomenon of intersexuality (term proposed in 1915) was discovered by separating it from gynandromorphism.

2. Normal sex determination is the result of a balance of female and male sex determiners, one within, one outside the X-chromosomes, the 1X–2X mechanism controlling quantitatively this balance. (This I called quantitative relation, since the decisive point is an imbalance.)

3. Zygotic intersexuality, as produced in *Lymantria* by racial crossings, is the result of a definite imbalance of these sex determiners that can be produced experimentally in any quantity.

4. Two types of intersexes exist, male and female ones, meaning genetically 1X or 2X individuals.

5. By appropriate genetic combinations all grades of both types of intersexes, including complete sex reversal, can be produced at will in 100 per cent of the respective individuals.

6. Intricate experiments showed that the results are due only to the quantity of the balance or imbalance and that these quantities can be handled as simple equations with always consistent results.

7. The morphology of the series of graded intersexes, up to complete sex reversal in both directions, found its explanation in the so-called time law, meaning that an intersex is an individual that begins development with its genetic sex and ends it, after a turning point, with the opposite sex. The time of the turning point determines the higher or lower grade of intersexuality. This time law was attacked by the school of my student and friend Seiler because some of his results in triploid intersexes did not seem to agree. After much discussion this criticism collapsed when Seiler himself proved that his intersexual development did not exist, but only female-male alternatives, which of course require the time law in order to explain the whole series.

8. In *Lymantria* an orderly series of geographic races exists with different conditions of the sex determiners as evidenced by the different but typical results of their crosses.

9. The female determiners in *Lymantria* are located in the Y-chromosomes and therefore must act in the unfertilized egg via the cytoplasm.

These are the main results. They stand today still untouched, though there are discussions possible about this or that detail, for example, single versus many sex determiners. In the course of the years I added innumerable details to these main facts that had been established by 1920, and only after almost twenty-five years of work I stopped crossing *Lymantria* and added more facts. Of course my three trips to Japan and its surroundings repeatedly furnished new material to extend the scope of the work, and, in addition, I returned again until 1953 to the theoretical aspect of the facts in order to fit them into more recent developments on the subject and to draw the attention of those geneticists who know only what has been done in the last five years to the foundations upon which they unwittingly stand.

In 1920 I incorporated the new insight into a book on the mechanism and physiology of sex determination, in which I tried to bring the balance theory into line with all other facts of sex determination in the animal kingdom. The book had a great influence on European work in the field, though only a few Americans understood its importance as a turning point in the study of sex. In 1933 it was followed by a voluminous monograph on the sexual intergrades, in which all the facts relating to the subject were assembled and integrated, and especially the relations between genetic and hormonic sex controls were amply discussed.

Speaking of books, I should mention that in 1911 I had already published an extensive textbook of genetics, *Einführung in die Vererbungswissenschaft*. Its origin was a lecture course in Munich, actually the first university course in genetics given in Germany, which was attended by more professors than students. The truth is that I wanted to learn genetics by teaching it, a kind of youthful daring, if not insolence, since at that time no German text existed. (Johannsen's book was not a text and, in spite of its brilliance, was not well suited for the zoological geneticists. Baur's book was to appear simultaneously with mine.) When I conceived the idea of making a text out of those lectures it was in my opinion a daring, if not "cheeky" experiment, because I had myself only begun with genetic experiments. Nowadays nobody hesitates to write a text without a firsthand mastery of the subject. But I still feel ashamed of that deed, with the qualification that in the course of four more editions I made the book into a really good (and very successful) one, which took its place in German scientific literature until the Nazis forbade its sale in 1933.

The same material, *Lymantria*, served during the same period of almost twenty years for another very extensive pioneer work involving the breeding of perhaps millions of individuals. When it became clear in 1914 that different sex races of this moth existed in different geographic regions, especially in eastern Asia, I embarked upon an analysis of the genetics of geographic variation. As a convinced Darwinian I believed geographic races to be incipient species. I hoped to prove by such an analysis the correctness of this idea. I was completely acquainted with what twenty years later was rediscovered as "the new systematics," and my convictions, as expressed in 1920 and 1923, were practically the same as those of present-day Neo-Darwinians.

This is important to state, since, at the end of this work, the facts forced me to change my basic ideas. But for almost twenty years I worked as a Neo-Darwinian, and if I had remained one my work would be touted as a classic of Neo-Darwinism. This pioneer work, performed at the same time as Sumner's work with mammals, contains an immense wealth of factual data and all the primary information on the genetics of natural subspecies and their adaptive nature, but not yet the later population genetics approach. Although it was called monumental by a British reviewer, since I changed my conclusions it is no longer known to the champions of the latest fashion in evolution.

It was not until 1932, when the analysis was finished on the basis of three field trips to eastern Asia and breeding experiments on a scale that only the generous Kaiser Wilhelm Institute could support, that I added to the many publications of the detailed facts an analysis of the conclusions. At the International Genetics Congress in Ithaca I presented my conclusion, that geographic variation is a blind alley leading only to microevolution within the species, and not the source of real evolution. On a move by Morgan I had to repeat my German lecture in English.

Such conclusions forced me to think of what addition to Darwinism was needed in order to account for the macroevolutionary processes. The solution was the existence of macromutants, which, in rare cases, could affect early embryonic processes so that through the features of embryonic regulation and integration at once a major step in evolution could be accomplished and fixed under certain conditions. I spoke half jokingly of the hopeful monster in my first publication on the subject, a lecture read by invitation in 1933 at the World's Fair in Chicago. We shall see how I returned to the subject in a later period.

The third major problem, attacked while still under the influence of the *Lymantria* work, was the theory of the gene. In 1915 I realized that the relation between the time of the turning point in intersexual development and the quantitative features of the con-trolling genic balance pointed to an enzymatic action of the genes controlling the rate of embryonic determining actions. After sur-veying the enzyme chemistry of that time I worked out a theory of genic action by intertwined and attuned and balanced velocities of reaction of determining processes, controlled by the quantities of the gene-enzyme system. This theory, later called the physiological theory of heredity, was written down in 1916 and published in 1920 as *Quantitativen Grundlagen von Vererbung und Artbildung,* a little book printed in only five hundred copies. I personally be-lieve that for the time of its publication it was a very remarkable book, and it impressed many European biologists. Historically I think it marks the beginning of physiological genetics, though much of its contents is now antiquated. It is worth mentioning that, while not many geneticists understood the meaning of this little book, the medical faculty of the University of Kiel, at the in-stigation of the biochemist R. Höber, conferred an honorary M.D. on me just in recognition of this work. The biochemist had realized that here was a beginning of bringing together genetics and bio-chemistry.

Needless to say, the ideas developed here continued to occupy my mind and lead to further and further elaboration of the theoretic construction. While in Japan in 1926 I worked again through all the material available and organized my ideas on physiological genetics into a book, *Physiologische Theorie der Vererbung,* a book that some people, including myself, consider a major performance. It is true that it is difficult reading for the average statistical geneticist, especially one unacquainted with dynamic thinking as well as with the problems of development. Thus it happened that its value was better realized by physiologists and experimental embryologists than by the narrow Mendelian geneticists. An American reviewer, who had obviously struggled through only the first chapter on the derivation of the general ideas from the theory of sex determination and then given up, wrote that he did not know whether the work was something worth while or pure bunk. He had not even noticed that a physiological theory of genetic action was developed.

The theoretical work of these years led me to start some other work with different material. Of this I shall mention only the work on the pattern of the butterfly wing, later continued by my student Sueffert. As this could be done only during the intervals in the

Lymantria work, it remained only an interesting beginning of what later became very important work in the hands of Kühn and Henke. Of course my time was not sufficient for tackling everything that came to my mind. At this point I should mention the extensive work on problems encountered during the work on geographic variation. These include the analysis of the genetics and physiology of the diapause, the inheritance of molting, the inheritance of differences in growth, and the first case in animals of cytoplasmic heredity.

I have loved all my life long to play from time to time with some problem that was rather remote from my main interest, and in the list of my publications quite a number of such odd papers can be found. In 1914 I was intrigued by the new technique of tissue cultures, which I thought might be used more widely as, of course, has been done since. Thus when I was in Harrison's laboratory in 1914–15 I proposed to try this technique on invertebrate material with the special goal of growing sex cells in vitro. I actually succeeded in obtaining spermatogenesis in vitro and thus in opening a new field in that line of work, which just now has become popular again in Williams' work. I repeatedly returned to the study of tissue culture and, many years later, had very interesting results with *Drosophila* tissues. I never published these, since my photographs were lost when I left Germany.

During these first twenty years of work in genetics I amused myself repeatedly, as I have mentioned, with my hobby of writing popular science. In my younger years I had already published two little volumes, one on protozoa (*Die Urtiere*) and one on the biology of reproduction (*Die Fortpflanzung der Tiere*). In the early days of the first World War I spent many otherwise lonely hours writing a popular biology (*Ascaris, eine Einführung in die Wissenschaft vom Leben*). The book had an immense success in Europe and was translated into many languages, with the greatest success in Russia. Count Keyserling, the traveling philosopher, called it in a review the best popular science ever written. In 1953 a third edition was published in German. An American edition was a failure; why this was so would be an interesting, though anything but cheering, problem to investigate.

While in the internment camp in 1918, I wrote a little popular work on Mendelism for agriculturalists, which went through a few editions. And in Japan in 1925 I wrote for a Japanese encyclopedia a popular work on genetics that was later also published in German as *Die Lehre von der Vererbung*. This sold fifteen thousand copies in Germany before the Nazis stopped it, and in 1953 a fourth edition appeared. It also was translated into many languages, and recently I adapted it to American conditions under the title *Understanding Heredity*. Finally, in 1927 I published a travel book on Formosa, Korea, Okinawa, Manchuria, and the Bonin Islands that, I think, is good reading, and especially now, when almost nothing remains of what I described then.

When, in the late 1920's, I realized that my work with *Lymantria* was drawing to a close, I began to play a little with *Drosophila* with the purpose of becoming acquainted with the material and special genetic techniques so that I might turn to *Drosophila* as material when *Lymantria* was finished. In 1928 I conceived the idea of trying on *Drosophila* some of the controversial temperature experiments that in Lepidoptera had led to the objectionable theory of parallel induction. The first result of the use of temperature shocks was the increase of the mutation rate. These results turned out to be unreliable, however, because by chance I had worked with one of the rare and still unexplained cases of mass mutation. But in 1929 another result turned out to be a major discovery, namely that, depending upon the time of application, the genetic material, and the type of shock, the shocks produced nonhereditary copies of almost all known mutants. In 1932, while discussing some problems of physiological genetics with J. B. S. Haldane, I quoted these results. Haldane said flatly that he did not believe them, so I started a repetition on a large scale and in 1935 published a fully documented account, proposing the name of phenocopy for the phenomenon. A huge amount of work has since been done in this field, some of it by myself and my students.

Thus started the last period of my scientific life, in which my experimental material was exclusively *Drosophila*. While my last experiments with *Lymantria* were being finished after my return from my third trip to Japan in 1930, I began large-scale work on problems of physiologic genetics in *Drosophila*. The most important part of this dealt with the genetically controlled clipping of the wings in the vestigial series. I found first that this phenomenon could be greatly influenced by the introduction of dominigenes (dominance modifiers). I isolated a number of these and made systematic series of homozygotes and compounds of the vg-alleles with and without these dominigenes. Thus I had two series that paralleled each other in their effects and permitted quantitative comparisons of genic action. Soon I found that the vg effect is based on secondary destruction of wing tissue at different times, earlier and earlier with increasing grade. Waddington later denied this destruction and proposed a very complicated and improbable interpretation of the developmental facts. I still think that my interpretation stands, perhaps with some additional features emphasized by Waddington. Parallel processes are known in Lepidoptera, and Waddington himself found a case in Lepidoptera of the destruction type. These time elements—the onset of destruction —could then be brought into line with the genetic facts, and a very attractive picture of genic action in relation to rates of differentiation could be presented.

At the time this work was finished the Nazis had already taken over. Since I had at once decided to leave Germany at the first opportunity, I wrote these papers in English and held them until three years later, when I took them with me to Berkeley. During the last years in Berlin I was most interested in the analysis of a strange stock that had appeared under my eyes and seemed to present phenomena of a high mutation rate affecting the same loci repeatedly. For many more years I puzzled over this material and finally published an extensive report on spontaneous mutation, combining many remarkable facts and groups of facts, probably of great significance but unfortunately very untransparent. I put an unbelievable amount of work into this paper, which nevertheless remained an unsatisfactory torso. This happens when one insists on analyzing things that are not of the common run and therefore lead into all kinds of corners. I should call this work a waste of time were it not for the conviction that I was struggling with something worth while, though unyielding. The paper contains a wealth of individual interesting facts, like the data on the remarkable silver alleles, the broad alleles, and the combination of both; the analysis of plexation; some significant details on minute rearrangements in the salivaries; and so on. A small section reporting on unproved but probable cases of interdependence of mutations is more suggestive than final, but worth keeping in mind.

The first year in Berkeley, finding myself without a proper laboratory, I settled down to write a comprehensive book on physiological genetics, as no such book had been written. It was reprinted twice and went out of print only recently. Besides reviewing the whole field, this book contained one of my first statements, after a few shorter hints, of some rather nonconformist

ideas about the nature of the gene involving the nonexistence of
the corpuscular gene. For some years I had entertained such ideas,
and I worked them out first in this book and in two papers, one
given at a Stanford symposium. The reception was what I expected: "Goldschmidt has gone crazy," and I am glad that I did not
myself hear the other comments.

In the following years I returned to the subject repeatedly,
trying to classify my own ideas and to assemble more material. In
the center of the critique stood the facts on position effect, and
in some of my experimental work of these years, and also the work
of some of my students, a number of interesting new facts on
position effect were presented. All of them were reviewed in a
paper in *Experientia* but, characteristically enough, were never
quoted by my critics.

In the course of the last few years the situation has changed.
Many of the critics of my "revolutionary" ideas (I call them
"evolutionary") came to realize that there is something behind
them. Many of the younger geneticists have joined me more or
less completely, and today Goldschmidt is no longer crazy, only
daring and, possibly, largely right. My friends called it a triumph
when in 1951 I was asked to open the symposium on the gene in
Cold Spring Harbor with a review of my ideas and thought. Some
diehard reactionaries tried to minimize the success, but I think that
a viable grain was sown here. I came back to the subject once more
in the presidential address at the Ninth International Congress of
Genetics, where I presented these views in a discussion of
philosophies of genetics. Later, while convalescing from a severe
illness, I wrote a volume for which I had collected the material
over a long period of time, in which these ideas and others are
built up into a work, *Theoretical Genetics*, that appeared in 1955.

This was not the only theoretical work I did in the years at
Berkeley, in addition to the continued experimental work in former
and new fields. In 1939 I had the honor of delivering the famous
Silliman lectures at Yale, and, since it is my opinion that such
lectures should not be dull reviews of one's work but something
stimulating and thought-provoking, I returned to my heretical
views on macroevolution and Neo-Darwinism and wrote a volume, *The Material Basis of Evolution*, in which I reviewed criti-
cally the evidence for Neo-Darwinian evolution and tried to prove
the necessity of macroevolution via macromutation. I extended my
argument especially to the aspect of the organism's ability to

323

change its development into new directions, and built up a strong argument for my ideas. I certainly had struck a hornet's nest. The Neo-Darwinians reacted savagely. This time I was not only crazy but almost a criminal. There were, of course, exceptions, like the deep thinker Sewall Wright, who criticized my work objectively and has recently moved much nearer to my views. And again the number of evolutionists who try at least to find a place for my views in evolutionary thinking is increasing. I am confident that in twenty years my book, which is now ignored, will be given an honorable place in the history of evolutionary thought.

After the work on spontaneous mutation, my experimental work again turned to the problems of physiological genetics and also of sex determination. In addition to a series of theoretical discussions with my Swiss friends and critics, I was occupied with a series of papers dealing with the unexpected discovery that *Drosophila* males containing the dominants beaded and minute become slightly intersexual. There cannot be any doubt that real intersexuality is involved, though the phenomenon overlaps with another abnormality. Perhaps the most interesting point in this analysis is that the feminizing action works also through the cytoplasm of the unfertilized egg, just as in a number of other cases discussed in these papers. Another piece of work related to sex was the analysis of a case of mutation within a secondary sex character (abdominal hair in *Drosophila* males). The very interesting and novel genetical results were used to present a full discussion of the topic of genetics of secondary sex characters.

While I was in Japan and afterward I was able, together with my student Katsuki who had done the breeding work without being able to analyze it, to do a piece of work on gynandromorphism and somatic mosaicism in the silkworms. This resulted in the most complete analysis of gynandromorphism that has been made, since both genetics and cytology were analyzed. It was shown that all results were explained by double fertilization of a polar body. A maternally inherited locus controls this phenomenon via cytoplasmic action. This series of papers is in my opinion one of the most elegant pieces of analysis I have been able to perform, and I am particularly proud of it, though the textbooks have taken no notice of it whatever.

For many years toward the end of my career I was engaged—together with some of my students, especially Leonie Kellen Piternick and Aloha Hannah—in an intensive analysis of what I called the podoptera effect, the final paper on this problem being an extensive monograph. In the homeotic mutants that I found, namely podoptera and tetraltera, the wing is transformed into a halterlike or leglike structure, with all transitions from normal to extreme change existing. The morphology is most interesting, since it involves different embryonic determination of different parts of the wing and their determinative change by genic action into other structures, namely one leglike structure and, from another section of the wing, thorax and scutellum tissue. The latter features, as analyzed in one of the last papers, are especially noteworthy from the point of view of both physiological genetics and evolution.

The genetics of podoptera is very remarkable. It is based upon main loci in the second chromosome and additional ones in all others. The details of how these control penetrance and expressivity are very remarkable. Penetrance factors seem to be ubiquitous, and lines can be isolated with all degrees of penetrance from almost nothing to 100 per cent. Selection from this cannot be performed gradually by slow steps, however, but only in major jumps, as analyzed on a large scale in the most recent paper of the series. There are innumerable special features in our fat monograph. One of the most important is the dependence on Y-chromosome material and a kind of spurious allelo-morphism between the different loci involved. Therefore the conclusion was drawn and elaborated that podoptera may represent a case of heterochromatic heredity, which, if proved by subsequent work, would be very important. Needless to say, these strange macromutations invited phylogenetic speculation and evolutionary discussions found in a number of different papers.

As in all periods of my life, I was interested during this last one in side issues. I might mention a few papers on human genetics, but more worth mentioning, I think, are a few general addresses of significance: one on politics and science, warning against organized and planned science, which brought me a large amount of fan mail; one on fifty years of zoology; one on fifty years of genetics; and one introducing the jubilee celebrating fifty years of Mendelism. I think they are all worth reading, and I certainly enjoyed their preparation. I still had students, and some of their work contained a larger than usual share of my own efforts. One of my last students, Tai Peh Lin, succeeded in solving a cytological problem with which I had struggled fifty years earlier, thus making the end of my career as a teacher a worth-while event.

Fate has continued to be good to me. Despite illness I was able to write *Theoretical Genetics*, a very serious and highly technical book, and this was followed by a little book of exactly the opposite nature. Both in Berkeley and at the University of Washington I had acceded to the wishes of students that I reminisce in informal talks about the great founders of modern zoology whom it was my good fortune to know. The contents of these talks were incorporated in *Portraits from Memory: Recollections of a Zoologist*. It is my greatest intellectual happiness that I can still work in my laboratory and even make interesting discoveries in the field of chemically induced phenocopies.

BIBLIOGRAPHY

ARTICLES

1. Protozoology

"Die Chromidien der Protozoen," *Arch. Protkd.*, V (1904), 126–44.

"Lebensgeschichte der Mastigamöben *Mastigella vitrea* n. sp. und *Mastigina setosa* n. sp.," *Arch. Protkd.*, Suppl. I (1907), 83–168.

"Über die Lebensgeschichte der Mastigamöben," *Sitzungsber. Ges. Morph. Physiol. München*, XXIII (1907), 1–6.

With M. Popoff. "Die Karyokinese der Protozoen und der Chromidialapparat der Protozoen- und Metazoenzelle," *Arch. Protkd.*, VIII (1907), 321–43.

2. Cytology

"Untersuchungen über die Eireifung, Befruchtung und Zellteilung bei *Polystomum integerrimum* Rud.," *Z. wiss. Zool.*, LXXI (1902), 397–444.

"Der Chromidialapparat lebhaft funktionierender Gewebezellen," *Biol. Centrbl.*, XXIV (1904), 241–51.

"Der Chromidialapparat lebhaft funktionierender Gewebezellen," *Zool. Jahrb.* (*Anat.*), XXI (1904), 1–100.

"Eireifung, Befruchtung und Embryonalentwicklung des *Zoogonus mirus*, Lss.," *Zool. Jahrb.* (*Anat.*), XXI (1905), 607–54.

"Über das Verhalten des Chromatins bei der Eireifung und Befruchtung des *Dicrocoelium lanceatum*, Stil. et Hass. (*Distomum lanceolatum*)," *Arch. Zellfg.*, I (1908), 232–44.

"Die Chromatinreifung der Geschlechtszellen des *Zoogonus mirus* Lss., und der Primärtypus der Reduktion," *Arch. Zellfg.*, II (1908), 348–70.

"Ist eine parallele Chromosomenkonjugation bewiesen?" *Arch. Zellfg.*, I (1908), 620–22.

With M. Popoff. "Über die sogen. hyaline Plasmaschicht der Seeigeleier," *Biol. Centrbl.*, XXVIII (1908), 210–23.

Kleine Beobachtungen und Ideen zur Zellenlehre, I," *Arch. Zellfg.*, VI (1910), 19–39.

327

"Some Experiments on Spermatogenesis in vitro," *Proc. Nat. Acad. Sci.*, I (1915), 220–22.

"Notiz über einige bemerkenswerte Erscheinungen in Gewebekulturen von Insekten," *Biol. Centrbl.*, XXXVI (1916), 160–67.

"The Function of the Apyrene Spermatozoa," *Science*, XLIV (1916), 544–46.

"On a Case of Facultative Parthenogenesis in the Gypsy Moth *Lymantria dispar* L., with a Discussion of the Relation of Parthenogenesis to Sex," *Biol. Bull.*, XXXII (1917), 35–43.

"Versuche zur Spermatogenese in vitro," *Arch. Zellfg.*, XIV (1917), 421–50.

"Kleine Beobachtungen und Ideen zur Zellenlehre, II. Die Spermatogenese eines parthenogenetischen Frosches nebst Bemerkungen zur Frage, welches Geschlecht bei den Amphibien das heterozygotische ist," *Arch. Zellfg.*, XV (1920), 283–90.

"Kleine Beobachtungen und Ideen zur Zellenlehre, III. Die Bedeutung der atypischen Spermatozoen," *Arch. Zellfg.*, XV (1920), 291–300.

"Die Reifeteilung der Spermatocyten in den Gonaden intersexueller Weibchen des Schwammspinners," *Biol. Centrbl.*, XLII (1922), 301–2.

"Kleine Beobachtungen zur Zellenlehre, IV. Die Sammelchromosomen der Schmetterlinge," *Arch. Zellfg.*, XVII (1923), 167–84.

With A. Fischer. "Chromosomenstudien an Carcinomzellen in vitro," *Z. Krebsforschg.*, XXX (1929), 281–85.

"Prä- oder Postreduktion der Chromosomen?" *Naturwiss.*, XX (1923), 358–62.

With M. Calvin and M. Kodani. "Effects of Certain Chemical Treatments on the Morphology of Salivary Gland Chromosomes and Their Interpretation," *Proc. Nat. Acad. Sci.*, XXVI (1940), 340–49.

With M. Kodani. "The Structure of the Salivary Gland Chromosomes and Its Meaning," *Amer. Natur.*, LXXVI (1942), 529–51.

With M. Kodani. "Pseudodeficiencies and Translocations of Chromosome Tips in Drosophila," *Genetics*, XXVI (1943), 108–13.

With A. Hannah. "One-Band Inversion," *Proc. Nat. Acad. Sci.*, XXX (1944), 299–301.

"The Blond-Silver Section of the X-Chromosome of *Drosophila melanogaster*," *Rec. Gen. Soc.*, XIII (1944), 18.

With T. P. Lin. "Chromatin Diminution," *Science*, CV (1947), 619.

"A Remarkable Structure in the Ovocytes of a Fish," in *Moderne Biologie, Festschrift Nachtsheim*, pp. 39–42. Berlin: F. W. Peters, 1950.

3. Embryology

"Zur Entwicklungsgeschichte der Echinococcusköpfchen," *Zool. Jahrb.* (*Anat.*), XIII (1900), 467–94.

"Bemerkungen zur Entwicklungsgeschichte des *Polystomum integerrimum* Rud.," *Z. wiss. Zool.,* LXXII (1902), 180–89.

"Über Bau und Embryonalentwicklung von *Zoogonus mirus* Lss.," *Centrbl. Bakteriol.,* XXXII (1902), 870–76.

"Notiz über die Entwicklung der Appendicularien," *Biol. Centrbl.,* XXIII (1903), 72–76.

"Eischale, Schalendrüse und Dotterzellen der Trematoden," *Zool. Anz.,* XXXIV (1909), 481–98.

"Untersuchungen zur Entwicklungsphysiologie des Flügelmusters der Schmetterlinge, I," *Arch. Entw. Mech.,* XLVII (1920), 1–24.

"Ein Beitrag zur Analyse der Doppelmissbildungen," *Arch. Entw. Mech.,* XLVII (1921), 654–67.

"Versuche zum Problem der Skelettbildung der Seeigellarven." *Biol. Gen.,* XI (1935), 44–48.

4. Histology and Neurology

"Histologische Untersuchungen an Nematoden, I," *Zool. Jahrb.* (*Anat.*), XVIII (1903), 1–57.

"Über die Cuticula von *Ascaris*," *Zool. Anz.,* XXVIII (1904), 259–66.

"Über die sogenannten radiärgestreiften Ganglienzellen von *Ascaris*," *Biol. Centrbl.,* XXIV (1904), 173–82.

"Mitteilungen zur Histologie von *Ascaris*," *Zool. Anz.,* XXIX (1906), 719–37.

"Einiges vom feineren Bau des Nervensystems," *Verhd. Dt. Zool. Ges.* (1907), pp. 130–31.

"Die Neurofibrillen im Nervensystem von *Ascaris* nebst Bemerkungen über den Chromidialapparat der Metazoenzelle," *Zool. Anz.,* XXXII (1908), 562–63.

"Das Nervensystem von *Ascaris lumbricoides* und *megalocephala,* I," *Z. wiss. Zool.,* XC (1908), 73–136.

"Das Nervensystem von *Ascaris lumbricoides* und *megalocephala,* II," *Z. wiss. Zool.,* XCII (1909), 306–57.

"Das Skelett der Muskelzelle von *Ascaris*," *Arch. Zellfg.,* IV (1909), 81–119.

"Das Nervensystem von *Ascaris lumbricoides* und *megalocephala,* III," in *Festschr. R. Hertwig,* II, 254–354. Jena: Gustav Fischer, 1910.

"Sind die Neurofibrillen das leitende Element des Nervensystems?" *Sitzungsber. Ges. Morph. Physiol. München,* XXVI (1911), 1–5.

5. Acrania

"Amphioxides, Vertreter einer neuen Acranier-Familie," *Biol. Centrbl.,* XXV (1905), 235–40.

"Amphioxides," *Wissenschaftliche Ergebn. Dt. Tiefsee-Exp., 1898–99 "Valdivia Expedition,"* XII (1905), 1–92.

"Notiz über *Branchiostoma elongatum* Sundervall," *Zool. Anz.,* XXIX (1905), 132–33.

"*Amphioxides* und *Amphioxus,*" *Zool. Anz.,* XXX (1906), 443–48.

"Das Bindegewebe des *Amphioxus,*" *Sitzungsber. Ges. Morph. Physiol. München,* XXIV (1908), 53–78.

"Die *Amphioxides*-Formen," *Deutsche Südpolar-Expedition 1901–1903,* XI (III. *Zoologie*) (1908), 233–41.

"A Note on *Amphioxides* from Bermuda Based on Dr. W. Beebe's Collections," *Biol. Bull.,* LXIV (1933), 321–25.

6. Gynandromorphism

With J. Machida. "Über zwei eigenartige Gynandromorphe des Schwammspinners *Lymantria dispar* L.," *Z. indukt. Abstl.,* XXVIII (1922), 249–58.

"Ein weiterer Beitrag zur Kenntnis des Gynandromorphismus," *Biol. Centrbl.,* XLIII (1923), 518–28.

With K. Katsuki. "Erblicher Gynandromorphismus und somatische Mosaikbildung bei *Bombyx mori,*" *Biol. Centrbl.,* XLVII (1927), 45–54.

With E. Fischer. "Erblicher Gynandromorphismus bei Schmetterlingen," *Arch. Entw. Mech.,* CIX (1927), 1–13.

With K. Katsuki. "Zweite Mitteilung über erblichen Mosaikbildung und Gynandromorphismus bei *Bombyx mori* L.," *Biol. Centrbl.,* XLVIII (1928), 39–42.

With K. Katsuki. "Cytologie des erblichen Gynandromorphismus von *Bombyx mori* L.," *Biol. Centrbl.,* XLVIII (1928), 685–99.

With K. Katsuki. "Vierte Mitteilung über erblichen Gynandromorphismus und somatische Mosaikbildung bei *Bombyx mori* L.," *Biol. Centrbl.,* LI (1931), 58–74.

"A Gynandromorph in Drosophila Produced by Double Fertilization," *Cytologia, Fuji Jubilee Vol.* (1937), pp. 78–79.

7. Intersexuality

"Über die Vererbung der sekundären Geschlechtscharaktere," *Münch. Med. Wochschr.*, XLVIII (1911), 2642–43.

"Erblichkeitsstudien an Schmetterlingen," *Z. indukt. Abstl.*, VII (1912), 1–62.

"Weitere Untersuchungen über Vererbung und Bestimmung des Geschlechts," *Münch. Med. Wochschr.*, LX (1913), 1688.

With H. Poppelbaum. "Erblichkeitsstudien an Schmetterlingen, II," *Z. indukt. Abstl.*, XI (1914), 280–316.

"Vorläufige Mitteilung über weitere Versuche zur Vererbung und Bestimmung des Geschlechts," *Biol. Centrbl.*, XXXV (1915), 565–70.

"A Preliminary Report on Further Experiments in Inheritance and Determination of Sex," *Proc. Nat. Acad. Sci.*, II (1916), 53–58.

"Experimental Intersexuality and the Sex Problem," Amer. Natur., L (1916), 705–18.

"Die biologischen Grundlagen der konträren Sexualität und des Hermaphroditismus beim Menschen," *Arch. Rass.-Ges.-Biol.*, XII (1916), 1–14.

"A Further Contribution to the Theory of Sex," *J. Exp. Zool.*, XXII (1917), 593–611.

"Intersexuality and the Endocrine Aspect of Sex," *Endocrinology*, I (1917), 433–56.

"Intersexualität und Geschlechtsbestimmung," *Biol. Centrbl.*, XXXIX (1919), 498–512

"Untersuchungen über Intersexualität," *Z. indukt. Abstl.*, XXIII (1920), 1–199.

"Zur Entwicklungsphysiologie der Intersexualität," *Naturwiss.*, IX (1921), 315–16.

With S. Saguchi. "Die Umwandlung des Eierstocks in einen Hoden beim intersexuellen Schwammspinner," *Z. ges. Anat.*, LXV (1922), 226–53.

"Untersuchungen über Intersexualität, II," *Z. indukt. Abstl.*, XXIX (1922), 145–85.

With K. Pariser. "Triploide Intersexe bei Schmetterlingen," *Biol. Centrbl.*, XLIII (1923), 446–52.

"Untersuchungen über Intersexualität, III," *Z. indukt. Abstl.*, XXXI (1923), 100–33.

"Richtigstellung zu Untersuchungen über Intersexualität, III," *Z. indukt. Abstl.*, XXXIV (1924), 1 p.

"Über die Erzeugung der höheren Stufen männlicher Intersexualität bei *Lymantria dispar,*" *Biol. Centrbl.*, XLV (1925), 134–36.

"Bemerkungen über triploide Intersexe," *Biol. Centrbl.*, XLV (1925), 536–41.

"Nachweis der homogametischen Beschaffenheit von Geschlechtsumwandlungsweibchen," *Biol. Centrbl.*, XLVI (1926), 193–200.

"Die zygotischen sexuellen zwischenstufen und die Theorie der Geschlechtsbestimmung," *Ergbn. Biol.*, II (1927), 554–683.

"Weitere morphologische Untersuchungen zum Intersexualitätsproblem," *Z. Morph. Oek.*, VIII (1927), 63–95.

"Untersuchungen über Intersexualität, IV," *Z. indukt. Abstl.*, XLIX (1929), 168–242.

"Untersuchungen über Intersexualität, V," *Z. indukt. Abstl.*, LVI (1930), 275–301.

"Bemerkungen zu dem Aufsatz von Plate, 'Einige Bedenken u. s. w.' in Bd. 24 dieser Zeitschrift," *Arch. Rass.-Ges.-Biol.*, XXV (1931), 108–11.

"Analysis of Intersexuality in the Gypsy Moth," *Quart. Rev. Biol.*, VI (1931), 125–42.

"Intersexualität und menschliches Zwittertum," *Dt. med. Wochenschr.*, Vol. LVII (1931).

"Neue Untersuchungen über die Umwandlung der Gonaden bei intersexuellen *Lymantria dispar* L.," *Arch. Entw. Mech.*, CXXIV (1931), 618–53.

"Untersuchungen über Intersexualität, VI," *Z. indukt. Abstl.*, LXVII (1934), 1–40.

"The Time Law of Intersexuality," *Genetica*, XX (1938), 1–50.

"Intersexuality and Development," *Amer. Natur.*, LXXII (1938), 228–42.

"A Lymantria-like Case of Intersexuality in Plants (Oehlker's Work) and Its Meaning for the Theory of Sex Determination in Plants," *J. Genet.*, XXXVI (1938), 531–35.

"The Interpretation of the Structure of Triploid Intersexes in Solenobia," *Arch. Julius Klaus Stiftg.*, XXI (1946), 269–72.

"New Facts of Sex Determination in *Drosophila melanogaster,*" *Proc. Nat. Acad. Sci.*, XXXIV (1948), 245–52.

"Neue Tatsachen zur Analyse der Geschlechtsbestimmung bei *Drosophila melanogaster,*" *Arch. Julius Klaus Stiftg.*, XXIII (1948), 539–49.

"The Intersexual Males of the Beaded-Minute Combination in *Drosophila melanogaster,*" *Proc. Nat. Acad. Sci.*, XXXV (1949), 314–16.

"The Beaded-Minute Intersexes in *Drosophila melanogaster* Meig.," *J. Exp. Zool.*, CXII (1949), 233–302.

"The Interpretation of the Triploid Intersexes of Solenobia," *Experientia*, V (1949), 417–24.
"The Maternal Effect in the Production of the Beaded-Minute Intersexes in *Drosophila melanogaster*," *J. Exp. Zool.*, CXVII (1951), 75–110.

8. *General Sex Determination, Sex-controlled Heredity*

"Das Problem der Geschlechtsbestimmung," *Umschau*, XIV (1910), 201–5.
"Bemerkungen zur Vererbung des Geschlechtspolymorphismus," *Z. indukt. Abstl.*, VIII (1912), 79–88.
"Vererbung und Bestimmung des Geschlechts," *Verh. Ges. Naturf. Ärzte* (1912), 14 pp.
"Geschlechtsbestimmung," in *Festschr. Kaiser Wilhelm Ges.*, pp. 90–95. Berlin: Julius Springer, 1921.
"Die Cytologische Untersuchungen über Vererbung und Bestimmung des Geschlechtes," in *Die Vererbung und Bestimmung des Geschlechtes*, by Carl Correns and Richard Goldschmidt, pp. 73–149. Berlin: Borntraeger, 1913.
"The Determination of Sex," *Nature*, CVII (1921), 780–84.
"Über Vererbung im Y-Chromosom," *Biol. Centrbl.*, XLII (1922), 481–87.
With E. Fischer. "*Argynnis paphia-valesina*, ein Fall geschlechtskontrollierter Vererbung," *Genetica*, IV (1922), 247–78.
With S. Minami. "Über die Vererbung der sekundären Geschlechtscharaktere," in *Studia Mendeliana*, pp. 65–77. Brünn, 1923.
"Bemerkungen zum Problem der Geschlechtsbestimmung bei *Bonellia*," *Biol. Centrbl.*, XLVI (1926), 441–52.
"The Quantitative Theory of Sex," *Science*, LXIV (1926), 299–300.
"The Quantitative Theory of Sex," *Science*, LXV (1927), 596–97.
"Zur sogenannten Indexhypothese der Geschlechtschromosomen," *Biol. Centrbl.*, XLVII (1927), 249–56.
"Zygotische Geschlechtsbestimmung und Sexualhormone," *Naturwiss.*, XV (1927), 609–14.
"La théorie de la détermination du sexe," *Scientia* (March, 1928), pp. 59–67.
"Geschlechtsbestimmung im Tier- und Pflanzenreich," *Biol. Centrbl.*, XLIX (1929), 641–48.
"Eine merkwürdige Beziehung zwischen Geschlechtsgenen, Entwicklungsgeschwindigkeit und Zahlenverhältnis der Geschlechter," *Naturwiss.*, XIX (1932), 735–36.
"Zwittertum," in *Brockhaus Convers. Lex.* 15th ed. Leipzig: F. A. Brockhaus, 1935.

"Multiple Sex-Genes in Drosophila? A Critique," *J. Genet.*, XXXI (1935), 145–53.

"A Critical Review of Some Recent Work in Sex Determination," *Quart. Rev. Biol.*, XII (1937), 426–39.

"Sex Determination in *Melandrium* and *Lymantria*," *Science*, XCV (1942), 120–21.

"Heredity within a Sex Controlled Structure of *Drosophila*," *J. Exp. Zool.*, CXXII (1953), 53–96.

9. Genetics and Evolution

"Die Artbildung im Licht der neueren Erblichkeitslehre," in *Die Abstammungslehre*, pp. 22–60. Jena: Gustav Fischer, 1911.

"A Preliminary Report on Some Genetic Experiments concerning Evolution," *Amer. Natur.*, LII (1918), 28–50.

"Untersuchungen zur Genetik der geographischen Variation, I," *Arch. Entw. Mech.*, CI (1924), 92–337.

"Untersuchungen zur Genetik der geographischen Variation, II," *Arch. Entw. Mech.*, CXVI (1929), 136–201.

"Untersuchungen zur Genetik der geographischen Variation, III. Abschliessendes über die Geschlechtsrassen von *Lymantria dispar* L.," *Arch. Entw. Mech.*, CXXVI (1932), 277–324.

"Untersuchungen zur Genetik der geographischen Variation, IV. Cytologisches," *Arch. Entw. Mech.*, CXXVI (1932), 591–612.

"Untersuchungen zur Genetik der geographischen Variation, V. Analyse der Überwinterungszeit als Anpassungscharakter," *Arch. Entw. Mech.*, CXXVI (1932), 674–768.

"Genetik der geographischen Variation," *Proc. 6th Intern. Congr. Genetics*, (1932), pp. 173–84.

"Untersuchungen zur Genetik der geographischen Variation, VI. Die geographische Variation der Entwicklungsgeschwindigkeit und des Grössenwachstums," *Arch. Entw. Mech.*, CXXX (1933), 266–339.

"Untersuchungen zur Genetik der geographischen Variation, VII," *Arch. Entw. Mech.*, CXXX (1933), 562–615.

"Some Aspects of Evolution," *Science*, LXXVIII (1933), 539–47.

"Einige Ergebnisse von Untersuchungen zum Evolutionsproblem, ausgeführt an japanischen Rassen des Schwammspinners," in *Jubiliäumsband der Deutschen Gesellschaft für Natur- und Volkerkunde Ostasiens*. Tokyo, 1933.

"Geographische Variation und Artbildung," *Naturwiss.*, XXIII (1935), 169–76.

"*Cynips* and *Lymantria*," *Amer. Natur.*, LXXI (1937), 508–14.

"A Note concerning the Adaptation of Geographic Races of *Ly-*

mantria dispar L. to the Seasonal Cycle in Japan," *Amer. Natur.*, LXXII (1938), 385–86.

"Evolution of Mouth Parts in Diptera," *Pan-Pacific Entomol.*, XXI (1945), 41–47.

"Podoptera, a Homoeotic Mutant of *Drosophila* and the Origin of the Insect Wing," *Science*, CI (1945), 389–90.

"The Structure of Podoptera, a Homoeotic Mutant of *Drosophila melanogaster*," *J. Morph.*, LXXVII (1945), 71–103.

"Mimetic Polymorphism, a Controversial Chapter of Darwinism," *Quart. Rev. Biol.*, XX (1945), 147–64, 205–30.

"An Empirical Evolutionary Generalization Viewed from the Standpoint of Phenogenetics," *Amer. Natur.*, LXXX (1946), 305–18.

"New Facts on Dependent, Successive and Conjugated Spontaneous Mutation," *J. Exp. Zool.*, CIV (1947), 197–222.

"A Note on Industrial Melanism in Relation to Some Recent Work with *Drosophila*," *Amer. Natur.*, LXXXI (1947), 474–76.

"Ecotype, Ecospecies and Macroevolution," *Experientia*, IV (1948), 465–72.

"Glowworms and Evolution," *Rev. Scientif.*, No. 3298, LXXXVI (1948), 607–12.

"Eine weitere Bemerkung über Glühwürmer und Evolution," *Naturwiss.*, XXXVIII (1951), 437–38.

"La evolución vista por un genetico," *Arbor* (Madrid), No. 66 (1951), pp. 229–49.

"Evolution as Viewed by One Geneticist," *Amer. Scientist*, XL (1952), 84–98.

"Homoeotic Mutants and Evolution," *Act. Biotheor.*, X (1952), 87–104.

"An Introduction to a Popularized Symposium on Evolution," *Sci. Month.*, LXXVII (1953), 182–89.

"Pricking a Bubble" (a critical review of N. P. Dubinin's 1948 paper on "Experimental Investigation of the Integration of Hereditary Systems in the Processes of Evolution in Populations"), *Evol.*, VII (1953), 264–69.

"Experiments with a Homoeotic Mutant Bearing on Evolution," *J. Exp. Zool.*, CXXIII (1953), 79–114.

10. *Genetics: Mendelian Analysis and General*

"Der Vererbungsmodus der gefüllten Levkojenrassen als Fall geschlechtsbegrenzter Vererbung," Z. *indukt. Abstl.*, X (1913), 74–98.

"Zuchtversuche mit Enten, I," *Z. indukt. Abstl.*, IX (1913), 161–91.

"Crossing-over ohne Chiasmatypie?" *Genetics*, II (1917), 82–95.

"Erblichkeitsstudien an Schmetterlingen, III. Der Melanismus der Nonne, *Lymantria monacha* L.," *Z. indukt. Abstl.*, XXV (1921), 89–163.

"Zwei Jahrzehnte Mendelismus," *Naturwiss.*, Vol. X (1922).

"Das Mutationsproblem." *Verhandlungen Dt. Ges. Vererbgwiss., Wien.* (1922) *Z. indukt. Abstl.*, XXX (1923), 260–68.

"Erblichkeitsstudien an Schmetterlingen, IV. Weitere Untersuchungen über die Vererbung des Melanismus," *Z. indukt. Abstl.*, XXXIV (1924), 229–44.

"Einige Probleme der heutigen Vererbungswissenschaft," *Naturwiss.*, XII (1924), 769–71.

"Experimentelle Mutation und das Problem der sogenannten Parellelinduktion," *Biol. Centrbl.*, XLIX (1929), 437–48.

"Vererbungslehre" (in German and Chinese), *Tung-Chi Med. Monatsschr.* (Shanghai), Vol. V (1929).

"Gibt es eine Vererbung erworbener Eigenschaften?" *Züchtungsk.*, VI (1931), 161–70.

"Protoplasmatische Vererbung," *Scientia* (Feb. 1933), 6 pp.

"Lymantria," *Bibl. Genet.*, XI (1934), 1–185.

"The Influence of the Cytoplasm upon Gene-controlled Heredity," *Amer. Natur.*, LXVIII (1934), 5–23.

"Does the Quantity of Chromatin Produce a Genetic Effect?" *Amer. Natur.*, LXXI (1937), 83–87.

With E. Gardner and M. Kodani. "A Remarkable Group of Position Effects," *Proc. Nat. Acad. Sci.*, XXV (1939), 314–17.

"Mass Mutation in the Florida Stock of *Drosophila melanogaster*," *Amer. Natur.*, LXXIII (1939), 547–59.

"Chromosomes and Genes," *Publ. Amer. Acad. Adv. Sci.*, XIV (1940), 56–66.

"A Mutant of *Drosophila melanogaster* Resembling the So-called Unstable Genes of *Drosophila virilis*," *Proc. Nat. Acad. Sci.*, XXIX (1943), 203–6.

With collaborators. "A Study of Spontaneous Mutation," *Univ. Calif. Publ. Zool.*, XLIX (1945), 291–550.

"On Spontaneous Mutation," *Proc. Nat. Acad. Sci.*, XXX (1944), 297–99.

"Cryptic Bobbed Alleles in *Drosophila melanogaster*," *Amer. Natur.*, LXXVIII (1944), 564–68.

"On Some Facts Pertinent to the Theory of the Gene," in *Science in the University*, pp. 183–210. Berkeley: University of California Press, 1944.

"Position Effect and the Theory of the Corpuscular Gene," *Experientia*, II (1946), 197–203, 250–56.

"Heterochromatic Heredity," *Hereditas,* Suppl. (1949), pp. 244–55.

"Fifty Years of Genetics," *Amer. Natur.*, LXXXIV (1950), 313–40.

With A. Hannah and L. K. Piternick. "The Podoptera Effect in *Drosophila melanogaster," Univ. Calif. Publ. Zool.*, LV (1951), 67–294.

"Marginalia to McClintock's Work on Mutable Loci in Maize," *Amer. Natur.*, LXXXIV (1950), 437–55.

"New Heteromorphoses in *Drosophila melanogaster* Meig.," *Pan-Pacific Entomol.*, XXVII (1951), 1–11.

" 'Repeats' and the Modern Theory of the Gene," *Proc. Nat. Acad. Sci.*, XXXVI (1950), 365–68.

"The Theory of the Gene," *Cold Spring Harbor Sympos. Quant. Biol.*, XVI (1952), 1–11.

"Different Philosophies of Genetics," *Science*, CXIX (1954), 703–10.

"A Remarkable Action of the Mutant 'Rudimentary' in *Drosophila melanogaster," Proc. Nat. Acad. Sci.*, XLIII (1957), 731–36.

"On Some Phenomena in *Drosophila* Related to So-called Genic Conversion," *Proc. Nat. Acad. Sci.*, XLIII (1957), 1019–26.

"Genic Conversion in *Oenothera?* A Critical Review," *Amer. Natur.*, XCII (1958), 93–104.

11. *Physiological Genetics*

"Genetic Factors and Enzyme Reaction," *Science*, XLIII (1916), 98–100.

"Einige Materialien zur Theorie der abgestimmten Reaktionsgeschwindigkeiten," *Arch. Entw. Mech.*, XCVIII (1923), 292–313.

"Gen und Aussencharakter," *Z. indukt. Abstl.*, Suppl. I (1928), 223–33.

"The Gene," *Quart. Rev. Biol.*, III (1928), 307–24.

"Die entwicklungsphysiologische Erklärung des Falls der sogenannten Treppenallelomorphe des Gens Scute von *Drosophila," Biol. Centrbl.*, LI (1931), 507–26.

"Bemerkungen zur Kritik der quantitativen Natur multipler Allele," *Bull. Lab. Genet. Leningrad*, IX (1932), 129–35.

"Genetics and Development," *Biol. Bull.*, LXIII (1932), 337–56.

"Gen und Asseneigenschaft, I. Untersuchungen an *Drosophila," Z. indukt. Abstl.*, LXIX (1935), 38–69.

"Gen und Ausseneigenschaft, II," Z. indukt. Abstl., LXIX (1935), 70–131.

"Gen und Aussencharakter, III," Biol. Centrbl., LV (1935), 535–54.

"A Remarkable Parallelism," Proc. Nat. Acad. Sci., XXIII (1937), 219–23.

"Gene and Character, IV–VIII," Univ. Calif. Publ. Zool., XLI (1937). "IV. Further Data on the Development of Wing Mutants in Drosophila," pp. 277–82; "V. Further Data on the vg Dominigenes in Drosophila melanogaster," pp. 283–96; "VI [with E. Honer]. Dominigenes and vg Allelomorphs," pp. 297–312; "VII. The 'Nonhereditary' kn Effect in Drosophila," pp. 313–26; "VIII. A Selection Experiment with Dominigenes," pp. 327–33.

"Spontaneous Chromatin Rearrangements and the Theory of the Gene," Proc. Nat. Acad. Sci., XXIII (1937), 621–23.

"Spontaneous Chromatin Rearrangements in Drosophila," Nature, CXL (1937), 767.

"The Theory of the Gene," Sci. Month., XLVI (1938), 268–73.

With E. Gardner. "A Further Contribution to the Analysis of Scalloped Wings in Drosophila melanogaster," Univ. Calif. Publ. Zool., XLIX (1942), 103–25.

"Additional Data on Phenocopies and Genic Action," J. Exp. Zool., C (1945), 193–201.

"A Note on the Action of the Bar Series in Drosophila," Growth, IX (1945), 259–64.

"One- or Two-Dimensional Action of Mutant Loci," Amer. Natur., LXXIX (1945), 97–103.

"Phenocopies," Scient. Amer., October, 1949, 4 pp.

"A Further Study of Homoeosis in Drosophila melanogaster," J. Exp. Zool., CXIX (1952), 405–60.

With L. K. Piternick. "New Experiments on Chemical Phenocopies," Proc. Nat. Acad. Sci., XLII (1956), 299–304.

"Problematics of the Phenomenon of Phenocopy," J. Madras Univ., XXVII (1957), 17–24.

"Discussion of Professor Landauer's Paper," Amer. Natur., XCI (1957), 91–94.

With L. K. Piternick. "The Genetic Background of Chemically Induced Phenocopies in Drosophila, I." J. Exp. Zool., CXXXV (1957), 127–202.

With L. K. Piternick. "The Genetic Background of Chemically Induced Phenocopies in Drosophila, II." J. Exp. Zool., CXXXVI (1957), 201–28.

12. Human Heredity

"Die Nachkommen der alten Siedler auf den Bonininseln," *Naturwiss.*, XV (1927), 449–53.

"Progressive Heredity and Anticipation," *J. Hered.*, XXIX (1938), 140–42.

"Anthropological Determination of Aryanism," *J. Hered.*, XXXIII (1942), 215–16.

"Ancient Chinese Knowledge of Human Heredity," *J. Hered.*, XXXVI (1945), 296.

"A Not Dominant Glaucoma Pedigree," *J. Hered.*, XLII (1951), 271–72.

"Materials for the Study of Dominant Personality Traits," *Folia Hered. et Pathol.*, II (1953), 267–95.

13. Biographical, Popular Science, Varia

"Theodor Boveri," *Science*, XLIII (1916), 253–70.

"Otto Bütschli. 1848–1920," *Naturwiss.*, VIII (1920), 543–49.

"Richard Hertwig und die experimentelle Zoologie," *Naturwiss.*, VIII (1920), 771–74.

"Jacques Loeb," *Münch. Med. Wochschr.*, LXXI (1924), 518.

"Pater Wasmann," *Vossische Ztg.*, (Berlin), 1929.

"Hans Spemann zum 60. Geburtstag," *Vossische Ztg.* (Berlin), 1929.

"Richard Hertwig zum 80. Geburtstag," *Naturwiss.*, XVIII (1930), 63.

"Jur. Philiptschenko," *Züchter*, II (1930), 237–38.

"Adolf von Harnack," *Dt. Med. Wochschr.*, LVI (1930), 1058.

"Carl Correns," *Vossische Ztg.* (Berlin), 1932.

"O. Bütschli: Mechanismus und Vitalismus," *Umschau*, V (1901), 681–85.

"Schenk: Geschlechtsbestimmung beim Menschen," *Umschau*, V (1901), 894–95.

"Ein Besuch des tätigen Aetnakraters," *Aus der Natur*, VI (1910), 161–66.

"Die Askarisvergiftung," *Münch. Med. Wochschr.*, XXXVIII (1910), 1–7.

"Die celluläre Grundlage des Geschlechtsproblems," *Naturwiss. Rundschau*, 1912, pp. 1–6.

"Vererbungslehre," *Südd. Monatsh.*, April, 1921, pp. 13–20.

"Zur Entwicklungsphysiologie der Intersexualität," *Naturwiss.*, IX (1921), 315–16.

"Die Vererbung und Bestimmung des Geschlechts," 1925. (Japanese translation published in Japan.)

"Das Problem der Geschlechtsbestimmung," *Der Naturforscher*, II (1925), 57–63.

"Die Vererbungswissenschaft," *Münch. N. Nachr.*, May 26, 1928.

Bimonthly reports on progress in biological research in *Frankfurter Zeitung*, 1928–29.

"Rückkehr zu Darwin," *Berliner Tageblatt*, 1929.

"Die japanischen Universitäten," *Minerva Ztschr.*, III (1927), 229–32.

"Die Bestimmung des Geschlechts und ihre Kontrolle," *Eugenik*, II (1931), 25–30.

"Was ist erblich?" *Die Räder*, XII (1931), 423–27.

"Die marine biologische Station auf den Bermudainseln," *Inter Nationes*, II (1932), 116–17.

"Das Kaiser Wilhelm Institut für Biologie in Berlin-Dahlem. Abteilung Richard Goldschmidt seit 1914," *Festschr. 25 Jahre Kaiser Wilhelm Ges.*, pp. 251–60. Berlin: Julius Springer, 1936.

Preface to a complimentary volume of the Japanese cytologist, Kan Oguma, *Imperial Univ. Sapporo Publ.* (1948).

Preface to an issue of *Iden*, Tokyo (1948).

"Research and Politics," *Science*, CIX (1949), 219–27. (Translated into Portuguese, German, French.)

"Charles Atwood Kofoid," *Biogr. Mem. Nat. Acad. Sci.*, XXVI (1949), 121–51.

"Fifty Years of Zoology," *Sci. Month.*, LXXI (1950), 359–69.

"L. Cuénot, 1866–1951," *Science*, CXIII (1951), 309–10.

"The Impact of Genetics upon Science," in *Genetics in the 20th Century*, ed. L. C. Dunn, pp. 1–23. New York: Macmillan Co., 1951.

"Harry Federley," *Science*, CXV (1952), 561–62.

"Otto Bütschli, Pioneer of Cytology (1898–1920)," in *Science, Medicine and History: Essays . . . in Honour of Charles Singer*, ed. E. A. Underwood, pp. 223–32. London and New York: Oxford University Press, 1953.

"Prof. Methodi Popoff," *Nature*, CLXXIX (1957), 289–90.

"A Chapter from Kitchen Zoology," *The Biologist*, XXXIX (1957), 18–21.

"Aus der Geschichte der Vererbungswissenschaft," in *Genetik: Wissenschaft der Entscheidung*. Stuttgart: Alfred Kröner, 1957.

Books

1. Technical

Die quantitativen Grundlagen von Vererbung und Artbildung. (Vortr. Aufs. Entwicklungsmech., No. 24.) Berlin: Julius Springer, 1920. 163 pp.

Mechanismus und Physiologie der Geschlechtsbestimmung. Berlin: Borntraeger, 1920. 251 pp. (Translated into English and Russian.)

Physiologische Theorie der Vererbung. Berlin: Julius Springer, 1927. 247 pp.

Die sexuellen Zwischenstufen. (Monogr. Gesamtgeb. Pflanzen, Tiere, No. 23.) Berlin: Julius Springer, 1931. 528 pp.

Les problèmes de la sexualité. 2nd ed. Paris: Doin, 1932. 193 pp.

Physiological Genetics. New York: McGraw-Hill Book Co., 1938. 338 pp.

The Material Basis of Evolution. (Silliman Lectures.) New Haven: Yale University Press, 1940. 436 pp.

Theoretical Genetics. Berkeley: University of California Press, 1955. 563 pp.

2. Textbooks

With Emil Selenka. *Zoologisches Taschenbuch für Studierende.* Leipzig: Georg Thieme, 1907. *Invertebrata,* 130 pp.; *Vertebrata,* 143 pp. 6th ed., 1912.

Einführung in die Vererbungswissenschaft. Berlin: Julius Springer, 1911. 568 pp. 5th ed., 1928. (Translated into Russian.)

Der Mendelismus. Berlin: Paul Parey, 1920. 78 pp. 2nd ed., 1926.

Understanding Heredity: An Introduction to Genetics. New York: John Wiley and Sons, 1952. 228 pp.

3. Popular

Die Urtiere. (Natur und Geisteswelt, No. 160.) Leipzig: Teubner, 1906. 96 pp. 2nd ed., 1914.

Die Fortpflanzung der Tiere. (Natur und Geisteswelt, No. 253.) Leipzig: Teubner, 1909. 123 pp.

Ascaris, eine Einführung in die Wissenschaft vom Leben. Berlin: Julius Springer, 1921. 3rd ed., 1953. (American, British, Russian, Polish, Yugoslav, and Hebrew editions.)

Die Lehre von der Vererbung. Berlin: Julius Springer, 1927. 216

pp. 4th ed., 1953. (Translated into Russian, Spanish, Polish, Japanese.)

Neu-Japan: Reisebilder aus Formosa, Ryu-Kyu Inseln, Bonin Inseln, Korea und dem Südmandschurischen Pachtgebiet. Berlin: Julius Springer, 1927. 303 pp.

Portraits from Memory: Recollections of a Zoologist. Seattle: University of Washington Press, 1956. 181 pp. (German translation, *Erlebnisse und Begegnungen: Aus der grossen Zeit der Zoologie in Deutschland.* Hamburg and Berlin: Verlag Paul Parey, 1959.)

In and Out of the Ivory Tower: The Autobiography of Richard B. Goldschmidt. Seattle: University of Washington Press, 1960.

INDEX